Statistics for Business
An Introduction

Statistics for Business

An Introduction

Paul Whitehead PhD (Cantab)
and
Geoffrey Whitehead BSc (Econ)

Pitman

PITMAN PUBLISHING
128 Long Acre, London WC2E 9AN

A Division of Longman Group UK Limited

© Paul & Geoffrey Whitehead 1984, 1992

First published in Great Britain 1984
Second edition published 1992

British Library Cataloguing in Publication Data
A catalogue record for this book is available from the British Library.

ISBN 0 273 03810 9

Text set in 9½ on 11 Sabon Roman
Printed and bound in Great Britain

Contents

Preface

Modern society requires business staff to be highly numerate, for the business environment is one which increasingly reflects advances in quantitative techniques. Routine calculations are now done in the twinkling of an eye and 'number crunching' takes place on an increasing scale, for the data can be processed at electronic speeds. Supermarkets are interested in turnover per metre of shelving and banks in 'credit cards per thousand customers'.

Much of the information made available to business today comes in numerical form. Much research is mathematical in nature, the influences at work are expressed in the form of mathematical equations which build into a mathematical model of the system under consideration. If we are to follow the arguments being put forward and evaluate them, we must have at least a nodding acquaintance with statistical method. We cannot allow ourselves to be 'marched up to the frontiers of our knowledge', unable to make decisions about the proposals under discussion.

This introductory text aims to provide business personnel with an insight into basic statistical method which will provide the quantitative background knowledge required in the modern environment. It is appropriate for both self-study and class use, and the amount of mathematics has been kept to a minimum. While this inevitably restricts the usefulness of the book to advanced students, it is hoped that the efforts made to explain things in a non-mathematical way will contribute to the understanding of business aspects of those who do intend to study statistics at a more advanced level.

Syllabuses covered include all GCSE and 'A' level statistics courses, RSA and LCCI intermediate courses, BTEC National and Higher National syllabuses with a statistical content and the introductory statistical syllabuses of all business professional bodies, and first year degree courses.

Paul G Whitehead
Geoffrey Whitehead

Acknowledgements

The authors wish to thank the following for permission to use various forms and statistics, which are acknowledged individually where they appear in the text.

George Vyner Ltd, Holmfirth, Huddersfield, publishers of Simplex Account Books
Formecon Services Ltd, Gateway, Crewe
The Business Statistics Office, Government Statistical Service
Finance and Development
STSC Inc for the use of the STATGRAPHICS material
Unilever PLC
McGraw-Hill Book Company Ltd

We are grateful to the Literary Executor of the late Sir Ronald A Fisher, FRS, to Dr Frank Yates, FRS and to Longman Group UK Ltd for permission to reprint Table III from their book *Statistical Tables for Biological, Agricultural and Medical Research* (6th edition).

1 What is statistics?

1.1 Definitions of statistics

Statistics may be defined as numerical facts, systematically collected and presented. The word has its origin in the Latin word for state, for from the earliest times the state has been interested in such matters as the number of its citizens, the wealth that they are creating every year, the volume of foreign trade, etc. Today managers are equally interested in the numerical facts affecting their businesses, in particular production figures, sales figures, financial projections, measurements of productivity and many other statistics.

Viewed in this way, as numerical facts systematically collected, we speak of the statistics as **data**. Thus, if five electric light bulbs are tested to destruction, we might find that they last as follows:

Bulb A	550 hours
Bulb B	595 hours
Bulb C	1232 hours
Bulb D	25 minutes
Bulb E	602 hours

We have five numbers in this set of statistical data. Our light bulbs seem to have an erratic life, ranging from 25 minutes to 1232 hours. The average seems to be around the 600 hours mark, but we might feel that with such disparities between bulbs showing up in only a small set of five it would be better to test a few more. Are bulbs C and D very unusual examples or are they quite common? In matters of **quality control** it is unwise to draw conclusions from an inadequate set of data. On the other hand we cannot test every light bulb to destruction or we shall have none to sell.

Sometimes when we use the word 'statistics' we do not mean data, but the technique, or method of investigating problems by analysing statistical facts. This **statistical method** is essentially a branch of mathematics. It requires us to understand such ideas as averages, trends, distributions, probabilities, etc. Viewed in this way we may define statistics as a *range of mathematical techniques for analysing problems in the real world*. In fact, mathematical statistics is of increasing importance in a wide range of activities, for example, in industrial mass production, medicine, biology, economics, politics, psychology, analysis of public opinion and other social sciences, agriculture, traffic studies, meteorology, physics and engineering.

In all of these areas data is used to test hypotheses and models can be developed for planning and forecasting purposes. For example, in the case of weather forecasting we could say that if it is raining now there is a good chance it will be raining in 1 hour's time. We could write this as an equation, ie:

$$\text{Rainfall}_{t+1} = \text{Rainfall}_t + E$$

where t is the current time, $t+1$ is the time in 1 hour and E is an error term. The error term is required since if we tested the equation against rainfall data, we would find that we were occasionally (if not frequently) wrong.

The error may reflect inadequate knowledge, so that we could reduce the error by improving the model, for example, by adding an additional factor such as a knowledge of wind direction. By contrast it may be due to chance influences whose outcomes on any particular occasion are not susceptible to prediction. Statistical methods can be used for testing hypotheses in many fields of endeavour.

1.2 Descriptive and analytical statistics

The two definitions given in Section 1.1 above are not unrelated to one another. The numerical facts which we collect about any matter that interests us help to describe the state of affairs existing at the time of the investigation. These are called **descriptive statistics**. They are usually presented in some way which improves the **raw data**, a term meaning 'untreated' data. A mass of raw data is very confusing. All the statistics recorded are as important, or as unimportant, as one another. To improve the description of the state of affairs under discussion we need to sort out the data to some extent. Thus the ages of students at a technical college might lead us to conclude that a large part of the student body were school leavers, while others left school only recently. Others might be postgraduates, ie those with a university degree who had decided to follow a further course which would apply their academic knowledge in some professional field. Yet others might be described as 'mature students' returning late in life to pursue some sort of advanced career training. By presenting this set of data in the form of a table (**tabulation**) showing the four groups, we describe the student body in a simple way.

Composition of student body: September 19——

Type of student	Age	Numbers
School leavers	16	582
Others under 21	17–20	984
Postgraduates	21 +	87
Other mature students	21 +	286
Total		1939

Analytical statistics seeks to go further than descriptive statistics. It seeks to analyse the data so as to enable us to reach decisions. The decision might be a positive one – such as a decision to expand production. Equally it might be a decision to take no action at all. Statistical conclusions may reinforce support for current policy, or overturn current policy in favour of a new approach. Sometimes a statistical inquiry may be set up to determine the viability of a project or proposal, to weigh the costs and benefits against one another. This is not easy, for costs and benefits may be difficult to quantify in numerical terms. A proposal to bridge an estuary and thus divert traffic from a busy up-river town, where a centuries-old bridge is at present coping with a huge traffic problem, might be the subject of such a **cost-benefit analysis**. We can easily calculate the mileage saved by the new bridge, and if we estimate the number of vehicles using it we can quantify the vehicle costs saved. How shall we quantify the happiness of the parents of the five children dying in road accidents at present each year, whose lives will be saved by the new bridge? There are many problems in any statistical inquiry: of definition, of bias and its avoidance, of quantification, standardisation, etc. Analytical statistics are sometimes referred to as **inductive statistics** in that they lead us to make generalisations or predictions from the data we have collected.

1.3   The range of problems requiring statistical treatment

Economic life seeks to provide satisfaction of the wants of mankind by the creation of goods and services. These goods and services may be provided by private enterprise – in other words by business units of one sort or another – or they may be provided by the 'public sector'. This is the sector of production which is state controlled, or controlled by local government. In the United Kingdom the private sector of business enterprise and the public sector are about equal in size. In other countries the public sector may dominate, as in the communist or socialist countries, while in others the free enterprise sector may dominate, as in the United States of America. Whichever type of society we live in the problems are really the same. How many people have we in our country? What standard of living do they enjoy and what aspirations have they for the future? What volume of goods and what types of services are required to achieve these aspirations? How shall we produce or provide them? What inputs of resources are required and what outputs can we expect? How shall we ensure uniform quality in the goods we produce and the services we offer? Since no nation is self-sufficient how much foreign trade is required? How shall it be financed and insured? What are the risks involved and what are the probabilities that a particular event will occur? What feedback control mechanisms in the light of management information revealed in the course of business activities are required to keep production, distribution and exchange activities at optimum levels?

Almost all these matters are susceptible to statistical inquiry. Many of them will be monitored continuously by government bureaux or by managements. In the United Kingdom, the Central Statistical Office was at one time part of the Cabinet Office. It has now been made into a separate department more remote from the centre of power, since it is important to avoid bias in statistics. It was felt by some critics that statistics were being manipulated by those at the centre of power. Every bank has its 'financial statistics division' and every major firm has a number of departments largely concerned with statistics of one sort or another. There will be quality control divisions in production departments, budgetary control divisions under the chief accountant, market research departments under the marketing manager, etc. Other problems may be investigated on an *ad hoc* basis, as difficulties arise, with a team appointed to solve the problem.

1.4 The stages of a statistical inquiry

The stages of a statistical inquiry may be listed as follows:

a The problem must be clearly stated

An inquiry cannot be launched in general terms. We must identify the cause for concern and state explicitly what the problem is. For example, an investigation into labour turnover may not affect all parts of a firm equally. No inquiry may be necessary in many departments where labour turnover is not abnormal. The area giving trouble may be a particular department, or a particular process or product. Stating the problem carefully gives those conducting the inquiry **terms of reference** from which they can start to collect relevant data for analysis.

b The best approach must be decided upon

In the light of the terms of reference provided by *a* above, how shall we tackle the problem? Statistical evidence may already be available from past records. Someone may already have faced the same problem, and it will be a waste of time to repeat an investigation. Many inquiries begin with a **'literature survey'** in which we read all the published material already available on this, or related topics. Other inquiries begin with a thorough survey of all past records available **'in house'**. For example, a 'labour turnover' investigation might begin with an examination of 'closed' personnel files. Why did people in this area leave? Did the explanations they gave fit into a pattern of behaviour that pinpoints the cause of our problem? Was it working conditions, levels of remuneration, supervisory problems or what?

c Census or sample survey

If available material cannot solve our problem we must commence the collection of data. An immediate problem is the extent of the inquiry. Shall it extend to include the whole **'population'**? This word has a special meaning in statistics – it refers to the whole of the material affected by the inquiry in hand. In some cases, such as the United Kingdom Census (held every 10 years in the first year of the decade) the population is every person living in the United Kingdom, and the word, therefore, has its ordinary dictionary meaning. In other cases, for example, an inquiry into labour turnover in the machine shop, it refers to every individual working in the machine shop. Probably an inquiry of this sort should investigate the views of every person concerned, but this might be a lengthy process if the numbers were large. We could perhaps get just as good a result by asking every tenth member for his/her views. This is called a **sample survey**. Special precautions are necessary to ensure that those interviewed are a **random sample**, not a biased sample which will give a biased result. For example, suppose the most convenient group to interview were those who arrived early for work. This might well be a biased sample. People who arrive early for work are frequently enthusiastic about their work and unlikely to be disgruntled and considering a transfer. Therefore, to ask only such employees may not produce a true answer to our problem.

d Is a questionnaire necessary?

One of the simplest ways to conduct an inquiry is to draw up a questionnaire. This ensures that all interviewees are asked all the questions we feel are relevant to the problem in hand. The questions should be posed in the same way to all so as to avoid biasing the answers by slightly different wording, or even an inflection of the voice. A **pilot inquiry** may be necessary (preferably in a different department) to test out the form and discover any weaknesses – ambiguous questions often produce irrelevant answers, not foreseen by those drawing up the questionnaire.

e Collecting the data

Many inquiries take the form of interviewing people, and it is essential to appoint interviewers, brief them adequately and ensure that they conduct the interviews in a proper manner. Any conclusions drawn from a badly conducted series of interviews will be meaningless. Other inquiries do not involve interviewing, data is collected by **enumerators** who record facts as they become available. Thus a traffic census requires enumerators to record traffic passing a specific point, using the five-barred gate principle illustrated in Fig 1.1. Other data may be collected electronically, by telemetering devices in rivers, for example, if the inquiry is about water quality.

f Editing and classifying the data

The result of *e* above is a mass of raw data, in a very indigestible form. Some of it may need editing to tidy it up. For example, in Fig. 1.1 on page 6 the editor will add up the total number of vehicles recorded on each part of the form and record it as shown in a circle. These should then be carried to a master sheet which will provide the total for the day under each heading.

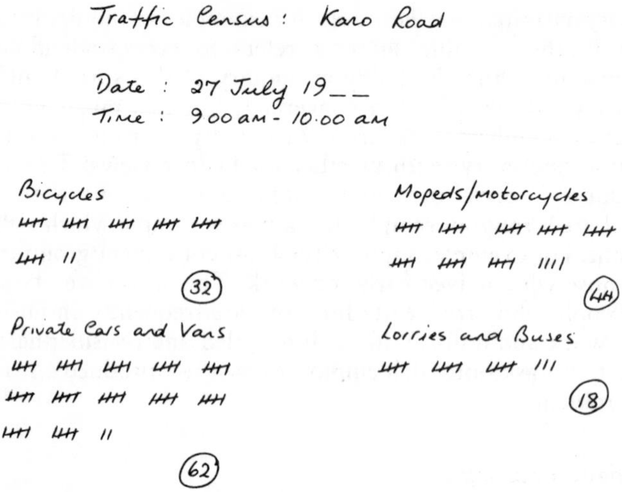

Traffic Census : Karo Road

Date : 27 July 19 _ _
Time : 9·00 am - 10·00 am

Bicycles

HHT HHT HHT HHT HHT
HHT //
(32)

Mopeds/motorcycles

HHT HHT HHT HHT HHT
HHT HHT HHT ////
(44)

Private Cars and Vans

HHT HHT HHT HHT HHT
HHT HHT HHT HHT HHT
HHT HHT //
(62)

Lorries and Buses

HHT HHT HHT ///
(18)

Fig 1.1 The five-barred gate system of enumeration

g Analysing the data

We are now in a position to analyse the data. Up to this point much of the work may have been done by enumerators who were neither skilled in statistical method nor knowledgeable about the matter under investigation. It might even be preferable to use such people during the collection of the data, since an enumerator who is vitally interested in the results may introduce unconscious or – worse still – conscious bias into the data. When analysing the data it is essential to have those who are knowledgeable about the subject matter and skilled in statistical method taking part. The various parties will act as a check upon one another and ensure valid conclusions.

h Presentation and report writing – including recommendations

The result of any survey is a set of proposals to remedy the problem originally faced, or to choose between alternative programmes and policies. In making these recommendations it is necessary to present the data in a simple and convincing style, as part of a report to the appropriate authority. The report will be addressed to the authority that ordered the investigation and will usually begin by quoting the terms of reference given to the team at the commencement of the inquiry. Tables, charts and diagrams will show what the survey found, suggest the causes or reasons for the original problem and make firm recommendations to resolve the difficulty.

In any statistical inquiry the subject of the exercise is to solve a problem. It may be a matter of product quality, market penetration, provision of an adequate service at reasonable cost or the improvement of the environment. There is no point in collecting statistics for their own sake, or to demonstrate our erudition. Statistical surveys are expensive, and we shall generally be judged by our cost effectiveness in demonstrating the true facts and recommending the most likely cure in the circumstances.

1.5 Statistics for business use

It is difficult and artificial to separate statistical data and statistical techniques into subject areas. They are not mutually exclusive. Thus population statistics are usually collected and presented by social statisticians but they may be of enormous importance to businessmen. Products suitable for particular age groups need to be available in increasing numbers as a bulge in the birthrate moves through its life cycle, and a businessman who is aware of the passing of the wave may expand output as it approaches and reduce output as it passes. The National Income and Expenditure Survey is not solely of interest to public-sector corporations, it may have many implications for private-sector firms.

All published statistics are really part of management information, but a great deal of statistical management information is generated in house. This will be generated both as raw data, and in treated form. We may have tables of output, sales, stock levels, personnel rolls, etc; charts of production, sales, machine utilisation, productivity, etc; ratios of stock turnover, gross profit, net profit, working capital, etc. Countless analyses will be made of products, customer trends, sales areas, sales periods, order size, distribution method, maintenance programmes, vehicle usage, vehicle mileage, debtor age, cash flow, etc. All such management information requires the manager to be aware of statistical techniques, familiar with statistical jargon (the specialised vocabulary of statisticians) and appreciative of its uses (rather than resentful of its intrusions into his/her cosy world). Corporate objectives are seldom realised by chance; they have to be achieved by managerial controls which keep the firm abreast of trends.

1.6 Statistics – a science and an art

The student who approaches the subject of statistics for the first time should bear in mind that it is both a science and an art. Statistical method is part of general scientific method and has the same fundamental ideas and processes. We are seeking to establish exactly what the present situation is in the economic or social field under investigation. We wish to make decisions about the future which will be beneficial in some way, by understanding the present and predicting likely results of various policies or activities. The figures we are dealing with are not simple, as they might be in chemistry or physics, but variable in an infinite variety of ways as different influences are brought to bear. Speaking of the problem of controlling the money supply one representative of the Bank of England said 'Any measure of money supply which is officially controlled promptly loses its meaning'. Having been at great pains to pin down and define the money supply so that it could be controlled, the Bank's statisticians then found that practical bankers, financiers, depositors and even ordinary householders varied their patterns of activity to escape the controls and drive an infinite variety of coaches and horses through the gaps in the Bank's definition.

Whilst keeping our scientific integrity we must also exercise our ingenuity in presenting our statistics in such a way as to command the respect of, and enlighten, our audience, whatever its level. A presentation to a board meeting or a panel of expert and influential decision-makers is an art that is not easily acquired. When watching media presentations on our television sets we see many attempts to present data in an attractive and simple form, but we are not always convinced by them. Indeed, there are many more critics of statistics than are supporters. Disraeli said 'There are lies, damned lies and statistics!' It is a popular belief that you can prove anything by statistics, and consequently all statistics are suspect. This public distrust of statistics is probably not a bad thing, especially if it inclines the statistician to take more than usual care to achieve precision in the statements he/she makes.

1.7 The use of calculators in statistics

Many calculations in statistics are lengthy and take a considerable time. Today many of the more difficult calculations can be performed on electronic calculators in seconds. This presents us with a dilemma. Does the student really understand what he/she is doing when, for example, at the touch of a calculator button, the standard deviation of a set of data is displayed on the screen? The student does not, of course, at this stage, know what is meant by 'the standard deviation of a set of data', but clearly there is little point in letting the machine do something which is a complete mystery to the student. For this reason the student is urged to work out most questions fully so as to become familiar with what is happening to the data being investigated, and to turn to the calculator only when absolutely confident of understanding what it has achieved in a fraction of a second. Then, when using the calculator in an examination, or in employment, the student will have a full understanding of what the results shown on the display panel mean.

For the level of work referred to in this book, a scientific calculator which has a statistical mode would be adequate. An ordinary hand calculator has only the arithmetical functions $+$, $-$, $\times$ and $\div$ plus a % key and a single memory. Scientific calculators have a number of other keys, some of which are statistical while others are mathematical and scientific. Many of the keys have two possible actions, one more routine and the other specialist in a particular field. To bring the keys up to the more specialist function, a key labelled 2nd F (second function) is touched and the double function keys then work in their second, more complex, activity.

More advanced statistical work requires a specialised computer program rather than a calculator and, although this particular text is not aimed at the more advanced student, some reference is made to such programs later in the text.

Summary

1 Statistics may be defined as numerical facts, systematically collected and presented. Another definition, using the word in a different way, defines statistics as a range of mathematical techniques for analysing problems in the real world.

2 Descriptive statistics may be collected and marshalled to present in some tabulated or diagrammatic form the actual situation at the time of an inquiry. Analytical statistics seek to go further, and assist decision-making by drawing general conclusions, calculating ratios and percentages, discovering trends in the data, etc.

3 The range of problems requiring statistical investigation is large. Many of them will be monitored continuously; others will be investigated as the problem arises.

4 The stages of a statistical inquiry are *a* a clear statement of the problem, *b* a literature or in-house records survey, *c* a 'census or sample' decision, *d* preparation of a questionnaire, *e* appointment and training of enumerators or interviewers, *f* collection of the data, *g* checking, editing and classification of the data, *h* analysis of the data and *i* presentation and report writing, including recommendations.

5 Statistics is both a science and an art.

Exercises

1 What is meant by the phrase 'terms of reference' in a statistical inquiry?

2 What are the main stages in a statistical inquiry? In your answer select one of the following to illustrate the stages you list. Either:
   a A traffic census involving the High Street of a small town. The High Street is part of a trunk road, and the investigation is to discover not only the true traffic situation but also the views of local inhabitants about the traffic problems. Or:
   b A proposal has been made to move a factory to new premises in a satellite town outside its present conurbation. Housing will be provided for staff wishing to move, and the inquiry is to establish the exact position of personnel should the move take place. In the opinion of the board of directors the move is viable from other business points of view.

3 In what ways is statistics a science? In what ways is it an art?

4 A motor transport department has 50 similar vehicles. Management suspects that its control of these vehicles is inadequate. What suggestions could you make for investigating vehicle use, and tightening managerial control over the department?

2 The collection of routine data

2.1 Facts – the decision-makers

Mark Twain, in his book *A Tramp Abroad*, tells of the delights of conversation while walking. It is, he says, at its best after the first 15 minutes, because, by that time, people have exhausted the topics about which they are knowledgeable, and have moved on to subjects where they can embroider the conversation imaginatively. Controversies can flourish in a situation where any reference to the real facts is avoided. Weary miles are covered unnoticed as fertile minds invent stories, and recall incidents to illustrate opinions held with a strength of conviction that is only matched by the weakness of the evidence. The last person one wants in such a group of happy wanderers is a companion who presents detailed factual information in a cogent way, which will kill the conversation by settling any arguments and revealing the inadequacies of the other travellers.

By contrast, the major activities of economic life – the production, distribution and exchange of goods and services, the redistribution of wealth through taxation and public-expenditure programmes and the general management of prosperity – call for factual knowledge of the most detailed sort. What are the true facts of resource availability? What are the optimum combinations of land, labour and capital in any production system? What choices should be made between consumption and capital creation, etc? Such decisions can only be made on the basis of facts collected by inquiries of one sort or another, and presented in a statistical form to highlight the significant information.

The availability of the statistical facts is therefore of peculiar importance in economic affairs; hence, the subject of 'business statistics'. The study begins at grass-roots level with the collection of business data as and where they occur. It is then necessary to collate the statistics, and make sense of them, separating off the significant data from the unimportant data. This will usually be a middle-management function of some sort, either an individual or a committee receiving the grass-roots data and analysing and reviewing it. The result of this review will be a report to top management on which policy decisions can be based. Where the data is of social significance (as, for example, with factory accidents which occur in business premises but impose social costs) it may be necessary for a government department to be the collating and reporting body. Statistics collected for social purposes are therefore frequently of great concern to businesses and may bring cost consequences, or even fines and imprisonment on responsible officers. The subject of business statistics is not therefore solely related to in-house statistics. To summarise, business statistics may be broken down into the following sections:

a the collection of data at a grass-roots level
b collation and analysis of the data
c reports and recommendations
d decisions and executive action

Collection of data at grass-roots level then begins again to provide data on the effectiveness of the action taken.

2.2 Types of statistics

Statistics are of two types, **primary statistics** and **secondary statistics**. Primary data are the raw data, obtained at first hand, as a result of some sort of inquiry. Because the data are collected for a specific purpose they will give us the exact information we require. Questions will be devised in such a way as to elucidate the information we need, and checks can be introduced to ensure accuracy and freedom from bias. By contrast, secondary data are obtained from some published source, or from some quite different investigation which may still have valuable information for the inquiry we are pursuing. Of course, all such published material was originally primary data, but it has been analysed and 'worked up' to some extent and presented in some way. Examples of secondary data are those published in the *Annual Abstract of Statistics* by the United Kingdom Central Statistical Office. It gives 400 tables, covering such major fields as population, vital statistics (births and deaths), education, labour, production, transport, distribution, external trade, balance of payments and many more.

Many businesses classify data as internal or external. **Internal data** is generated in house, and is therefore largely primary data. A major source of in-house data is the **routine report** on such matters as sales, quality control, capital expenditure, labour turnover, etc. Other in-house data may be produced by an *ad hoc* **inquiry** set up to deal with a particular problem and discover the facts which will enable a solution to be found.

By contrast, **external data** are not generated in house but are made available from official or private sources. A very wide range of data is published officially in such periodicals as the *Monthly Digest of Statistics, Economic Trends, Social Trends, The National Blue Book on Income and Expenditure, The Pink Book on Balance of Payments, the Family Expenditure Survey*, etc. These are British publications. Overseas readers might like to draw up lists of official published statistics for their own countries.

2.3 Routine statistics and management by exceptions

Many statistics are collected routinely. Their variety is enormous, and varies from institution to institution. Thus a manufacturer will need statistics about *a* production (raw-material volumes and costs, outputs, wastage, overheads, etc), *b* sales (stocks in hand, sales volumes, selling prices, distribution costs, etc), *c* payrolls (labour, wages, labour turnover, training costs, etc), *d* capital expenditure (premises, plant and machinery, warehousing, vehicles, office equipment, etc) and *e* many other items. A central government will need statistics about national output, income and expenditure, employment, exports, imports, etc. A local-government body needs statistics of education, welfare, transport, the infrastructure of its area, recreational needs, etc.

The sources of such records may be listed as follows:

a Permanent records (for example, about staff, customers, suppliers, residents, tenants, etc). Names, addresses, telephone numbers and other details on the matter in hand will be essential permanent records.

b Current records (for example, sales invoices, purchases invoices, payroll sheets, regular returns from salesmen, agents, departments and subsidiaries).

c Regular returns are often called for by government departments, local authorities, etc, on a wide variety of topics (for example, accidents at work, attendances at schools and colleges, out-patient treatment at hospitals, etc). They are a special form of current records.

A word or two about each of these is desirable at this point.

a Permanent records

Permanent records are usually arranged on some sort of card indexed, loose-leaf or computer-based system. It is essential to be able to insert new records in the correct place alphabetically (or whatever other filing system is in use). Where records are frequently referred to a visible index system is often helpful, unless the records are computerised and available as part of a database.

b Current records

Current records, such as invoices, credit notes, etc, in business matters, or incident reports, accident reports, parking offences, etc, in police work, provide the raw data from which regular summaries can be prepared on trends in sales, purchases, labour turnover, crime, etc. The data for these summaries may today be captured on computerised records in large organisations, a simple program being prepared to collect the information desired. In smaller organisations it is necessary to extract the data onto summaries; only the essential data being taken to the summary. For example, in sales records it is not necessary to know the names and addresses of the customers, only the amount of the invoice. Figure 2.1 shows such a summary for takings used in the Simplex System of bookkeeping. The weekly figures for takings have been carried to the summary, which is arranged in four quarterly summaries giving an annual total. The result is that the manager or proprietor of the business concerned can compare the figures for each week with the corresponding

Week no	Amount	Week no	Amount	Week no	Amount	Week no	Amount
1	326.42	14	525.60	27	784.60	40	721.30
2	372.56	15	485.90	28	886.20	41	562.55
3	428.60	16	721.60	29	634.40	42	472.80
4	418.55	17	732.50	30	420.50	43	459.60
5	422.30	18	426.50	31	428.50	44	473.28
6	384.60	19	388.60	32	556.60	45	426.40
7	372.60	20	785.60	33	495.90	46	389.85
8	426.50	21	685.60	34	480.01	47	427.30
9	732.80	22	526.60	35	630.27	48	625.46
10	688.80	23	430.40	36	680.48	49	752.80
11	725.60	24	480.40	37	690.25	50	1120.50
12	642.40	25	492.60	38	685.72	51	1750.25
13	486.30	26	721.60	39	738.60	52	408.39
Total 1st qtr	6428.03	Total 2nd qtr	7403.50	Total 3rd qtr	8112.03	Total 4th qtr	8590.48

Total summary for year	
1st qtr	6428.03
2nd qtr	7403.50
3rd qtr	8112.03
4th qtr	8590.48
TOTAL	30534.04

Fig 2.1 A summary of weekly takings (courtesy of George Vyner Ltd, Simplex Account Books)

figure for the previous year's records which are available in last year's account book. Similarly, the quarterly figures can be compared with one another and with corresponding figures for earlier years, and, of course, this is also true of the annual figure. The result is a regular check of business trends, available almost at a glance.

When preparing summaries of this sort, and in particular when designing the summary form, it is essential to make the form as foolproof as possible. It may be necessary to define such things as 'weekly takings' – for example, what is to be done about 'sales returns'? Are returns of goods sold in a previous week to be deducted from the sales for that week, or from the sales of the current week? The first gives more accurate figures but involves altering figures already inserted in the summary. The second choice is therefore more convenient.

c **Regular returns**

In every field of economic and social activity management seeks to control the enterprise by calling for regular reports. They are often called 'returns' because the necessary forms are sent out at prescribed intervals, to be returned by a specific date. A monthly return is often convenient, but weekly returns or even daily returns may be called for. The disadvantage of monthly returns is that the months vary in length from 28 days to 31 days. Any comparison between monthly figures is therefore difficult. Sometimes a 4-weekly 'month' is adopted, to give 13 months in the year. It depends upon the statistics being collected and the use made of them as to whether such considerations are important. Since the aim of the statistician is to avoid error and serve truth, it is essential to arrange these routine activities in such a way that the bare, verifiable facts are called for. The report must be compulsory, and failure to deliver the required data by the required time calls for an immediate inquiry. Generally speaking, delay is suspicious. The data may be unpleasant, reflecting adversely upon the person required to present them. Some sort of spot check may be called for, especially if false returns are suspected.

One of the chief uses of regular reports is **management by exceptions**. An example we are all familiar with is the ordinary register used in schools and colleges. In Fig 2.2 the exceptions to the general rule that students attend for 10 sessions a week are clearly shown. S Thomas has been absent for the 2 weeks shown, and P Johnson was absent for 8 days, but has now returned. The other exception is P Svenson, whose erratic attendance calls for inquiry. Is he in bad health, or truanting, or has he domestic problems which call for some sort of social casework? An alert teacher or lecturer might pinpoint the difficulty and resolve any problem.

Abbott M	/ \ / \ / \ / \ / \ / \ / \ / \ / \ / \
Green T	/ \ / \ / \ / \ / \ / \ / \ / \ / \ \
Howard H	/ \ / \ / \ / \ / \ / \ / \ / \ / \ \
Johnson P	O O O O O O O O O O O O O O O O / \ / \
Malik A	/ \ / \ / \ / \ / \ / \ / \ / \ / \ \
Mason T	/ \ / \ / \ / \ / \ / \ / \ / \ / \
Svenson P	/ \ / \ O O / \ O O / \ O O / \ O O O O
Thomas S	O O O O O O O O O O O O O O O O O O O O
Uhuru R	/ \ / \ / \ / \ / \ / \ / \ / \ / \
Zweig T	/ \ / \ / \ / \ / \ / \ / \ / \ / \

Fig 2.2 Managing the classroom 'by exceptions'

A similar situation which is not quite as obvious is shown in the monthly returns submitted to an education authority from a particular evening institute. The management problems presented by such establishments involve the exercise of choice about which courses should be provided. Public expenditure is involved, although a certain part of the costs is borne by the students in the form of admission fees. The question is which courses deserve a subsidy, and how much is justified in each case? It is usual to set minimum numbers, below which it is no longer worth while keeping a course open. Some courses may be deemed more socially valuable than others. All such decisions are debatable, but in the example given an examination course is considered more valuable than a recreational course, or a course which, while educational in nature, does not lead to the attainment of a recognised qualification. The notes which appear below Fig 2.3 on page 15 explain the situation.

Management by exceptions may be used in a wide range of supervisory activities. For example, area managers might control the effectiveness of a force of salesmen by comparing their records on the following matters:

a sales for the month
b calls made in the month

No	Name of class	Category (E, Ex, R)	Week commencing November				
			1	8	15	22	29
1	BTEC General	Ex	27	28	32	31	31
2	BTEC National	Ex	43	41	42	39	37
3	Bookkeeping	Ex	14	15	13	14	16
4	Economics	E	11	12	9	5	4
5	Photography	R	17	13	8	6	5
6	Ladies keep-fit	R	34	28	29	36	33
7	Typewriting I	E	18	17	22	23	17
8	Typewriting II	Ex	11	8	7	8	9
9	Geography	E	12	11	12	10	7
10	Physics	E	9	8	9	3	9

Fig 2.3 Decision-making at the education office

Notes
 i The minimum number for educational courses (E) is 12, for examination courses (Ex) it is 10 and for recreational courses (R) it is 15.
 ii Any course which falls below the minimum for 3 weeks will be closed, unless special pleading with the Chief Education Officer persuades him/her that continuance is justified.
 iii For the examination courses typewriting II is the exception. It has already fallen below the minimum for more than 3 weeks, and should logically be closed. The usual course is to merge such classes with similar groups and typewriting I is available. However, typewriting courses do depend on the number of machines available. We cannot merge classes if it means some students have no machine. Management will keep its eye on this course, but for the moment it is not going to close Typewriting II.
 iv Which of the educational courses would you close at once? Which of them is in danger of closing? What special case could you make with the Chief Education Officer about physics, bearing in mind that the attendance in the week beginning 22 November was affected by unusually bad weather?
 v Which recreational class should be closed at once?
 vi The printed illustration in Fig 2.3 does not quite bring out the exceptions as easily as the real returns would do, for it is usual to complete the returns in red if the weekly figure is below the minimum attendance required. Thus in economics the figures 9, 5, 4 would be in red, and in physics all the figures would be in red.

 c sales per call made
 d new customers per month
 e repeat orders from old customers per month
 f expenses per month
 g kilometres covered
 h motor vehicle expenses per month
 i kilometres per litre of fuel used
 j sales per kilometre travelled

ACCIDENT/DANGEROUS OCCURRENCE REPORT

In accordance with the Merchant Shipping (Safety Officials and Reporting of Accidents and Dangerous Occurrences) Regulations 1982. S.I. No. 876 (1982) 11.(3)(6).

Employer

Report No. (Consec.)	Ships Position	Voyage No.	Name of Vessel	Official No.

Accident or Dangerous Occurrence			Date of Incident		
Notifiable on D.O.T. form ARF.1	YES/NO	Time	Local		GMT
Conditions	Wind & Sea		Weather		
	Ship movement			Lighting	

DETAILS OF INCIDENT. State precise Location (attach sketch if necessary). cause and circumstances of incident. Also give names and parts of any equipment involved.

Continue on separate sheet if insufficient space above.

Personnel involved in incident		Witnesses (attach Statements from Witnesses).	
Name(s)	Rank/Rating	Name(s)	Rank/Rating

Details of Injuries

Action Taken / Recommendations to prevent future similar incident

TOP COPY FOR EMPLOYER — BOTTOM COPY FOR SAFETY OFFICER'S RECORDS

Date	Signature	Rank

Fig 2.4 Collecting statistics on merchant shipping accidents and dangerous occurrences

Notes

i The detailed report will enable a proper investigation to be held into each incident, so that the employer can take immediate steps within his own organisation to avoid a recurrence and deal in a proper manner with any compensation problems, etc.

Of course, the generation of all these statistics costs time and money, but the knowledge that such figures are calculated may have a salutary effect upon performance. A salesman will hesitate to miss a call if it means that the omission is sure to be detected, while the use of the car for non-business purposes may adversely affect 'sales per kilometre travelled' by increasing motor vehicle distances without any corresponding increase in sales. The use of such statistics calls for comparison charts which will enable the efforts of the sales force to be compared, so that the exceptions can be pinpointed.

2.4 An example of routine data collection

When data are collected on a routine basis the essential thing is to have a simple form which ensures that the details required are provided in a standard manner which makes their eventual collation and analysis easy. These ideas can best be understood by considering a particular case, and the example given on page 16 is the Merchant Shipping (Safety Officials and Reporting Accidents and Dangerous Occurrences) Regulations 1982, which are published as SI No 876 (1982). (SI stands for Statutory Instrument. This is a document produced by a government department – in this particular case the Department of Trade – under the authority of an earlier Act of Parliament.)

The regulations begin by defining exactly what an accident or dangerous occurrence is. In these regulations an accident is defined as an event causing death or personal injury involving incapacity for more than 3 days (not counting the day of the accident). Alternatively, if the injury was serious enough to require a sailor to be put ashore – so that the ship sailed without him – this is notifiable. As a great many accidents are reportable under different regulations, such as the off-shore installations regulations and the submarine pipeline regulations, these are therefore excluded from the regulations.

A dangerous occurrence is defined to include the collapse or overturning of any lift, hoist, ramp, etc; the explosion, collapse or bursting of any vessel, boiler, etc; any electrical short circuit or overload; any sudden release of inflammable gas or liquid and any release of a noxious substance. Clearly, the statistics, when collated, will separate off these classes of occurrences to discover any particular piece of ship's gear which shows defects with a view to rectifying the problem. Other events

---

ii The submission of the report to the Department of Trade will enable them to collate the report with others coming in from all other employers, to see if similar events are occurring on other ships. This will result in a nationwide awareness of the failure of particular items of ships' gear or merchant-shipping practices (for example, such procedures as the cleaning of tanks on very large crude carriers).

iii The discovery of some defect in this way would be investigated by scrutiny of all the reports concerned, to discover the pattern of events. This would give a clue to the remedial measures required and lead to a review of design and operating procedures.

are the bursting or collapse of pipelines, the parting of tow ropes, any fall overboard, collapse of a hatch cover or contact with loose asbestos fibre (other than for those wearing protective apparatus).

The employer must investigate every case, and complete and sign a report which must then be submitted to the Department of Trade. The regulations give the detailed requirements to be covered in the report. This makes it relatively simple for any enterprising firm in the stationery field to design a form which will meet the requirements. The example in Fig 2.4 shows one company's solution to the problem of collecting these routine statistics.

Finally, we may note that the penalty for failure to keep proper records of accidents or dangerous occurrences is a fine of £1000 or imprisonment for up to 2 years, or both. Here is the 'compulsion' element in the collection of comprehensive data on these matters.

2.5 Computer collection and storage of data

Data obtained from routine surveys should be filed in an orderly and systematic manner to ensure rapid access when it is required by managers and other data users. It is important that the data filing system be organised such that data are easily assembled for quick scanning and review of results. The data should also be arranged so that the statistical analysis and report preparation may be readily carried out.

Although manual recording and analysis will still be a feature of many inquiries, electronic data storage and processing is becoming increasingly common for all large-scale inquiries. The importance of developing and maintaining an efficient data-processing and storage system cannot be overemphasised. In recent years the cost of computers has fallen dramatically with an equally astonishing increase in computer power. For example, a computer system costing hundreds of thousands of pounds in 1970 can be bought today for £10 000 and there is a further range of small-business and home computers available below this price. All computers have some method of storing data whether it be in a direct random-access memory (RAM), computer discs or magnetic tapes. A typical small computer system is shown in Fig 2.5 on page 19.

In general, direct random-access memory storage is fairly limited since this space is reserved for storing computer programs (ie instructions for the particular task the operator wants the computer to perform). These are entered from the keyboard, or via the disc or tape, and are erased from the memory when the power is turned off. Computer discs and magnetic tapes store large quantities of data more permanently and can be read by the computer in the same way as a turntable plays records, in the case of a disc, or as with a normal cassette tape deck, in the case of a magnetic tape.

Computers can handle large quantities of data rapidly and efficiently and can even be used as the primary means of collecting routine data. For example, in the case of chemical process plant, instruments measuring such variables as temperature, pressure or chemical concentrations can be telemetered directly into a computer and the data stored automatically

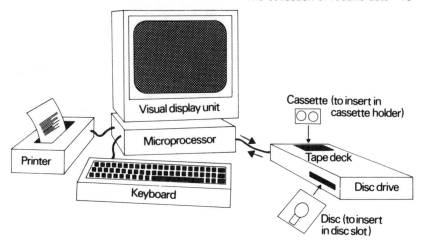

Fig 2.5 Typical components of a small computer system

Notes
 i The microprocessor in this layout is situated in the base of the visual display unit (VDU) and is the brains of the computer.
 ii The keyboard is used to input instructions into the computer and also to input the data from the 'raw' form in which it was collected.
 iii The disk drive/tape deck accepts stored data on disc or cassette and inputs it into the computer. After processing, the data, perhaps in a modified form, will be put out to storage again on the disc or tape.
 iv When attached, the printer can be used to output data or conclusions in readable form.

on discs or magnetic tapes. Such data can be retrieved at any time by management to check on process performance or to obtain statistical summaries. The computer in this situation is used to read in the current data and store them together with all the routine data. A typical print out of such routine data is given in Fig 2.6.

Derived statistics   Derived statistics are statistics obtained as part of the analysis of raw data. For example, we may find averages, or percentage figures, as part of the process of summarising the raw data and trying to make sense of it. Some derived statistics are shown in Fig 2.7 on page 20.

Although the data shown in Fig 2.7 have been derived from a similar set of data as collected in Fig 2.6 they do not actually relate to that particular set of data. The computer has been programmed to calculate average figures, and deviations from the average. These calculations will be explained in later chapters of this book. The ability of the computer to perform these calculations (which can be quite tedious) instantaneously is obviously a great help to statisticians.

In many chemical processing plants automatic computer monitoring is essential since it would be impossible to collect all the data manually. Whilst such processing-plant data have immediate value for operational

Date	Time	Dissolved oxygen (% saturation)	Temperature °C	Conductivity (μ siemens)	Ammonia concentration (mg/l)	pH
19.8—	09.09	50.00	15.60	947.21	0.04	7.73
19.8—	11.20	64.06	15.79	966.74	0.04	7.83
19.8—	11.49	66.79	15.79	966.74	0.04	7.86
19.8—	12.16	71.48	15.79	956.97	0.04	7.88
19.8—	12.19	72.26	15.89	956.97	0.04	7.89
19.8—	12.24	73.43	15.89	956.97	0.04	7.89
19.8—	12.34	75.78	15.89	956.97	0.04	7.93
19.8—	12.39	76.95	15.89	956.13	0.04	7.83
19.8—	12.44	76.56	15.89	956.97	0.04	7.99
19.8—	12.49	77.73	15.89	956.97	0.04	7.95

Fig 2.6 Routine data monitored, stored and listed by computer from river sensors

Notes
 i The measurements are made on the same day, 19 August. (The year has been shown as —.)
 ii Times for taking measurements are pre-set according to the sampling programme being undertaken.
 iii The automatic sensors measure oxygen concentrations, water temperature, the conductivity of the water, ammonia levels and acidity (pH) values.

Instrument	No. of samples	Minimum	Maximum	Mean	Standard deviation	Units
Dissolved oxygen	7	48.8	105.1	75.9	22.70	% saturation
Temperature	7	14.0	15.5	14.6	0.51	Celsius
Conductivity	7	869.1	957.0	927.7	33.35	μ siemens
Ammonia (as N)	7	0.04	0.04	0.04	0.00	mg/l
pH	7	7.7	8.3	8.0	0.21	—

Fig 2.7 A statistical summary of routine data

management they may also be of use to management at a later stage. For example, they can be used to investigate a fault in the process, or to investigate the variability of the final product. The data may be stored as a permanent record on the disc or magnetic tape and the data saved. A common term used to describe such permanent records in data storage is a data bank, analogous to the bank we store our money in. Such a permanent data bank is frequently used to store data obtained from manual surveys. This is explained in the next chapter.

Summary

1 The availability of statistical facts is particularly important in business and government affairs.
2 The stages of business statistics are *a* collection of facts at a grass-roots level, *b* collation and analysis of the data, *c* reports and recommendations and, *d* decisions and executive action.
3 Primary data are raw data, collected for a specific inquiry; secondary data are published data which have been worked up from some inquiry but may provide useful information for business purposes on other, quite different, inquiries.
4 Many statistics are collected on a routine basis. They may be required by management in the form of regular 'returns'. A policy of *management by exceptions* permits decisions to be made on a whole host of matters in line with declared policy (for example, boardroom policy, council policy, departmental policy or governmental policy).
5 Data collected as a result of routine surveys must be filed in an orderly manner for processing in due course. This may be done manually, but increasing use is being made of computerised storage of data. Much routine data are measured by sensors (telemetry) and reported to minicomputers which record, process and summarise it.

Exercises

1 Coldstore Ltd manufacture refrigerators, which are marketed nationwide through domestic hardware stores. You are the area manager for the south-east region. Consider what types of statistics would be necessary to control a labour force of commercial travellers.
2 Distinguish between internal statistics and external statistics. Suggest types of external statistics which would be of interest to a shoe manufacturer making children's shoes and juvenile sportswear?
3 Under the statutory sick-pay regulations for the country of Westland employers are obliged to pay wages in full to all workers who are sick. If an employee is sick for more than three consecutive days a PRSP (period of recoverable sick pay) begins. The employer can claim a refund of the wages paid from the government. For the purpose of 'consecutive' days, weekends and public holidays do not count – so that absence on Wednesday, Thursday, Friday and Monday (Saturday and Sunday being the weekend in Westland) would count as a PRSP. Devise a form to keep regular records of each employee's absences during a 'month' of 4 weeks. Mark in absences showing a period of PRSP and three shorter periods of absence, pay for which is not refundable by the state. Absence is shown by a letter A.
4 Repeat Exercise 3 above showing a period of absence of 11 days, and two occasions where sick pay would not be recoverable.
5 A test department has installed monitoring equipment in 6 grain silos which takes the temperature in each at 3-hourly intervals. Which silos appear to have a problem, in that grain is overheating?

Date	Time	Silo 1 (°C)	Silo 2 (°C)	Silo 3 (°C)	Silo 4 (°C)	Silo 5 (°C)	Silo 6 (°C)
27.1.19--	03.00	9.5	9.4	9.8	9.5	9.8	9.8
27.1.19--	06.00	9.5	9.5	9.8	10.5	9.7	9.7
27.1.19--	09.00	10.0	9.8	9.9	10.8	9.8	9.6
27.1.19--	12.00	9.5	10.0	9.9	11.3	9.8	9.7
27.1.19--	15.00	9.5	11.5	9.9	13.2	9.9	9.8
27.1.19--	18.00	9.5	11.7	9.7	15.1	9.9	9.9
27.1.19--	21.00	9.5	12.5	9.7	17.5	10.0	9.8
27.1.19--	24.00	9.5	13.0	9.7	20.3	9.9	9.9

6 Devise a 'returns' form for use in a youth club or evening institute to return statistics to the education office about attendance at classes. The form requires spaces to record 10 classes, giving 5 weeks' attendances (some months have 5 weeks), the weeks to commence on Sundays. Instructions at the top require numbers in attendance to be in blue or black ink, except where attendance falls below 10, when they are to be completed in red. Fill in some imaginary classes and their attendances.

3 Methods of inquiry – censuses and sampling

3.1 The collection of data

If data cannot be obtained as a matter of routine, requiring those in possession of the facts to render an account of them to management, or to government or some designated authority, they must be collected by launching an inquiry. Data may be collected in five chief ways. These may be listed as follows:

a observation
b inspection
c abstraction from records
d written questionnaire
e interview

The essentials of each of these methods must now be considered.

a Observation

The situation under investigation is monitored unobtrusively by trained observers who have been provided with a list of points to be observed, and a simple method of recording them. If the observation is direct – as when traffic is counted by an observer stationed on a bridge over a motorway – the information is of actual events occurring, over as long a period as the inquirer requires (or can afford) and there is no interruption of events. Other investigations – for example, interviewing – would interrupt the natural flow of events. Those who have been caught in a traffic survey of this sort – flagged down by a police officer and called into a coned-off section of a layby where an interviewer can pose a series of questions – will known how inconvenient it can be. It also introduces bias into the statistics – for example, ambulances with flashing lights are waved through.

The disadvantages of observation are many. It frequently costs a good deal – observers have to be selected, trained and paid. They must be reliable and unbiased in their approach if valid results are to be obtained. Unless it is possible to be totally unobtrusive – for example, observing from behind a two-way mirror – those observed will soon become aware that something is going on. They may vary their pattern of behaviour – even to the extent of calling the police – and consequently the observation will be atypical.

Even when observation is indirect – as when closed-circuit television is used – some of the observed may become aware of the camera and vary their patterns of behaviour.

When collecting this type of data a convenient method must be available for recording each observation. Thus entrants to an exhibition are often counted by an observer stationed at the door who presses a button on a counting machine each time a visitor arrives. Bias can creep in if this machine is operated by one of the organisers rather than by a completely independent enumerator. Another method of recording observations is the 'five-barred gate' method illustrated in Fig 1.1 on page 6.

b Inspection

Inspection is used when the data required is about objects. We may need to know the weight, composition, colour, tensile strength, etc, of objects manufactured, grown or mined. This may require tests which destroy the object in the process, or the tests may have no effect. Thus tests carried out on cement require it to be mixed in a proper manner, given time to harden and then stressed in a variety of ways to find at what point it breaks down. We must use samples for this purpose – if we tested everything we should have nothing to supply to our customers. By contrast, the specific gravity of beer and wines can be tested to discover the stage which the fermentation has reached without serious effect on the product.

Inspection requires standardised procedures based upon experience of the product under test. Variations in test procedure may lead to incorrect results. Bias, even deliberate falsification of results, may occur. Inspection should preferably be carried out by independent teams of researchers with no vested interest in the results. We all know of human tragedies in industries like the pharmaceutical industry because inspection of new drugs was not conducted rigorously enough, or 'awkward' results were disregarded. For such inspection procedures a form will usually be designed for recording the results of each test. A typical test card is shown in Fig 3.1.

c Abstraction from records

When the investigation we wish to conduct involves the analysis of past records we are said to abstract the data from the records. It does not always follow that the records we examine will contain the exact data we require, for they may have been collected for some quite different purpose. It may be necessary to examine the specifications laid down at the time the original records were collected and see what differences exist between them and the specifications for the present inquiry. An adjustment might then be made for the differences. Thus an investigation into waste in the factory canteen may be helped by an analysis of past records of swill sold to a local pig farm over the years, but it will not tell us much about the type of waste occurring at that time. Probably only the volume or weight and the price received will be recorded.

When records are available abstraction can give useful information at very low cost, but the data have their limitations. They may be out of date; they may not be as relevant as we think to today's situations, since changes in the interval since the data were collected might have been very

Batch no	Item selected		Colour	
Dimensions Overall length	Shaft diameter		Bulb diameter	
Fragility test	Pass	Fail	Signature	
Colour test	Pass	Fail	Signature	
Viscosity test	Pass	Fail	Signature	
Special report			Date	
			Final result	
			Pass	Fail

Fig 3.1 An inspection docket used in quality control

significant. For example, family incomes change over the years and alter the pattern of demand for many products. Many fields of inquiry (public health, for example) have been transformed in recent years.

When abstracting from records in this way it is helpful to have a chart on which the details abstracted from the records can be recorded.

d Written questionnaires

One of the most useful methods of collecting data is the written questionnaire. The basis of the method is the preparation of a series of questions pertinent to the matter under investigation, which is sent to those we feel have the information we are seeking to discover. We might send this to everyone interested, or we might use a sample of those interested. The advantages of the method may be listed as follows:

a The questionnaire can be designed in such a way as to investigate the problem fully (within the limit set by the time available to those responding and their willingness to cooperate).
b The responses required can be made very simple, a tick in a box, or ringing a particular reply.
c The cost is relatively low compared with other methods such as interviewing. Mailing to 1000 addresses can easily be done by one person in a day. It would take months to interview the same number.
d A questionnaire is more likely to find the correct person to complete it than an interviewer. It is sorted in the mail on arrival into the in-tray

of the most likely person to deal with it. Thus a questionnaire about export trade would be passed to the export manager, and one about fleet transport would go into the transport manager's tray.

e The person responding does not have to make instantaneous decisions as with an interview. It is possible to turn up records, check facts and give more accurate replies as a result.

f Responses do not all come in at once. The data arriving can be handled routinely, each day's post being recorded at once and the responses filed away for future reference if required.

Against these advantages we must set certain disadvantages. These are:

a The **response rate** may be poor. If we have no way of compelling a reply from the individuals concerned we may have to be satisfied with a low response rate. Since the statistical reliability of any conclusions we draw depends upon having a reasonable response to the inquiry we may need to send to a larger sample. Thus if a 50% response rate is to be hoped for and 1000 replies is the least we can consider as giving a fair cross-section of the population, we need to send out 2000 questionnaires. Often the response rate is much less than 50%.

b The response may be biased. This is because those most interested in the subject matter of the inquiry tend to respond – others may set it aside and never get around to answering it. Some, with strong views about the subject of the investigation, may reply to the questions in such a way as to bias the result towards the views they hold.

c The replies are prepared without the presence of an interviewer, and may be irresponsible. Some respondents may send 'joke' answers. Others may ask other people what they think, and send in a communal response.

d Literate people enjoy answering questionnaires; those who find reading difficult may not reply, or may misread the question. One respondent to an inquiry abut burglaries mistook the word and thought it referred to budgerigars. The answers caused considerable confusion – reference to teaching them to sing had not been expected in an investigation about burglars, and the colours of the burglars, blue/green, seemed curious too.

e The design of the questionnaire is very important. The questions must be straightforward, but this may not be good enough for a sophisticated subject. The simplest questions to answer are those where a yes/no reply is possible. The views of the respondent may call for a more thoughtful reply, and may be difficult to record and evaluate. This topic is dealt with later in this chapter (see Section 3.2).

e Interviewing

Interviews, if conducted by an impartial interviewer, give the best results in most inquiries. The popularity of the interview in recent years, when regular polls are conducted on many political matters and market research based upon interviews has become very common, has perhaps reduced the response rate. Even so, it is usually much better than the response to questionnaires.

The interviewer is present, and can ease the respondent along when answering questions, clearing up any difficulties of understanding as the interview proceeds. The replies will have a spontaneity which is lacking when questionnaires are completed. This gives more subtle opinions a chance to be aired, but on factual matters may be less reliable since the respondent cannot consult records.

The interview may be evaluated afterwards by the interviewer, to give his/her impression of the respondent, the likely truth of the replies, etc.

Against these advantages we must list the following disadvantages.

a The cost – an interview takes time to organise, time to conduct and time to evaluate. It costs money to contact respondents, arrange appointments and travel to them. The quality of the interviewer is crucial. We have to recruit, induct and train them.

b Interviews must be conducted according to a standard procedure; the interviewer taking the respondent through a schedule of questions very similar to a questionnaire. If this is too short it will be a waste of time, but if it is too long the respondent may lose interest and the interviewer, sensing this, may ask the questions in a hurried manner and record incorrect answers. We have to distil the questions so we extract the essence of the respondent's views in as few questions as possible, but with adequate safeguards to ensure understanding and considered responses by the respondent.

3.2 The design of questionnaires and schedules

The word 'questionnaire' is usually used for a set of questions sent out by post, or delivered by hand to the respondents, who are asked to complete it unaided. A 'schedule' is the rather similar list of questions which an interviewer poses to a succession of interviewees. A schedule can be slightly more complex than a questionnaire because the interviewer will be trained to complete it, and by the time 30 or 40 interviews have been conducted will be thoroughly familiar with it. This is not the situation when a questionnaire is completed, and instructions on how to complete it must be clear and simple.

Points to bear in mind when drawing up a questionnaire are as follows:

a Keep it as short as possible. Few people enjoy completing forms or answering questions and the more questions they have to answer the sooner they will reach a point where they ask 'By what right am I being asked all this?'

b If the completion of the form is voluntary, explain this, and solicit the cooperation of the respondents. Explain the purposes of the inquiry, and the benefits that should follow. Stress the non-personal nature of the enquiry – it is to provide statistics, not evidence for use in other ways.

c If the completion of the form is compulsory make this clear, state by what authority it is required and the penalties that will be incurred if it is not completed.

d Keep each question short, and if possible answerable by a simple 'yes' or 'no', or by a name or a figure. Where a subjective opinion is being asked for, limit the possible responses. Thus a question like 'What did you think of the seminar on environmental problems?' would produce a mass of comments, some quite lengthy perhaps. It could be rephrased to read: 'Underline the one of the following four comments which best describes your opinion of the seminar on environmental problems: excellent; good; fair; poor.'

e If questions are soliciting personal details it is important to avoid offence, and to keep the sequence logical and natural. Thus the following sets of questions are in the correct sequence.

4 Are you married?
5 How many children (if any) have you?
6 Give the names, and date of birth, of each.

If question 4 were asked after question 5 it might well give offence.

f So far as possible devise a simple response, such as a tick or a cross inserted in a particular box, for each question on the paper. If people have to write something, many will hesitate to do so because they spell poorly or cannot write neatly. Many people type today, and as typewriters do not have a 'tick' it is usual to put a cross in the box chosen when completing a questionnaire in the typewriter. Rather like voting at an election, the selection made is shown by an ×.

g Give clear instructions how the questionnaire is to be returned, including the address, postcode, etc.

A typical questionnaire is shown in Fig 3.2 on pages 29 to 32.

3.3 Taking a census

A census is an investigation into a complete set of data. The word 'census' itself, in everyday language, means the counting of the population. In the United Kingdom this type of census is held every decade in the first year of the decade, unless some major difficulty presents itself. Thus there was no census in 1941 because the Second World War (1939–1945) was being fought at the time. To count an entire nation of 57 million people presents many problems, and it has to be done on a particular day or, rather, night. Every householder, hotel-keeper, etc, is required to record every person in the house, hotel, caravan site, etc, on the chosen night. There are penalties for failure to record the tally properly – some people may have good reasons for wishing to conceal where they are on a particular night. To reduce the difficulties the census is also held to be completely confidential, so that there are penalties for revealing personal details recorded in a census paper – the intention is that the census shall only be used for statistical purposes, not as evidence in divorce courts, etc.

More generally, a census, as an investigation into a complete set of data, uses the word 'population' in a special way. It means 'all those people, or things, affected by the inquiry'. Thus an investigation into the

A Compulsory Inquiry conducted by
the Government Statistical Service
IN CONFIDENCE

| FV | | | **PA920** |

← Please quote
in any enquiry

Please amend
where appropriate
the name, address
and postcode

NOTICE UNDER SECTION 3 OF THE STATISTICS OF TRADE ACT, 1947

The Secretary of State for Industry hereby requires you by law to provide to the Business Statistics Office the information called for in this inquiry form. Your return should be made for the year ended 31 December 19.., unless no figures are available for that period when the return may be made for your business year which ends between 6 April 19.. and 5 April 19.,. The return should be completed and returned to the Business Statistics Office as soon as possible but, in any event, not later than 15 June 19..

NB   The information given by you will be treated as confidential in strict accordance with the Act and subject to the further restriction that information about individual businesses will be used and disclosed under Ministerial direction to other government departments for statistical purposes only, except that the names and addresses of individual businesses, their industrial classification and the numbers of persons of different descriptions employed by them may, if a Minister so directs, be made available to Ministers and officials of government departments who need them for carrying out their functions.

Department of Industry
BUSINESS STATISTICS OFFICE
Newport Gwent NPT 1XG

Telephone: Newport (0633) 56111 Ext 2695
Telex: 497121 Answer Back BSONPT G

ANNUAL CENSUS OF PRODUCTION FOR 19..

Dear Contributor

We conduct this Annual Census to obtain up-to-date statistical information about the structure and development of industry in the United Kingdom. Census results are used in the construction of national accounts, the index of production and other statistical indicators. They also provide measures of industrial performance for use in industry and government departments. Comparisons may be made with results of similar inquiries that are being conducted in other countries of the European Community. The census has been designed in consultation with the Production Statistics Advisory Committee which is appointed under the Statistics of Trade Act 1947 and includes members from industry, the trade unions, the accountancy profession and the public services.

Forms are sent to all larger establishments but sampling methods are used for medium sized establishments in most industries. Smaller units generally are excused from the obligation to complete the form.

Census results consisting of individual industry reports and a summary volume will be available from Her Majesty's Stationery Office or from the above address.

Notes to help you complete your return are enclosed. If you have any difficulties or would like further information my staff will be pleased to help you. The telephone extension of the appropriate enquiry point is given above.

Yours faithfully

R. ASH
Director

Fig 3.2 An official questionnaire (reproduced by courtesy of HMSO)

IMPORTANT: PLEASE READ THE ENCLOSED NOTES

1. PERIOD COVERED BY THE RETURN

Your return should relate to the calendar year 19.. If no figures are available for the calendar year, the return may be made for a business year, ending on any date from 6 April 19.. to 5 April 19..

Period covered by the return from | Code **11** | day / | month / | year | to | Code **12** | day / | month / | year

2. EMPLOYMENT (average number employed during the year)

Working proprietors | Administrative, technical and clerical employees | All other employees (Operatives)
201 | **202** | **205**

3. SALES, WORK DONE AND SERVICES RENDERED (exclusive of VAT; i.e. net selling value as invoiced)

£ thousand

3.1 Sales of goods of your own production **261**

3.2 Work done and industrial services rendered. **262**

3.3 Sales of goods bought and resold without processing (i.e. merchanted or factored goods) **266**

3.4 Other services rendered (include e.g. rents for industrial buildings and amounts received for hiring out plant and machinery, provision of transport) **267**

4. EXPENDITURE (exclusive of VAT)

£ thousand

4.1 Gross wages and salaries paid to:

(a) Administrative, technical and clerical employees **301**

(b) All other employees (operatives) **304**

(c) Remuneration paid to outworkers (i.e. homeworkers) . . . **314**

4.2 Employers' national insurance contributions and contributions to other pension and welfare schemes . . . **315**

4.3 Purchases of materials and fuel **734**

4.4 Goods purchased for resale without processing (i.e. for merchanting or factoring) **733**

4.5 Amounts payable for work given out (i.e. subcontracted) and for repairs and maintenance **623**

4.6 Hiring, leasing or renting plant, machinery and vehicles . . . **655**

4.7 Rent paid for industrial and commercial buildings **656**

4.8 Rates (exclude water rates) **277**

4.9 Commercial insurance premiums paid **625**

4.10 Bank charges (exclude interest) **626**

4.11 Road vehicle licences (include those relating to passenger vehicles) . . . **276**

4.12 Other services received (e.g. professional, postal, telecommunications, transport, travel, research, advertising, publicity etc., services from other organisations) . . . **630**

Fig 3.2 (*continued*)

PA920

5. **DUTIES, SPECIAL LEVIES, SUBSIDIES, ALLOWANCES, ETC.** Not applicable

6. **STOCKS (exclusive of VAT)**

	Materials, stores and fuel £ thousand	Work in progress £ thousand	Goods on hand for sale £ thousand
6.1 Value at beginning of year	401	403	413
6.2 Value at end of year	402	404	414

6.3 If the values given above are not for the calendar year 19. . please give a combined stocks total (corresponding to the total of all the three categories shown above) for the calendar year . . . .

	1 January 19. . £ thousand	31 December 19. . £ thousand
450		

7. **CAPITAL EXPENDITURE IN THE YEAR (exclusive of deductible VAT; do not make any deductions for depreciation)**

Note: You are particularly asked to give the information at Questions 7.2 to 7.9 for the calendar year 19. . If this is not possible please provide information for your business year in 7.2 to 7.9 and also a single figure at 7.10 of net capital expenditure, estimated if necessary, for the calendar year 19. .

	day	month	year
7.1 The information given at 7.2 to 7.9 is for the year ending	17	/	/

ACQUISITIONS   Cost of:

£ thousand

7.2   New building work   501

7.3   Land and existing buildings   502

7.4   New and second-hand plant, machinery, office equipment and other capital equipment   517

7.5   New and second-hand vehicles (include Customs and Excise Car Tax)   504

7.6   Work of a capital nature carried out by your own staff and included in questions 7.2 to 7.5 above   252

DISPOSALS   Proceeds from disposal of:

7.7   Land and buildings   503

7.8   Plant, machinery and other capital equipment   518

7.9   Vehicles   505

To be completed **only** if capital expenditure figures given above are **not** on a calendar year basis.

7.10 Total net capital expenditure for calendar year 19. . (i.e. cost of acquisitions less proceeds from disposals)   519

UNITS NOT YET IN PRODUCTION

Please state yes or no

Have you any additional capital expenditure at sites not covered by this return and at which production has yet to commence . . . .

Fig 3.2 (*continued*)

8. LIST OF UNITS COVERED BY THE CENSUS RETURN

A list, CRIA, is enclosed for completion if your return is thought to cover more than one unit (e.g. factory, workshop or site). If your return covers more than one unit and no CRIA is enclosed, see Note 8.

9. CLASSIFIED LISTS OF BUSINESSES

To assist industry, classified lists of manufacturing businesses compiled by the Business Statistics Office have been published from time to time. The latest list was published by HMSO as Business Monitor PO1007.

The lists show only the names and addresses of manufacturing units and the industrial classification of the businesses to which they belong. If you are willing for the business to which this return relates to appear in future lists made available to the public, please give your consent below. If you do not wish this limited information to be made available please delete the statement.

I agree that the name(s) and address(es) of the business to which this return relates may be included in any classified lists to businesses made available to the public.

Signature . . . . Date . . . .

Position in business . . . .

10. NAME AND ADDRESS OF PERSON WHO SHOULD BE CONSULTED IF QUESTIONS ARISE ABOUT THIS RETURN (BLOCK CAPITALS PLEASE)

. . . .

. . . .

. . . .

Telephone No . . . . Ext . . . . Telex No. . . . .

FOR OFFICIAL USE ONLY			8		ACTION	INIT. and date
2		5		10	Receipted	
3		7		13	Data take-on	
4		9				
					Examined	
					P.A. check	

Fig 3.2 *(continued)*

markings on giraffes might have as its 'population' every giraffe in the United Kingdom. There may be as many as 100 zoos or safari parks, and some of them might have several giraffes, but the total population would not be too great for enumeration. By contrast, we could not hope to do a census of all the giraffes in Africa. An inquiry into student opinion of canteen food might, in a small college, take the form of a census. We could not possibly ask the entire student population of the United Kingdom what they thought of their canteen meals.

3.4 Samples

If we cannot take a census of the whole population because of the amount of work involved we have to settle for discovering data from a **sample survey**. The idea of a sample survey is that a small group of people, or objects, is taken to represent the whole population. We there-fore use the term **representative sample**. By investigating the sample we discover information which is relevant to the whole population. Con-sider the possible samples that might be extracted from an organisation like the US Army. Suppose we decide our sample should consist of 50 persons. We might take 50 generals, 50 colonels, 50 technical corporals or 50 master-sergeant cooks. Could we regard these as a representative sample of the US Army? Clearly we could not, for there are no privates or corporals. We should feel a lot happier about our 'representative' sample if it had representatives of each rank in the army, and also repre-sented the variety of skilled and unskilled trades in such a large organisa-tion. Indeed, we might decide that 50 was too small a group to give adequate representation to the full range of ranks and trades – 500 might be a better sample, or even 5000.

Having decided the general composition of our sample we now have to pick the actual individuals to be interviewed or to be sent our

---

Notes on the Annual Census Production Form reproduced on pages 29 to 32
  i The introductory page makes it clear that completion of the form is compul-sory under the Act; but reassures the person completing the form that the information will be kept confidential and used for statistical and other official purposes only.
 ii It also makes quite clear what period the inquiry covers, and the date by which it must be returned.
iii The questions on pages 30 to 31 are clearly numbered and subnumbered for easy reference by both parties. The answers are to be written in coded boxes which help collation of the replies.
 iv In several places it is made clear that the values to be placed on items are exclusive of VAT, so that the figures required are the net-of-VAT charges.
  v A set of notes (not reproduced here) accompanies the form and exhortations to read the notes are included on the form in several places.
 vi Finally in case a follow-up call has to be made for any reason the Government Statistical Service asks for the name and address, telephone and telex number of a responsible person who can deal with any queries.
vii The collation of the material clearly commences on the form itself – where the phrase 'For official use only' appears. It appears that the data would then be taken onto a computer for data processing.

questionnaire. If there is to be one master-sergeant cook, who shall it be? We cannot pick the one who happens to be most conveniently situated, in the camp up the road from our headquarters. The individual should ideally be selected 'at random'. This means that all the master-sergeant cooks should have an equally good chance of being selected. This might be done, like picking a number in a raffle, by putting all the names on similar sized pieces of paper, putting them in a hat and choosing one.

The essential features of a random sample are as follows:

a All members of the population are included in the selection procedure.
b Every member of the population has the same chance of being selected. (In one investigation where numbers were written on cardboard discs and placed in a revolving drum, some of the discs were of shiny card and the others were on card of a rougher material. It was found that the shiny discs slipped easily to the bottom of the drum, and the majority of the discs selected were of the rougher materials. The selection was not therefore random, but biased.)
c There is no way of predicting which item will be selected for inclusion in the sample. (*Note:* If a selected item is returned to the collection before a further selection is made we say we have 'sampling with replacement'. If the selected items are not returned we have 'sampling without replacement'. In choosing winners in a lottery it is usual to return the winning numbers before a further prize is chosen. In selecting a sample for interviewing it is not usual to return the selected individuals to the pool, for we would not wish to interview them twice.)

a The sample 'frame'

At a race meeting the runners and riders names appear in a frame, and those, obviously with little understanding of statistics, who propose to back a horse, may choose any name in the frame. There is no point in picking a name that is not in the frame, for those are the only horses running. In selecting a sample from a 'population' the sample 'frame' is a list of members of the 'population'. Every member of the 'population' should appear in the frame, so as to have a chance of selection. An inaccurate frame, which is out of date or contains errors, will reduce the accuracy of the results obtained from any sample chosen. Typical population frames are the register of electors, the lists of members of professional organisations (doctors, dentists, lawyers, clergymen), the list of members of clubs and societies, etc.

b Why should a sample represent a population?

In sampling we hope to achieve a knowledgeable opinion about a population from the consideration of a sample only. Why should we feel this is possible? The answer is that the basic laws of statistics support the idea. The *Law of Statistical Regularity* holds that a set of data composed of items selected at random from a larger group tends to display the characteristics of that group. Clearly this becomes more and more so as the sample selected gets larger (5% of male schoolchildren will display the characteristics of the whole class of male schoolchildren, but 95% will display an almost undetectable similarity to the whole group).

The *Law of the Inertia of Large Numbers* holds that large groups or collections of data are more stable than small groups. Any variations in the individuals in the major group will tend to cancel one another out, keeping the characteristics of the whole group stable. This does not mean that the aggregate does not change over a period of time, but its rate of change as an aggregate will be slower than the rate of change of smaller groups, and certainly of individuals. Consider a piece of research into the body weight of 1000 adults. Over a period of time individuals may put on weight or lose weight. The total weight of all the adults might well remain stationary, the gains and losses cancelling one another out. More likely, perhaps, the group as a whole may slowly gain (or lose) weight as the standard of living improves (or deteriorates). This would indicate the **trend** in bodily weight in the society under investigation, but it would be a slow and stable development rather than the volatile change that might occur in a particular small group experiencing changing fortunes within the larger population. Thus where structural unemployment (a change in employment due to a change in the structure of industry) occurs, a group badly affected might change weight more than the population as a whole. When the cotton industry declined in the United Kingdom, the Lancashire operatives experienced hard times (and no doubt many of them lost weight), whereas the overall trend was an improvement in the standard of living in the United Kingdom at that time.

3.5   Types of sample

Theoretical considerations about the selection of a sample to represent a population often come up against practical difficulties, especially time factors and cost factors. Consequently, a variety of 'short-cut' methods of sampling have been developed, each of which inevitably reduces the perfection of the sample chosen – but samples are inherently imperfect anyway. If we have 100 motor vehicles, 5 of which are in fact faulty, any 10% sample chosen could include 5, 4, 3, 2, 1 or no faulty cars. If a sample happened to include all 5 we might conclude that 50% of the cars were faulty – much worse than the true position – whereas if the sample included no faulty cars we might conclude that all were in excellent condition. Even a satisfactory sample can therefore give an unsatisfactory result, and any conclusions drawn must bear in mind the possibility that a particular sample is unrepresentative in some way. When we start to use a sampling method that takes short cuts to save expense we may distort results again. Let us look at some of these methods of sampling.

a Random samples

Ideally all samples should be random samples, defined as samples selected without any bias whatsoever, every individual in the population having an equal chance of selection. The best example of everyday use of a random sample is the game of 'Bingo'. Players are issued with cards each of which has a selection of numbers from 1 to 99 on it. Tiny pieces of card are also available to cover up the numbers on the card as they are selected. A caller selects the numbers at random and calls them out – the players covering over each number as it is called if it happens to appear on their cards. The first player to cover all the numbers on his/her card wins a prize. To ensure random selection the numbers drawn are inscribed on identical wooden discs, or in some cases they are painted upon table tennis balls which are captured in a jet of air and trapped in turn as the selected items.

More simply a table of random numbers can be used. Table 3.1 contains a list of random numbers. Suppose a quality controller wants to test 10 castings randomly from a batch of 90 numbered castings. He/she would use the table starting at any arbitrary point (say line 3 column 4) and read the numbers horizontally. The 10 numbered castings are 44, 17, 75, 11, 71, 8, 72, 33, 93 and 23. In this case the number 93 does not identify an actual casting and this number is ignored and the next number in the sequence used. Similarly repeated numbers are ignored. By adopting this procedure a random sample of the 90 castings is tested for quality.

Table 3.1 Random numbers

11	74	21	82	26	29
00	43	40	72	61	19
68	02	40	44	17	75
11	71	08	72	33	93
23	05	79	82	64	57
31	06	06	51	19	26
48	64	73	53	43	36
19	94	36	42	75	34
55	71	15	47	44	91

Many computers have a random-number generator which can be used to create a similar table to that shown in Table 3.1. Should you have a small business computer the handbook of program instructions will contain a random-number generator function generally called RAND (Y). You can use this to generate your own series of random numbers. There are many different systems but the general idea is to provide the function with a seed number and the random number is returned as Y. The RAND function can be used within a loop to generate a sequence of random numbers.

b Systematic, periodic or equal interval sampling

In practice random sampling can be very tedious, for every single item selected has to be chosen by random methods. An easier method is to select systematically. This can best be explained by considering an example. Suppose we wish to have a 10% selection from a population of 30 individuals. This means that 3 of the 30 are to be selected. We could systematically select every 10th one. However, this would not be random, since the 10th, 20th and 30th items would be certain of selection and the others would have no chance of selection at all. We can restore random selection by choosing the starting point by random methods. Thus if we put the first 10 numbers in the hat and select one of them (say 7) by random methods, our choice of items starts at the 7th and continues with the 17th and 27th items. This is shown in Fig 3.3.

c Stratified (representative) sampling

It is sometimes possible to reduce the costs of random sampling by using a smaller group than the entire population, but taking steps to ensure that the various strata in the population are included in the sample used. Thus an inquiry into the opinions of car users which only questioned the owners of Rolls-Royce cars would give an unrepresentative sample. If motor vehicles can be separated into strata – the Rolls-Royce stratum, the luxury saloon stratum, the popular saloon stratum and the mini-car stratum – and selections are made at random from these groups we can obtain a relatively unbiased sample. If the numbers selected are proportional to the number of cars in the various strata, in the whole population we have a 'proportional stratified random sample', and come as near as possible to a representative sample of the whole population. In a purely random sample the proportion of car users in the various groups would be left to chance, but in the stratified sample it is not and the final sample consequently is more representative of the whole population than a purely random sample. The selection process is shown in Fig 3.4.

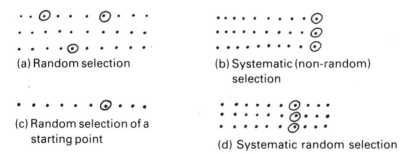

(a) Random selection

(b) Systematic (non-random) selection

(c) Random selection of a starting point

(d) Systematic random selection

Fig 3.3 Systematic random selection

Population of 2000 cars

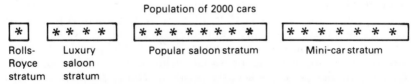

Rolls-Royce stratum   Luxury saloon stratum   Popular saloon stratum   Mini-car stratum

Fig 3.4 A proportional stratified representative 1 percent random sample

d Multistage sampling (area sampling)

Rather similar to stratified sampling – which may be built into it – but a system of sampling designed to reduce the volume of work to manageable proportions, multistage sampling is a method of reducing a national survey to a number of local inquiries. The essence of the scheme is that random selection on a national basis is abandoned in favour of the random selection of a few areas (hence the alternative names 'area sampling' and 'cluster sampling'). In the United Kingdom the most convenient basis chosen for stage 1 is the random selection of a number of rating authorities out of a total of some 400 authorities available. At this stage a certain amount of stratification might be introduced by ensuring that a fair selection of metropolitan, industrial, residentiual and rural authorities is included. Within the selected areas at stage 2 we now choose by random methods a further section of subareas – possibly the electoral wards. Within the few areas now selected for our inquiry we select the actual households from the electoral roll by random methods – probably by systematic random selection as described earlier. We now have the problem of actually locating and interviewing these householders, but they are conveniently clustered together in a few areas – not necessarily very close to one another – but each area is a compact base for a small team of interviewers. Multistage sampling is illustrated in Fig 3.5.

Stage 1	400 rating authorities	
	Select 2% = 8 rating authorities	
Stage 2	8 rating authorities = 70 electoral wards	
	Select 10%	= 7 wards
Stage 3	7 wards	= 25 000 households
	Select 5%	= 1250 households

Fig 3.5 Multistage sampling

e Quota sampling

One of the problems with random sampling is the low level of responses. The individuals found in the sample may not be available, or may refuse to give their views. Repeat calls can be expensive and there is often no way of compelling replies from those who refuse to cooperate. One way of overcoming such difficulties is to allow the interviewer to substitute any other person who is available. Probably one view is as good as another. However, bias might creep in if the interviewer only has to fulfil his/her quota without any considerations of stratification. A paid interviewer might reduce the effort required by always asking the same group of people, neighbours and acquaintances. They might reflect the interviewer's own social group or social inclinations – middle-aged frequenters of the same public bar, perhaps. Young people, or retired people, might be inadequately represented in the quota.

For this reason the quota is usually stratified to some extent: by age, by social class, by trade or profession. Such stratifications are illustrated in Fig 3.6.

Age	Sex Male (No required)	Female	Socioethnic group	Caucasian	Negro	Asian
Under 15	0	0	Profession/			
15–29	4	4	managerial	8	2	2
30–44	9	9	White-collar	10	3	2
45–59	7	7	Blue-collar	10	3	1
60 and over	5	5	Senior citizen	6	2	1
Total	25	25	Total	34	10	6

Fig 3.6 Quotas for sampling

f Attribute sampling

This is a very simple method of sampling because it selects individuals who display a certain attribute – such as those born in April. In one long-term inquiry all children in the United Kingdom born on a particular day were followed up throughout their entire lives – well, at the moment they are still in their thirties. The early data were about weight, height, etc. As they passed successively through infancy, childhood and adolescence they proved to be a valuable source of data about educational attainments, intelligence, etc, and the intention is to continue the process throughout their lives. One disadvantage of such attribute sampling is that you cannot predict how many people will be caught by such a sampling method.

Summary

1 Data may be collected by observation, inspection, abstraction from records, written questionnaire and interview.
2 With observation the observer records the data as they are observed, and with a minimum of disturbance of the pattern of behaviour. Training is necessary, and integrity of the observers is important if bias is to be avoided.
3 Inspection is used where manufactured objects or natural products are being tested for quality. Sampling is necessary and strict procedures must be adopted so that 'awkward' results are not disregarded. The inspectors should be independent if possible, with no vested interest in the results of the inquiry.
4 Abstraction from records collected for other purposes may be a cheap method of discovering data for a particular inquiry, but they may not be as relevant, or as up to date, as data from a new inquiry.

5 Written questionnaires are a form of inquiry which is cheap, comprehensive, simple to answer and administratively convenient. However, the response rate may be poor, answers may be biased and the design of a questionnaire is a specialist activity.

6 Interviewing gives good results if interviewers are well trained, the time available for the interview is adequate and the procedure followed is systematic. This implies a panel of questions similar to a questionnaire, but the responses recorded by the interviewer in the light of the responses made. The costs are high, interviewers have to be trained and paid, their expenses met and the possibility of repeat calls envisaged where those selected for interview are not available. Multistage (area) sampling can group interviews into convenient localities.

7 In designing a questionnaire it is essential to keep the whole questionnaire and the individual questions as short as possible. Questions should be in a logical sequence, and call for simple responses like 'yes', 'no', or a figure or name, date of birth, etc. Other responses might involve ticking or encircling or marking a × in a box.

8 A census is an investigation into a complete set of data. The term 'population' means 'all those people, or things, affected by an inquiry'.

9 A 'sample' is a selection from a 'population'. It should preferably be a representative sample, selected at random. A random sample is one selected in such a way that every member of the population has an equal chance of being selected, and there is no way of predicting who will be selected. A sample frame is a list of the members of a population from whom a sample may be selected.

10 Random samples must be selected from the entire population, possibly by the use of a table of random numbers. A systematic sample is one which selects a starting point by random methods and then selects items systematically from that starting point, as with the 7th, 57th, 107th and 157th items.

11 Stratified sampling selects a representative sample by dividing the population into strata, and ensuring that a fair proportion of items from each stratum appear. Multistage sampling reduces the work involved in an inquiry by selecting subareas of a total population and then finding the individuals to be interviewed from a random selection in the few subareas selected.

12 Quota sampling is cheaper than other methods where interviewing is concerned. The interviewer is only required to collect the opinions of a quota of people, stratified in some appropriate way. Actual named individuals are not specified, or if they are and prove to be unavailable, another person in the same stratum may be substituted (but preferably not from the interviewer's close circle of friends).

Exercises

1 What is meant by 'observation' as a method of collecting data? A study is to be made of the way export documentation is dealt with

in an office where the present system is that individuals who are knowledgeable about particular areas of the world – Africa, South America, etc – deal with all aspects of documentation for consignments destined for that area. What difficulties might be found in observing procedures in this type of situation. How might they be overcome?

2   Observers are to be stationed on a bridge overlooking a motorway to record *a* the number of vehicles and *b* the types of vehicles using the motorway. Suggest how this should be done, and design a form to be used. What practical difficulties might arise and how may they be overcome. Mention in particular any decisions that might need to be made about the timing of the investigation.

3   A supermarket manager is concerned that not all tills are used equally intensively. She suspects that this is something to do with the layout of the checkout positions. There are 7 checkouts which can all be viewed from a balcony overlooking the food hall. Suggest how an investigation of the use of the tills might be implemented to provide some firm evidence for presentation to management.

4   An investigation is to be conducted into the nationality of origin of motor vehicles leaving a car park in a busy shopping centre. Draw up an observation chart with room for recording *a* cars made in your own country, *b* cars from the four most likely foreign countries and *c* one further section headed 'all other foreign cars'. Actually visit a car park in your own home area and record the vehicles as they leave. Write a short report on the results you have obtained, including any difficulties encountered.

5   A work-study enthusiast proposes to observe the way shop-floor workers in an engineering factory use their time. Discuss the difficulties inherent in such a proposal.

6   What do you understand by 'abstraction of data'? A personnel officer believes that since the introduction of statutory sick pay, which permits the firm to claim back sick pay from official government agencies, supervisors are much less strict about absenteeism, since it does not now cost the firm money to pay for sick pay. This ignores the drastic effects on productivity of repeated absences from work. How would the personnel officer establish the truth of this belief?

7   You are conducting an inquiry into business studies teaching at your school or college and the contribution it has made to the career of students who left 5 years previously. You propose sending out a questionnaire to the 160 students in that year, whose addressess are available. You wish to know the following points:
a the subjects studied
b the examination successes achieved
c their present employment (and the salary earned per annum)
d their previous employments
e their opinions about the importance to them in their actual employment of (1) typewriting, (2) book-keeping and accounting, (3) economics, (4) secretarial studies, (5) business calculations and (6) English language

    f the subject which has been the most directly beneficial in their careers

    g whether they consider they benefited greatly, only a little, or not at all from their business studies course

Devise a questionnaire to obtain these answers.

8   A manufacturer of a new window-cleaning product wishes to discover *a* the extent of the market, *b* the relative popularity of other brands and *c* the likely price customers would be willing to pay. He proposes to conduct a survey in three areas: *a* a rural area, *b* a surburban area and *c* an inner city area. You are required:

    i to draw up a questionnaire which will discover the necessary information

    ii to advise him how best to select his three areas, bearing in mind the nature of the product

9   Write notes on three of the following:

    a simple random sampling

    b quota sampling

    c stratified sampling

    d multistage sampling (area sampling)

10 What is a random sample? A personnel officer conducting an inquiry decides to ask the first 25 members of staff who enter the gates on the first Monday in June to complete a questionnaire. Discuss whether this is a random sample.

11 Discuss the relative advantages and disadvantages of a sample survey and a census for the collection of data. Refer in your answer to an investigation of the views of the 100 members of the Riversdale Canoe Club about the purchase of rights to use a certain river area, and an investigation of opinions of students nationwide about affiliation to a certain political organisation.

12 What is a systematic sampling? Mr A proposes to select interviewees for an inquiry systematically by selecting the 50th, 100th, 150th, etc, member of the published list of the professional body concerned. Advise him about the random nature of his sample.

13 What is quota sampling? An interviewer is asked to pose three questions about local education to 50 people, made up as follows:

    a 10 boys under 18 years of age who are still at school/college

    b 10 girls under 18 years of age who are still at school/college

    c 10 male parents

    d 10 female parents

    e 10 other adults

Criticise this quota structure.

14 Design a questionnaire to be used to keep a record of accidents in a small factory. The forms will be sent to head office to acquaint them with all the particulars of each accident, date, time, nature of the occurrence, who was involved, who treated the injured person, etc. A space for the signature of the supervisor concerned should be provided.

4 Classification and tabulation of data

4.1 Raw data

The result of any census or sample inquiry is a mass of data. Rarely is it possible to extract any sense at all from considering these raw data, for it is usually the case that the really significant data are very ordinary in appearance whereas the items which stand out are of no real significance. A giant and a dwarf both stand out in a crowd, but the mass of people of average height are statistically more important. The first task of the statistician is to reduce the mass of data to manageable proportions by classifying it and summarising it so that we can pick out the shape of the wood from the trees. The process is one where we extract from the questionnaires or interview schedules the answer to each separate question, and discover the range of replies to each.

Before doing this it is usual to scrutinise the questionnaires, as they arrive, to eliminate manifest absurdities. Some people send in 'joke' replies, others clearly did not understand the nature of the inquiry and their replies will consequently be useless. Some forms may be incomplete, and may need to be followed up. Once the responses have been scrutinised, the valid questionnaires can now be examined in detail and the answers to individual questions recorded and collated. If this task is performed manually it can be very time consuming and tedious. Fortunately mechanical and electronic methods of analysing responses are now available.

4.2 Classification

First it is necessary to classify the data, ie arrange them into classes. Every inquiry will have its obvious classes into which a particular statistic naturally falls. Thus if we classify cars according to their colour we shall group all the black cars together. If we classify them by engine size we shall have all the 2 litre cars in the same class. A 1000 cc car will not be in the 2 litre class, but naturally belongs in the 1 litre class. When we classify data we arrange them into classes, each member of which displays the same attributes as the others. Thus businesses may be classified according to turnover, and the classes used may be narrow ranges of turnover per annum, say: under £10 000; £10 000 but under £20 000; £20 000 but under £30 000, etc. In the class £20 000 but under £30 000 there will be many items – all of them businesses whose turnover falls within this narrow range. They all display this attribute, and businesses displaying a smaller turnover or a larger turnover do not appear. Any attribute that can be displayed in quantitative terms (such as turnover) is called a **variable**. Where a variable changes over time, and regular measurements of the data can be taken to bring out changes, the result is a 'series', or 'time series'. Attributes measured according to location are referred to as 'spatial distributions' – for example, sales of a firm may be collected on a geographical basis.

The rules for classifying data are as follows.

a The categories must be comprehensive

We have a mass of responses to a particular inquiry. Every response must be capable of being included in one of the classes chosen. In some inquiries we deliberately have one class which is used to collect together any items which do not appear to fit in the other categories. This class might be labelled 'other items', or 'other activities', according to the nature of the inquiry.

b The categories should not be too numerous

Generally, six to ten classes is enough. Too many classes makes it difficult to draw conclusions from the data. The whole purpose of classification is to reduce the data to manageable proportions. A few large classes reduces the bulk of the data, while at the same time leaving a sufficient spread of information to bring out the range of data under consideration.

c The categories should not overlap

If categories overlap there is a difficulty in deciding where to place a particular statistic. Thus if ages are classified as 0–5, 5–10, 10–15 and 15–20 we are not quite sure whether to put a 5-year-old into the first or the second group, while a 10-year-old could go in both the second and the third group. If the classes are reclassified as 0–5, 6–10, 11–15 and 16–20 the overlap is eliminated and the difficulty is resolved.

Common methods of expressing class intervals are as follows:

a	b	c (Correct to nearest whole number)
Under 10	0–	0– 9
10 and under 20	10–	10–19
20 and under 30	20–	20–29
30 and under 40	30–	30–39
40 and under 50	40–	40–49
50 and under 60	50–	50–59
60 and under 70	60–	60–69
70 and under 80	70–	70–79
80 and under 90	80–	80–89
90 and under 100	90–	90–99

In *a* the class intervals are perfectly clear and do not overlap. In *b* the class intervals are exactly the same as in *a* except for the last class interval which is open ended. 0– means from zero up to the next class which begins at 10.

In *c* the classes are expressed to be correct to the nearest whole number. Because, in correcting up, a number of exactly a half is rounded to the nearest even number (see Section 4.6*b* below) it means that the second group 10–19 includes items from 9.5 to 19.4999. Other ways of expressing class intervals are possible, of course.

d The categories should be homogeneous

In general, the members of any class will display the same characteristics, and the names given to the class will describe the characteristic clearly. Where a class is used to collect together those items which do not fit into any other class the membership may not display the same characteristics and consequently few valid conclusions can be drawn from it. Thus in an inquiry about fish caught by vessels from a certain port we might find a number of miscellaneous varieties lumped together in a group 'other varieties'. They might include a shark, a sting ray, 5 lobsters, 2 crabs and some whitebait. Such groupings will be largely irrelevant to the main inquiry, and only included for the sake of comprehensiveness (see *a* above).

Bearing these rules for classifying data in mind, the work proceeds by rearranging the data in the form of an array, from which a frequency distribution can be developed.

4.3 Arrays and frequency distributions

Consider the responses to an inquiry about average monthly take-home pay shown in Table 4.1. There are 150 responses, a very confusing collection of replies at first glance. On a more detailed look we find that the smallest pay packet contains £128, while the largest contains £925. This spread, from £128 to £925, is called the **range** of the data.

One way of sorting out these data is to rearrange them in the form of an array. This means that we rearrange them in increasing order of size – starting with the smallest pay packet, £128, and finishing with the largest, £925. The array therefore displays the full range.

	£		£
The array would start	128	and would end	826
	129		836
	129		882
	154		925
	157 etc		

A slightly simpler arrangement is to prepare a **frequency distribution**. The array is still in increasing order of size but this time the frequency with which each individual statistic occurs is indicated, instead of repeating the quantity, as with 129 in the partial array shown above. The

Table 4.1 Average monthly take-home pay: year 19—
(Correct to nearest £1 sterling)

£	£	£	£	£
160	162	238	295	492
184	324	426	425	265
195	297	326	276	624
385	179	164	254	426
626	326	157	186	265
164	325	253	166	171
172	331	246	321	318
296	264	321	632	724
295	333	626	188	621
185	721	262	246	184
836	429	725	426	129
725	192	269	248	194
429	284	184	716	246
326	327	495	129	325
154	365	273	296	195
257	203	325	736	362
363	278	295	276	428
725	426	168	584	275
484	128	426	314	165
246	158	186	726	373
495	208	264	429	366
186	232	325	391	317
176	365	195	325	316
238	427	283	411	342
425	217	287	426	562
761	712	296	514	882
325	925	429	325	243
826	225	295	275	286
714	729	363	265	372
194	188	168	238	478

frequency distribution is shown in Table 4.2. A frequency distribution may be defined as 'a table which shows the frequency of occurrence of the different values of any variable'.

This is slightly simpler than the original data but the reader will notice that it is still very difficult to know much about the pattern of take-home pay from such a large number of individual values. To clarify the picture we must change to a **grouped frequency distribution**. This is shown in Table 4.3.

The number of groups or classes has been reduced to nine 'natural' divisions which are easily assimilated. The frequencies in each group are sufficiently large to be readily comparable with the whole – for example, statements such as '33 out of 150 employees take home pay packets in

Table 4.2 Frequency distribution of average monthly take-home pay: year 19—

(Correct to nearest £1 sterling)

Value (£)	Frequency	Value (£)	Frequency	Value (£)	Frequency	Value (£)	Frequency
128	1	225	1	316	1	478	1
129	2	232	1	317	1	484	1
154	1	238	3	318	1	492	1
157	1	243	1	321	2	495	2
158	1	246	4	324	1	514	1
160	1	248	1	325	7	562	1
162	1	253	1	326	3	584	1
164	2	254	1	327	1	621	1
165	1	257	1	331	1	624	1
166	1	262	1	333	1	626	2
168	2	264	2	342	1	632	1
171	1	265	3	362	1	712	1
172	1	269	1	363	2	714	1
176	1	273	1	365	2	716	1
179	1	275	2	366	1	721	1
184	3	276	2	372	1	724	1
185	1	278	1	373	1	725	3
186	3	283	1	385	1	726	1
188	2	284	1	391	1	729	1
192	1	286	1	411	1	736	1
194	2	287	1	425	2	761	1
195	3	295	4	426	6	826	1
203	1	296	3	427	1	836	1
208	1	297	1	428	1	882	1
217	1	314	1	429	4	925	1

Table 4.3 Grouped frequency distribution of average monthly take-home pay: year 19—

(Correct to nearest £1 sterling)

(£)	Frequency
100 but under 200	33
200 but under 300	42
300 but under 400	31
400 but under 500	20
500 but under 600	3
600 but under 700	5
700 but under 800	12
800 but under 900	3
900 but under 1000	1
Total	150

the lowest band of £100–199' are quite meaningful and convey a clear impression of the earnings of a substantial body of the employees.

A grouped frequency distribution may be defined as '*a table which shows the frequency of occurrence of variables within specified classes, or bands of value*'

The full range of data is divided into a number of subgroups or classes, using subdivisions as naturally as possible. Thus to divide a range into classes of 100, or 50, would assist comprehension while the choice of 70 as a subdivision for each class would not be 'natural' since we do not usually think in terms of 70s. Overlapping of classes is avoided – in Table 4.3 the five employees in the £600 but under £700 range had take-home pay of at least £599.50 but not more than £699.49 (since the data is given correct to the nearest £1 sterling). It is conventional to regard the class designation as the **independent variable**, and the frequency as the **dependent variable** (since it depends upon the class intervals chosen).

4.4 Cumulative frequencies

The grouped frequency distribution can be extended to present the data in cumulative form. The accumulation is usually done from start to finish, but may be reversed (from finish to start). In Table 4.4 below the two cumulative columns may be used to read off such statements as the following (looking at the £400 but under £500 group):

a 126 of the 150 employees took home less than £500 per month
b 44 of the 150 employees took home more than £400 per month

Table 4.4 Cumulative columns on a grouped frequency distribution of average monthly take-home pay: year 19—
(Correct to nearest £1 sterling)

Take-home pay (£)	Frequency	Cumulative frequency	Reversed cumulative frequency
100 but under 200	33	33	150
200 but under 300	42	75	117
300 but under 400	31	106	75
400 but under 500	20	126	44
500 but under 600	3	129	24
600 but under 700	5	134	21
700 but under 800	12	146	16
800 but under 900	3	149	4
900 but under 1000	1	150	1
Total	150		

Table 4.5 Investors in International Producers PLC, December 19—
(Source: company secretary's report)

Class of holder	Number of holdings	Amount of holdings (US$)	%
Bank and discount houses	4 883	1 068 750	2
Financial trusts	112	310 499	1
Insurance companies	843	8 118 631	18
Investment trusts	180	577 000	1
Pension funds	236	2 484 055	5
Trade unions	3 585	12 989 658	28
Other companies	1 235	2 234 728	5
International Producers' Trust	1	8 443 887	18
Individuals	61 831	9 539 607	21
Totals	72 906	45 766 815	100

Note
The apparent error in the % column (it totals 99 really) is due to rounding.

Notes
 i A table should have a clear and concise title, stating exactly what the table is about. Do not sacrifice clarity for brevity. If units are involved, make it quite clear what units are being used. For example, dollars are used by many countries – make it clear US$; A$; Hong Kong$; etc.
 ii A source reference should be given, perhaps in italics.
 iii The class description should appear as a heading above the various classes shown on the rows lower down. Thus the words *Class of holder* appear in Table 4.5 and below, in the individual rows, the classes of holder are listed, with the number and value of their holdings in the columns alongside.
 iv The column headings may be for actual data, or for derived data such as percentages, cumulative frequencies, etc.
 v Totals should always be checked for accuracy. It is used to make the totals stand out by having one rule below the data being totalled and a double rule below the totals. However many offices do develop their own house style. Our publisher's house style is shown in Table 4.4 above.
 vi Sometimes footnotes and source notes are required, but these should be kept to a minimum. They are often needed in a time series collected over several years, to pinpoint a break in the table caused by a change of classification – so that earlier statistics and later statistics are not strictly comparable.

4.5 The essentials of tabulation

Tabulation is the presentation of data in the form of a table. It is the most widely used and the simplest method of presenting data. It is very adaptable, for there is an infinite choice of headings, subheadings, columns and rows available. Table 4.5 and the notes below it make most of the essential points. The reader should note that in practice the eventual tabular presentation is envisaged at the start of an inquiry, since nothing concentrates the mind more when drawing up a questionnaire then the need to present a final report as lucidly as possible. In outlining how the tabular presentation will appear in the final report it may become apparent that it can only be produced if certain information is available, and one or two questions can be added to the questionnaire to elicit the necessary information.

The importance of tabulation and frequency distributions

What, it might be asked, is the point of all this? The answer depends very much on the inquiry we are conducting. Statistics is a technique for examining problems. Many tabulations are the result of the routine collection of data month after month and year after year. Because they are organised routinely does not mean they have lost their point – we are still examining the original problem, trying to detect changes which will throw our plans awry. If production starts to fall we shall not be able to fulfil the orders we are taking from customers. If people start to spend their money in different ways the Treasury's plans for the economy may be upset. If banks start to loan money on easy terms people will go ahead with expenditure which perhaps they – and perhaps the nation – cannot afford. So firms keep track of production, the Treasury keeps track of expenditure and the Central Bank monitors the banks' loan policies.

Frequency distributions are a way of sorting out data, and tables are a way of presenting data so that we can understand them almost at a glance. The manager or accountant who goes home with the latest statistics in his brief case and ponders them at home over the weekend, lifts the phone on Monday morning and starts to give orders which will correct adverse trends in the firm; cut down output of tyres and increase the production of gear boxes; put pressure on debtors who are overdue and arrange for a loan from the bank until they actually pay. Statistics is not a dull activity with a mass of raw data – it is decision-making material for management.

4.6 Some examples of tabulation

a Simple tabulation

Many tables are made up of relatively simple data, presented to display the data in a straightforward manner, bringing out totals wherever possible and possibly such derived statistics as percentages. Thus the following data might be presented as shown in Table 4.6.

Example 1 Weekly production of two different models of an appliance in a certain factory taken from weekly reports were as follows during the month of March: Standard model: week 1: 37 285; week 2: 42 656; week 3: 40 758; week 4: 39 500. De luxe model: week 1: 7853; week 2: 8594; week 3: 9251; week 4: 12 285. Arrange these in a table to bring out weekly and monthly totals.

Note: The best layout for such a table shows the weekly production figures side by side in rows, and added to give the weekly total, while the monthly totals are in columns, to give a grand total. Now see Table 4.6.

Table 4.6   Production of appliances: March 19—
(Source: weekly reports)

Week	Standard model	De luxe model	Weekly total
1	37 285	7 853	45 138
2	42 656	8 594	51 250
3	40 758	9 251	50 009
4	39 500	12 285	51 785
Monthly total	160 199	37 983	198 182

b Simple tabulation, with rounding

Frequently, sets of data contain more figures than can be readily comprehended by most people, and it is better to round the figures to simplify them. Thus to say that the United Kingdom has 55 295 321 people may be 'true' at a particular moment, but is it meaningful? It is difficult to visualize 55 million people, but quite impossible to visualize 55 295 321. We could round the figure to thousands (55 295 thousands) or, better still, to millions (55 million).

The rules for rounding are as follows:

a Decide the level of accuracy required to make the data easily intelligible (millions in the example given above).
b Look at the part of the figure to be discarded (295 321 people in the example given above). Is this as great as half a million? Answer 'No!' Then round the number downwards to 55 million, and discard the rest, since the population *correct to the nearest million* is 55 million.
c Consider the situation if the population had been 55 729 326. In this case we would be discarding more than half a million people, and the population, correct to the nearest million is 56 million. We must round up to the figure above 55 million if the discarded fraction is more than half a million people.
d If the balance is exactly half (as with a population of 55 500 000) the rule is to round off to the nearest *even* number (of millions in this case). Thus 55 500 000 becomes 56 million, but if the population had been 54 500 000 we should round *down* to 54 million. This policy means that in a whole set of statistics the rounded totals would even one another out to some extent.

Example 2   The populations of the 12 states in the European Community are found to be as follows in the year 19—: United Kingdom, 55 930 000; France, 52 605 802; Germany, 61 645 000; Belgium, 9 650 944; Holland, 2 215 876; Luxembourg, 338 500; Italy, 56 024 000; Eire, 2 978 248; Denmark, 4 921 156; Greece, 8 736 367; Spain, 38 882 954; Portugal, 10 212 595. Round these populations to the nearest tenth of a million and present them in tabulated form to show the total population of the EC. Using these rounded statistics calculate the percentage of the total EC population in each country. Include these statistics in your table.

The result is shown in Table 4.7.

Table 4.7   Population of the European Community, year 19—

Country	Population (millions)	%
United Kingdom	55.9	18.4
France	52.6	17.3
Germany	61.6	20.3
Belgium	9.7	3.2
Holland	2.2	0.7
Luxembourg	0.3	0.1
Italy	56.0	18.4
Eire	3.0	1.0
Denmark	4.9	1.6
Greece	8.7	2.9
Spain	38.9	12.8
Portugal	10.2	3.4
Total	304.0	100.0

Note
The apparent error in the % column (it actually totals 100.1) is due to rounding.

c Bi-variate tables

A bi-variate table is one where we wish to show more than one variable in a table and to do so we must either subdivide the rows, or subdivide the vertical columns. Since the eye takes in columns of figures more easily than rows of figures it is usual to subdivide the vertical columns. An example is given in Table 4.8.

Exercises on simple tabulation and rounding

1   Sales of strawberries at a 'pick-your-own' farm were as follows in the third week of June, according to the weekly sales records: Sunday, 387.5 kg; Monday, 145 kg; Tuesday, 195.5 kg; Wednesday, 394.5 kg; Thursday, 203.5 kg; Friday, 295 kg; Saturday, 624.5 kg. Arrange them in tabular form bringing out the sales by weight and by value each day, and the total for the week. The charge to pickers is £1.50 per kilogramme.

2   Output from two mills owned by a firm in the cotton industry is as follows according to the production reports for the 4-week period 4–31 July inclusive: week 1: mill A, 24 702 m; mill B, 13 975 m; week 2: mill A, 31 560 m; mill B, 15 295 m; week 3: mill A, 28 850 m; mill B, 16 170 m; week 4: mill A, 34 252 m; mill B, 15 850 m. Present these figures in tabular form to show the weekly production, the total weekly production, the monthly production of each mill and the total production of the firm for the month.

3   Employment figures in the year 19— are given in a Department of Employment Report as follows: agriculture, 432 754; mining and quarrying, 363 175; manufacturing industries, 7 830 495;

Table 4.8 Marketing report: Rozier (Camside) Engineering PLC: Sales, 19— (£m)
(Source: annual returns)

Sales sector	Motor vehicles			Other machinery			Total			Grand total (£m)
	UK	Other EC	Rest of world	UK	Other EC	Rest of world	UK	Other EC	Rest of world	
Personal	3.2	2.9	1.4	0.8	1.3	0.7	4.0	4.2	2.1	10.3
Business clients	14.3	11.8	7.7	12.8	15.4	5.2	27.1	27.2	12.9	67.2
Public corporations	1.4	3.2	1.8	4.2	1.6	1.3	5.6	4.8	3.1	13.5
Government bodies	5.9	7.8	11.7	11.7	5.8	7.7	17.6	13.6	19.4	50.6
Totals	24.8	25.7	22.6	29.5	24.1	14.9	54.3	49.8	37.5	141.6

Notes

i The table gives a grid of information showing the sales achieved, in each sector of business and each geographical area.

ii Care is needed when cross-totting totals – we only need to add together the appropriate figures, for example the two UK figures, to get the UK total.

iii The grand total shows the sales in all sectors and all geographical areas.

construction, 1 379 500; gas, electricity and water, 344 395; transport and communication, 1 523 850; distributive trades, 2 743 975; insurance, banking and finance, 1 058 500; professional services, 3 250 499; catering and hotels, 793 895; miscellaneous services, 1 388 733; national government service, 607 845; local government service, 977 490. Round these figures to the nearest thousand, and present them in tabular form, showing the total in employment.

4 Capital expenditure in the New York distributive and service industries for the year 19— is investigated by a research organisation. The results are as follows: wholesale distribution, $394 273 816; retail distribution, $738 246 712; shipping, $386 959 090; leasing, $572 498 389; other finance, $1 251 826 374; other industries, $1 656 738 240. Round these figures to the nearest million dollars and present them in tabular form, to show the total capital expenditure, and also the percentage of capital expenditure (to the nearest 0.1%) invested in each industry.

5 The supply of coal in the United Kingdom during the year 19— is as follows: deep-mined coal, 128 725 386 tonnes; opencast coal, 34 278 425 tonnes; imports, 9 425 386 tonnes; exports, 4 024 900 tons. Draw up a table to show, to the nearest thousand tonnes, *a* total home-produced coal supplies, *b* net imports (or exports) and *c* total coal available for domestic use. In a note at the foot of the table say what percentage of coal *used* at home is imported coal. In doing this calculation use the corrected figures, not the full statistics, and give your answer correct to two decimal places.

6 In England and Wales offences are divided by the police into indictable offences and non-indictable offences. In a certain year, 19—, the indictable offences consisted of 112 murders, 256 cases of manslaughter, 31 369 cases of wounding and 1434 other offences against the person. There were 7204 charges of a sexual nature, 64 115 burglaries, 2767 cases of robbery and 204 061 cases of theft or the handling of stolen goods. Fraud and forgery totalled 17 705 and there were 45 895 other indictable offences.

   a Present these figures in a table, to bring out the total of serious crimes.

   b Calculate what percentage of these crimes were murders, and what percentage were burglaries (give answers correct to two decimal places).

7 Draw up a bi-variate table showing the the enrolment in a college, which has 4 departments; general education, business studies, science and engineering and tourism and catering. Figures are required for the following age groups: under 17, 17, 18, 19, 20 and 21 and over. They are also to be divided into males and females. Total are required (males and females) for each department and each age groups (males and females), combining to give a grand total of enrolments in each department and each age group. The figures are:

   General education: Under 17, 86 males (m), 79 females (f); 17-yr-olds, 49m, 55f; 18-yr-olds, 49m, 62f; 19-yr-olds, 46m, 59f; 20-yr-olds, 46m, 38f; 21 and over, 62m, 97f.

   Business studies: Under 17, 74m, 66f; 17-yr-olds, 95m, 88f;

18-yr-olds, 62m, 71f; 19-yr-olds, 38m, 48f; 20-yr-olds, 62m, 71f; 21 and over 84m 126f.

Science and engineering: Under 17, 24m, 6f; 17-yr-olds, 42m, 18f; 18-yr-olds, 36m, 62f; 19-yr-olds, 42m, 26f; 20-yr-olds, 72m, 61f; 21 and over, 42m, 14f.

Tourism and catering: Under 17, 32m, 56f; 17-yr-olds, 42m, 46f; 18-yr-olds, 38m, 68f; 19-yr-olds, 40m, 29f; 20-yr-olds, 72m, 18f; 21 and over, 44m, 38f.

4.7 Frequency distributions

The full procedure for drawing up frequency distributions has already been discussed earlier in this chapter. It consists of the following stages:

a Arrange the data in an array, in ascending order of magnitude.
b Draw up a frequency distribution showing the number of times each item appears.
c If there are too many items decide how to group them together (ie decide the class intervals to be used in the classification). From these groups we can now draw up a grouped frequency distribution.
d Add cumulative frequency columns, or other derived statistics if these are helpful in understanding the table.
e Use the rules for tabulation to draw up the table in proper form.

A short-cut procedure may be used as follows:

a Examine the data to discover the range, ie find the smallest item and the largest item.
b Having found the range decide upon the number of classes or groups to be used, and the class interval of the body of the table. There may be classes at the beginning or the end of the table which are different – collecting together scattered items towards the limits of the range.
c Prepare a draft table with class intervals on the left-hand side and a space for frequencies on the right-hand side. Using the original data and the five-barred gate system of recording record the actual items in the various groups at once. This eliminates the 'array' and 'ungrouped frequency' stages and enables us to prepare the final table more quickly. Example 3 illustrates the method.

Example 3 Examination marks scored by 50 candidates in an examination in Cargo Insurance were as follows:

25	72	96	54	92	67
42	35	72	56	63	46
36	81	100	72	57	38
84	49	14	64	55	49
72	75	34	73	48	56
95	36	84	62	43	55
63	25	25	48	44	93
66	88	56	53	72	45
46	52				

The lowest score is 14, the highest is 100.

It is decided to have an open class 'under 30' to begin with and then build in tens, 30 and under 40, 40 and under 50, etc. The final group will be 90 and over, and will thus include 100. The sorting out process is then done as shown in Fig 4.1. The table might then be laid out as in Table 4.9 below.

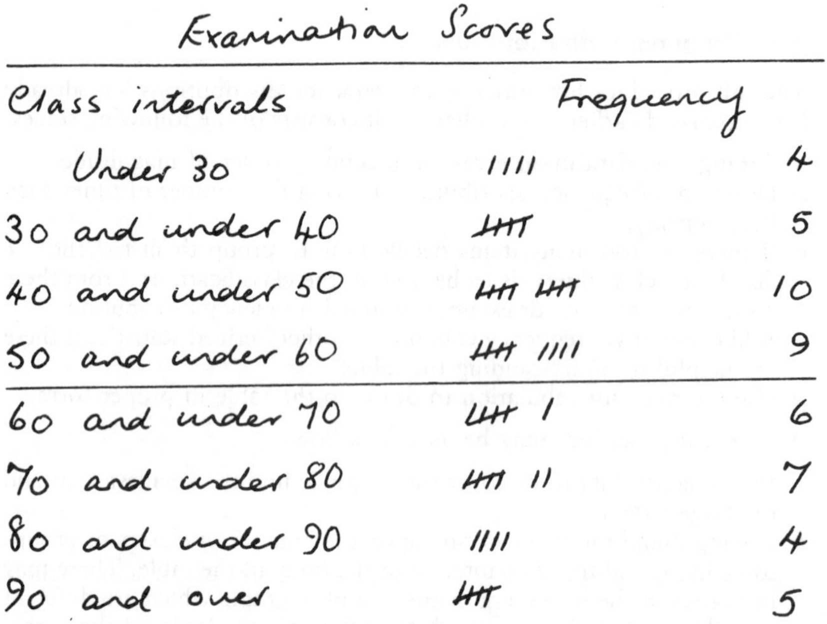

Examination Scores

Class intervals	Frequency	
Under 30	/III	4
30 and under 40	LHT	5
40 and under 50	LHT LHT	10
50 and under 60	LHT IIII	9
60 and under 70	LHT I	6
70 and under 80	LHT II	7
80 and under 90	IIII	4
90 and over	LHT	5

Fig 4.1 Raw data recorded as a frequency distribution

Table 4.9 Examination scores: Cargo Insurance

Scores	Frequency	Reverse cumulative frequency
Under 30	4	50
30 and under 40	5	46
40 and under 50	10	41
50 and under 60	9	31
60 and under 70	6	22
70 and under 80	7	16
80 and under 90	4	9
90 and over	5	5

Note
The reverse cumulative frequency is chosen because we can tell from this how many people will pass the examination if a particular cut-off point is chosen. Thus if the pass mark is 50 the number passing the examination will be 31, for 31 people altogether scored 50 or more marks.

Summary

1 Raw data must be scrutinised to eliminate manifest absurdities and joke answers. It must then be classified to reduce the mass of data to manageable proportions.
2 The essentials of classification are to group items together naturally in easily comprehensible groups. Categories should be comprehensive (able to embrace all the data). They should not be too numerous; they should not overlap and the classes should be homogeneous – except perhaps for a final class which sweeps up 'any other items'.
3 Raw data may be presented as an array, in order of increasing value. This brings out the range of the data, and its spread between the extremes.
4 A frequency distribution is similar to an array, but shows the frequency of each item, rather than repeating an item that occurs more than once. A grouped frequency distribution shows the frequency with which items fall into groups or classes, selected as outlined in 2 above. Further columns can be added to show the cumulative frequency of the data, as we move from group to group.
5 Tables must be clearly titled, with a source reference (if any) given. The classes should be natural, and follow the rules for classification given in 2 above. Totals and other derived statistics should be included as required, to bring out the salient points of the inquiry. Rounding to eliminate excessive detail may be helpful.

Exercises on arrays and frequency distributions

1 The lives of 60 electric light bulbs subjected to a quality control investigation were as follows:

Hours	Hours	Hours	Hours	Hours	Hours
72	5 minutes	424	724	97	712
594	242	127	636	537	615
624	363	363	719	479	495
836	1846	725	824	629	12
137	5042	616	243	516	139
449	395	494	240	724	725
347	696	727	371	638	623
626	727	1046	268	456	304
594	816	952	1724	395	180
1726	96	121	23	327	175

Arrange these 'lifetimes' in an array. What is the range of the data?
2 Earnings of office juniors per month are found by questioning 30 young people about their gross monthly pay (pay before deductions).

The results are as follows:

£	£	£	£	£
140	180	620	148	240
220	240	320	180	300
280	140	246	375	380
320	220	142	580	142
600	280	340	280	180
220	350	350	375	140

Arrange these earnings in a frequency distribution and add a cumulative frequency distribution column to bring out the total number earning a given amount, or *less*.

3   Houses in a certain town are on offer at the following prices. Draw up a grouped frequency table in bands of £10 000, the first group being £1–10 000.

£	£	£	£	£
18 000	32 500	42 500	11 250	14 250
15 500	36 750	35 000	23 550	33 500
20 000	48 500	69 050	28 750	41 500
17 250	3 250	65 000	17 500	40 500
38 000	5 000	17 750	12 500	21 500
34 000	51 250	8 750	87 500	23 850
78 000	18 250	23 750	85 000	72 500
85 000	19 000	25 000	12 750	18 500
19 500	35 000	29 850	17 950	16 250
8 250	58 000	86 000	7 250	18 000

4   Output by operatives in a newly industrialised country are listed below. The figures show the number of garments made. Prepare a grouped frequency distribution in bands of 100 garments. Present it as a table, with a cumulative frequency column.

Garments manufactured by operatives of the Indira Clothing Co, March 19—

72	320	720	240	320
165	360	186	460	800
850	54	142	320	780
560	186	59	760	630
490	290	180	480	320
360	580	480	360	240
120	660	650	429	560
800	420	720	512	780

5 Weekly turnover for 50 shops in a pedestrian precinct in Newtown
are found to be as follows:

Turnover (£)

£	£	£	£	£
3 350	980	2 500	15 000	14 250
2 350	380	2 000	775	740
10 000	4 200	1 980	400	11 750
12 500	3 780	380	5 850	625
790	1 470	5 950	630	12 500
1 230	695	3 680	8 650	6 950
670	4 800	13 600	3 890	8 750
800	1 820	6 880	2 460	6 400
500	480	1 020	9 500	2 750
9 750	1 600	9 500	980	14 500

a From these figures prepare a grouped frequency distribution, in
bands of £2500, the first group being £1–2500.

b Add a column showing the percentage of shops in each group, and
another column showing the cumulative percentage of shops from
the lowest turnover to the highest turnover.

5 Approximations and errors

5.1 Statistical accuracy

The statistician is in the unfortunate position of always striving for accuracy, but always knowing he/she cannot achieve it. Unfortunately, those who quote the statistics that result from an inquiry rarely appreciate as well as the statistician the limitations of the figures provided. What is stated with reservations by the statistician may be quoted with 'authority' by less careful politicians or captains of industry. Inferences may be drawn which do not necessarily follow, and so on. It is the function of the statistician to discriminate between 'good' and 'bad' data, to monitor such data as are collected under his/her auspices and eliminate mistakes wherever possible.

Mistakes may occur at several levels. Some of these are:

a At the interview or questionnaire stage. The interviewer may record a wrong answer, or misinterpret the answer given. A response to a questionnaire may be made under a misapprehension of the question asked.

b At the classification stage. There may be mistakes in transferring the answers to the computer input, or to the tabulation or frequency distribution. Errors may be made in classifying the answers, the choice of classes may be poor, or ambiguous situations may have been overlooked and uncertainties introduced.

c At the evaluation stage, when the tabulated data are analysed, mistakes may be made in the calculation of derived statistics. The table headings may be misunderstood or derived statistics may be wrongly calculated.

d Many published statistics do not pretend to give exact figures, for absolute accuracy is impossible to achieve. With population statistics based upon a census, the figures for the census can rarely be 100% reliable, and a census cannot be held every year. In subsequent years we adjust the census figures to take account of births, deaths, emigration and immigration, but all these figures are subject to error. The statistician, recognising the nature of the statistics, expresses the population to the nearest 1000, or perhaps 10 000, settling for an approximate value.

Most published statistics are of this sort; production figures are often quoted to the nearest million tonnes, or thousands of units of output. Frequently, the actual figures are not important, it is the trend which is important. Managements and governments need to take action to correct adverse tendencies or take advantage of favourable trends. Corrective action needs to be taken quickly, and therefore time is of the essence. Absolutely accurate figures, which have to be double-checked and consequently cause delay, may therefore be positively disadvantageous.

5.2 Approximations

The usual way of approximating figures (ie indicating that they are not given precisely) has already been described – it is known as rounding. Depending upon the statistics, and the purpose for which they are to be used, we may round to the nearest 10, 100, 1000, etc. If the use to which the figures are to be put is to give a general impression of a situation, then figures rounded to easily comprehensible numbers are all that are required. For example, the population of most major countries is best discussed in millions – there are 57 million United Kingdom citizens, 60 million Germans, etc. If a detailed analysis of the statistics is to be made, or they are to be used to start some social programme, we may need to work to much smaller units – say rounded off to hundreds if we are preparing costings for a relief programme.

We have seen in Chapter 4 that rounded figures in a table expressed to be rounded to a certain degree of accuracy would be shown as follows:

	Population ('000)
Hereford	47
Gloucester	90
etc	

Note that the limit of accuracy must be shown in the table heading; in this case 'thousands'. The implication is that the last figure in each case has been rounded off – in other words the population of Hereford lies between 47 499 and 46 501. Another way of saying the same thing is that the population of Hereford is 47 000 ± 500 (but remember the way figures like 47 500 and 46 500 are corrected to the nearest 1000).

5.3 Bias

Bias is the tendency of statistics to be influenced in a particular direction, and thus to give an incorrect impression. Thus if we ask redundant executives applying for new posts late in their working lives what age they are, there will be a tendency to understate their ages. The 'age' statistics will be biased downwards.

Similarly, in costing work based upon departmental cost forecasts prepared by managers it is usual to find that managers exaggerate likely future costs. The cost forecasts are biased upwards.

When rounding, it is sometimes decided to round to the nearest thousand above, or the nearest thousand below. This produces **biased** errors.

Normally rounding, while it cannot help producing errors, produces **unbiased errors** in that the errors cancel one another out sooner or later, and the more numbers in the series the more likely it is that the errors will balance one another out. Remember that the rules for unbiased rounding are:

a If the portion of the data being discarded is more than half, round up (eg 27 675 if rounded to the nearest 1000 would be 28 000).
b If the portion of the data being discarded is less than half, round down (eg 27 125 is rounded to 27 000).
c If the portion is exactly half round to the nearest even 1000 (eg 27 500 becomes 28 000 but 26 500 becomes 26 000).

Examples of biased rounding are shown in Table 5.1.

Table 5.1 Unbiased and biased rounding

Town	*i* Population of towns	*ii* Unbiased rounding ('000)	*iii* Biased rounding ('000 above)	*iv* Biased rounding ('000 below)
A	32 590	33	33	32
B	27 230	27	28	27
C	36 500	36	37	36
D	38 499	38	39	38
E	23 500	24	24	23
F	17 895	18	18	17
G	24 230	24	25	24
H	36 725	37	37	36
J	19 826	20	20	19
K	48 394	48	49	48
Total	305 389	305	310	300

Notes
  i The rounding of C (36 500) and E (23 500) to 36 000 and 24 000, respectively, in column *ii* balances out the errors, because we have rounded both to the nearest even 1000.
 ii The total of column *ii* rounds off to the same total of thousands as the actual figures of column *i*, because the tendency is for the errors to balance out in normal rounding. Of course, had the discarded figures happened to be closer to one another (suppose for example A, F, H and J had all had the last three figures in the 500–600 range) there could be a disparity between the rounded totals of columns *i* and *ii*. In that case column *i* would have totalled less than 305 000 but columns *ii* would still have given a rounded total of 305 000. However, the more numbers in the series the less likely this becomes, and the overall tendency is for the errors to balance one another out.
iii With biased rounding the errors are sometimes large and sometimes small, but they are cumulative and the disparity between the rounded total and the true total becomes greater as the number of statistics increases.

It sometimes happens that the figures of a table are rounded, and the totals do not come out right as a result. For example, consider the following two sets of figures for persons in employment.

	Actual figures	Rounded figures ('000)
Males	13 477 950	13 478
Females	8 704 521	8 705
Total	22 182 471	22 182

The rounded figures do not sum correctly. In presenting these rounded figures we do not alter the total to agree with the figures given. We have shown in the table that the figures are rounded to the nearest thousand and therefore a discrepancy between the rounded data and the total may be expected to occur in some cases. On average, rounding errors cancel one another out, but this will not always be the case. (Sometimes – to help the uninitiated – we write on the table 'Totals do not sum correctly due to rounding'.)

5.4 Absolute and relative errors

Approximations inevitably introduce small errors into figures and when manipulating such data it is important to know the degree of error that is likely to be introduced by the arithmetical processes being used. For example, suppose the numbers 14 and 19 are to be multiplied together after being corrected to the nearest 10. In their corrected form 14 and 19 become 10 and 20. Multiplied together the result is 200; but $14 \times 19 = 266$. Small errors in the correcting up become large errors when multiplied together. In calculating errors there are two concepts – **absolute error** and **relative error**.

Note: The word 'error' in statistics does not refer to mistakes in the data. It refers to the difference arising in a set of statistics due to rounding.

Absolute error

The absolute error is the actual arithmetic difference between the approximate figure and the original quantity. In the total of Table 5.1 the absolute error in rounding 305 389 to 305 thousand is 389.

Relative error

This is the more significant error. We consider the absolute error as a fraction of the rounded total. Consider 389 as a fraction of 305 000:

$$\frac{389}{305\ 000} = 0.0012754$$

This fraction is a very small error, but it can perhaps be best understood if we turn it to a percentage, ie 0.12754%. This is about one-eighth of 1% and therefore seems to be a relatively small error.

Relative errors are probably a more helpful concept than absolute errors for they enable us to compare figures of quite different magnitudes. Thus, is an error of 5 pence in a £1 better or worse than an error of £63.20 in £8000?

$$\text{Relative error of 5 pence in a £1} = \frac{5}{100} \times 100 = 5\%$$

$$\text{Relative error of £63.20 in £8000} = \frac{63.20}{8000} \times 100$$

$$= \frac{6320}{8000}$$

$$= 0.79\%$$

Clearly an error of 5 pence in the £1 is a much greater error relatively than an error of £63.20 in £8000. Viewed absolutely, £63.20 seems a much bigger error than 5 pence. Viewed relatively, it is smaller.

5.5 Calculations with rounded figures

Whenever calculations are performed with rounded figures and we know the degree of error in the figures, we can estimate the error arising in the final result. We need to consider each process – addition, subtraction, multiplication and division.

Addition: Add together 78 000, 64 000 and 52 000. The first is correct to 5%, and the others to 3% and 1%, respectively:

78 000	5% of this is	3900
64 000	3% of this is	1920
52 000	1% of this is	520
194 000		6340

The answer is 194 000 but how accurate is it? The answer is that each of the figures could in fact be wrong to the maximum degree shown. Therefore the possible error is ± 6 340 and the answer should be stated as 194 000 ± 6 340. The possible absolute error is the sum of the errors in the original statistics.

Subtraction: Subtract 64 000 from 78 000. The first of these is correct to 3% and the other to 5%:

78 000	5% of this is	3900
64 000	3% of this is	1920
14 000		5820

The difference between the two figures is 14 000. However, the possible error can range to a maximum in two situations. If 78 000 is exceeded by its maximum error 3900 it will be 81 900. If the other figure is reduced by its maximum error it will be 64 000−1920 = 62 080. Therefore the result will be 81 900−62 080 = 19 820. This is an error of 5820. Similarly if 78 000 was reduced by its maximum error 3900 it would be 74 100, but if at the same time 64 000 was exceeded by 1920 it would be 65 920. The difference of these is 74 100−65 920 = 8180.

This is an error of − 5820. The maximum possible absolute error in the answer of 14 000 is the algebraic difference of the original absolute errors, which actually comes out to the sum of the original absolute errors.

Therefore, in both addition and subtraction, the maximum possible error is the sum of the original errors in the data.

Multiplication: Consider the error when 18 000 (correct to the nearest 1000) is multiplied by 900 (correct to the nearest 100). The product of 18 000 × 900 = 16 200 000. The maximum possible error in the figures is that 18 000 could have been as high as 18 500 and 900 could have been as high as 949:

$$18\ 500 \times 949 = 17\ 556\ 500$$

Therefore the maximum possible error is:

$$
\begin{array}{r}
17\ 566\ 500 \\
-\ 16\ 200\ 000 \\
\hline
1\ 356\ 500 \\
\hline
\end{array}
$$

This is a relative error of:

$$\frac{1\ 356\ 500}{16\ 200\ 000} \times 100 = 8.4\%$$

Now note this:

a The relative error in the original 18 000 was

$$\frac{500}{18\ 000} \times 100 = 2.8\%$$

b the relative error in the original 900 was

$$\frac{50}{900} \times 100 = 5.6\%$$

$$2.8\% + 5.6\% = 8.4\%.$$

So we may say that the relative error of a product is equal to the sum of the relative errors in the original components. This is always approximately true and is generally used as an estimate of the error in a product.

Division: Consider the error when 19 500 (correct to the nearest hundred) is divided by 880 (correct to the nearest ten). The quotient is:

$$\frac{19\ 500}{880} = 22.16$$

What is the possible error in this answer? The greatest error would occur when the largest possible dividend (19 549) is divided by the smallest possible divisor 875 (or when the smallest possible dividend is divided by the greatest possible divisor). Using the first of these alternatives:

$$\frac{19\ 549}{875} = 22.34$$

This is an error, of 0.18 in 22.16. Therefore the relative error is:

$$\frac{0.18}{22.16} \times 100 = 0.81\%$$

The relative errors in the original figures were:

$$\frac{49}{19\ 500} \times 100 = 0.25\% \qquad \text{and} \qquad \frac{-5}{880} \times 100 = -0.57\%$$

The algebraic difference of these is $0.25 - (-0.57) = 0.25 + 0.57 = 0.82\%$. So we may say that the relative error of a quotient is equal to (or approximately equal to) the algebraic difference of the original relative errors. We may summarise these rules as follows.

To establish approximately the degree of error in an answer after an arithmetical process has been carried out:

Addition: The absolute error of a sum equals the sum of the absolute errors in the original figures:

9000 (to the nearest 100) added to 500 (to the nearest 10)
$(9000 \pm 50) + (500 \pm 5) = 9500 \pm 55$

Subtraction: The absolute error of a difference equals the sum of the absolute errors in the original figures (actually the algebraic difference):

9000 (to the nearest 100) has 500 (to the nearest 5) subtracted from it
$(9000 \pm 50) - (500 \pm 5) = 8500 \pm 55$

Multiplication: The *relative* error of a product is the sum of the relative errors in the multiplier and the multiplicand:

9000 (to the nearest 100) is multiplied by 50 (to the nearest 10)
$(9000 \pm 0.56\%) \times (500 \pm 1\%) = 4\ 500\ 000 \pm 1.56\%$

Division: The *relative* error of a quotient is the algebraic difference of the relative errors in the dividend and the divisor (the maximum error is therefore the same as the sum of the relative errors):

9000 (to the nearest 100) is divided by 500 (to the nearest 10)
$(9000 \pm 0.56\%) \div (500 \pm 1\%) = 18 \pm 1.56\%$

Summary

1   All statistics contain mistakes and it is necessary to check rigorously to preserve the quality of the data.
2   Since absolute accuracy is often impossible to achieve, we frequently publish statistics which are correct to a certain figure – in other words approximations. The usual method of approximating is called 'rounding'. We must state the limit of accuracy used in the heading of any table using approximations.
3   Bias is a tendency to distort statistics. If correctly done rounding produces unbiased data. This means that the errors caused by rounding tend to be low, since they balance one another out to a considerable extent.
4   The term 'error' in statistics does not refer to mistakes made in the collection and analysis of data, but to the errors arising from rounding off data. These can be exaggerated in the course of mathematical manipulation and the degree of accuracy in the answer to any mathematical procedure should be stated. The method of calculating errors resulting from addition, subtraction, multiplication and division are given in the text and should be memorised (see pages 64 to 66).

Exercises

1   What is meant in statistics by *a* absolute error and *b* relative error? The numbers 60 000, 75 000 and 8500 are correct to 5%, 1% and 0.05%, respectively.
   a Calculate the absolute error in the aggregate of these numbers.
   b Express this error as a percentage of the aggregate value (answer to one decimal place).
2   The output of coal in the United Kingdom is given in a particular year as 143 725 000 tonnes. This is rounded to 144 million tonnes.
   a What is the absolute error?
   b What is the relative error (give answer correct to two decimal places)?
3   Rewrite the table below, with the figures correct to the nearest 1000.
   a What is the absolute error in the rounded total?
   b What is its relative error (give answer correct to two decimal places)?

Sales by geographical area	Machines sold
North	27 254
North-east	33 816
East	57 942
South	62 425
South-west	19 475
West	27 285
Total	228 197

4 From a table of emigration statistics for the year 19— you are able to read off that 13 000 people emigrated to Canada and 34 000 to Australia, out of a total of 174 000. These figures are given correct to the nearest 1000.

 a What percentage of emigrants went to Canada (answer correct to one decimal place)?

 b What percentage went to Australia (answer correct to one decimal place)?

 c What is the relative error in each of these percentages?

5 The table below shows the monthly salary bill of three companies which together form the ABC Group. It also shows the numbers of employees. The figures have been rounded to the nearest £1000 for wages and to the nearest 10 for employees.

Monthly salaries bill

Company	£'000	Numbers employed
A	280	520
B	430	630
C	800	780

 a What is the average monthly salary paid by each company, and by the group as a whole (answer to the nearest £1)?

 b What is the maximum possible error due to rounding in the figures for the group in each area, ie i total wage bill, ii total employed and iii average wage (give the answer correct to the nearest £1)?

6 Subtract from $38\ 500 \pm 50$ the following figures (make clear in each case the maximum possible error in your answer): a 3250 ± 5, b $17\ 200 \pm 50$ and $18\ 255 \pm 2\frac{1}{2}$.

7 Multiply the following sets of figures, and indicate in your answer the maximum error possible as a result of rounding:
 a $50\ 000 \pm 500 \times 250 \pm 5$, b 6000 to the nearest 1000×320 to the nearest 10 and c $3600 \pm 50 \times 125 \pm 2.5$.

8 Divide 3850 ± 25 by the following figures: a 30 to the nearest 10 and b 500 to the nearest 100 (make it clear in your answer what the maximum possible error is as a result of rounding).

6 The pictorial representation of data, 1: charts and diagrams

6.1 Graphical communication

In the last quarter of a century a new art – graphical communication – has appeared. It is an extension of old skills, such as surveying and engineering drawing, into much wider fields. We now see in a single day more illustrations than our ancestors saw in a lifetime; our children build up 'graphics' on their home computers, the advertising world invades every waking moment with attempts to convey, in pictorial form, the essence of its clients' products and no statistical presentation is complete without its diagram or chart.

The chief feature of graphical communication is the display, in a simple pictorial form, of the essential facts of any situation. Tabular presentation is one way of presenting statistical facts in a table of figures, rounded to reduce complexity and promote understanding, but there are many people who are not particularly 'numerate'; people for whom some pictorial representation would be more appropriate. This chapter is about the use of such pictorial methods of displaying data, to promote wider statistical understanding.

The chief types of pictorial representation may be listed as follows:

a graphs
b pictograms
c bar charts
d pie charts
e Gantt charts
f histograms

The first of these, graphs, gave their name to the whole art of graphics. They are of such importance that a separate chapter has been devoted to them (Chapter 7). The others are described in this chapter, which cannot however be exhaustive.

6.2 Pictograms

As its name implies a pictogram conveys statistical facts in picture form. The usual method is to choose some appropriate symbol to represent the data concerned. Thus wine production might be represented by a vat of wine, or wine consumption by a bottle, or perhaps a glass, of wine. Sometimes the symbol is obvious and springs naturally to mind. Others may not be so obvious, and it is up to the ingenuity of the designer to choose an appropriate symbol. For the purposes of this discussion we will use a bottle of wine as an appropriate symbol.

Imagine that wine consumption in country A in year 19.0 is 1 million litres per year, but that due to a change of taste or fashion it doubles to 2 million litres per year in year 19.1. There are two different ways of showing the increase – we can double the number of symbols or we can increase the size of the symbol. This is illustrated in Fig 6.1a and b.

a *Doubling the number of symbols*　　　b *Increasing the size of the symbol*

Fig 6.1 Alternative ways of showing an increase in consumption

Notes

i The difficulty with method **b** is that the increase in size has to be related to the area of space enclosed by the symbol. If the dimensions are doubled the area is quadrupled. This method is therefore unsatisfactory for it is difficult to calculate the dimensions for a symbol of twice the area, nor can the average eye detect the size of the change.

ii By contrast, doubling the number of symbols is easy to follow, so method **a** is acceptable.

It helps if the symbol can be divided into at least four parts, to represent fractions of a unit. Thus a drawing of a television set is still comprehensible as half a television set or one-quarter of a television set. By contrast half a glass of wine may be meaningful in a pictogram, but one-quarter of a glass of wine is rather less satisfactory. Some appropriate scale must be chosen to enable the full data to be displayed on the page where it is to appear. Thus if wine consumption in various countries ranges from 5 million bottles per year in the country with the smallest consumption to 14 million bottles per year in the country with the largest consumption, we might need to use 1 bottle to represent a million bottles. The pictogram would then range from 5 bottles to 14 bottles. Wine consumption in Europe is shown in Fig 6.2 on page 71. The notes on page 71 deal with certain difficulties encountered with pictograms. Study the illustration and the notes now, before trying some exercises on pictograms.

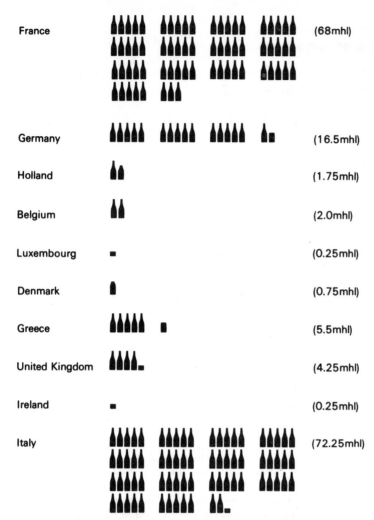

France (68mhl)

Germany (16.5mhl)

Holland (1.75mhl)

Belgium (2.0mhl)

Luxembourg (0.25mhl)

Denmark (0.75mhl)

Greece (5.5mhl)

United Kingdom (4.25mhl)

Ireland (0.25mhl)

Italy (72.25mhl)

Fig 6.2 Wine consumption in the European Community (mhl = million hectolitres): (source: Annual Reports of the EC, 19—)

Notes
  i The symbol chosen must be appropriate to the data being presented.
 ii The symbol should, if possible, be divisible into four parts, so that halves and quarters of a unit can be portrayed. In this illustration three-quarters of a bottle and half a bottle are comprehensible but a quarter of a bottle is less satisfactory. If we wish to represent smaller fractions than one-quarter (and in a decimal world tenths are often represented) it is usual to break up the height of a symbol, as in Fig 6.2, rather than the width.
iii The scale is chosen to represent the data on the size of page available — in this example 1 bottle represents 1 000 000 hl. The figures are given to the nearest $\frac{1}{4}$ million hl. To have chosen 1 bottle to represent 1000 hl would have made it quite impossible to draw the diagram in the space available.
 iv Frequently, comprehension is improved by giving at the end of each row the total figure represented by the pictogram.
  v The source of the data must be given — though in this illustration, to save endlessly revising the illustration, we have taken the liberty of not revealing the actual year to which the data relates.

Exercises on pictograms

1 New housing construction in the country of Ostland for the last 5 years has been as follows:

Year 1	25 000 new houses
Year 2	38 000 new houses
Year 3	45 000 new houses
Year 4	62 000 new houses
Year 5	94 000 new houses

Draw a pictogram to illustrate these data. The source is the Ostland Annual Abstract of Statistics.

2 A manufacturer of baby carriages is considering the expansion of his factory. He asks you to prepare a report on the feasibility of this project. In the course of your investigation you discover that the number of live births has been as follows in the last 6 years, according to a report of the Population Bureau:

Year 1	750 000
Year 2	728 000
Year 3	685 000
Year 4	675 000
Year 5	650 000
Year 6	598 000

Present these data in a pictogram and suggest in a few sentences what the implications of the data are for the proposed extension of the factory.

3 An international agency assesses world population in the year 19— as follows: low-income countries, 2500 million; middle-income countries, 850 million; high-income countries, 600 million. Illustrate these data with a pictogram. The source of the data is the Agency Population Survey.

4 Manpower PLC employs the following staff: *a* 125 senior management personnel, *b* 375 middle-management personnel, *c* 1500 office workers and *d* 3825 manual workers. Using a *different* symbol for each group display this data in pictogram form, with each symbol representing 250 members of staff.

6.3 Bar charts

Although pictograms are useful in presenting data in an attractive way with symbols relevant to the data, they can be tedious to draw and require some artistic ability. A bar chart is almost as useful for comparing sets of data, and is more easily drawn. Information is related to the horizontal or vertical length of a bar or thick line. Bar charts should

not be confused with histograms (see Section 6.6 below) which are used
to display frequency distributions. Bar charts are used to display sets of
data from different times, or from different places. Thus they might be
used to compare one year with another, or one place with another. The
length of the bar is the basis of the comparison, not the area or volume
of the bar, even though, for artistic purposes, a three-dimensional view
may be given. As to three-dimensional views, see 'Three-dimensional bar
charts' (pages 77–79).

In Fig 6.3 below a shopkeeper has recorded sales in a given week under
various headings. Such a bar chart brings out the comparable situation
clearly, and might lead to a business decision to change the amount of
space allocated to the various departments. We might decide to phase out
altogether the sale of wines and spirits, which do not represent a large
proportion of turnover. Alternatively, we might attempt to increase sales
in this area. It might be even more valuable to do another bar chart to
discover the contribution to profits made by each of these departments.
Margins of profit on groceries may be very different from those on
tobacco and it might help our decision-making to know more about the
profitability of each area.

In designing such a bar chart we have to decide on the following
points:

a *Scale*   The scale must be chosen so that all the data can appear easily
   in the space available. The largest piece of data should use up almost
   the whole scale. Where one figure is much larger than the others and
   would make the others appear totally unimportant if a scale was
   chosen to accommodate it, it is usual to break the bar – as shown in
   Fig 6.4. Students may find it helpful to remember that squared paper
   can be turned through 90° (landscaped) to give more room when
   required.

b *Bars*   The bars should all be of the same width, since only the length
   of the bar is used to compare the data. The length of each bar is a
   matter of simple calculation. If the scale chosen in Fig 6.3 was

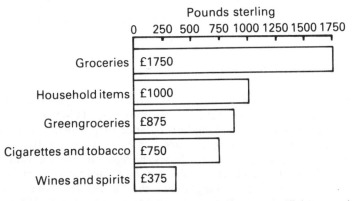

Fig 6.3 An analysis of retail turnover (£ sterling) week 17 (source: departmental
sales report)

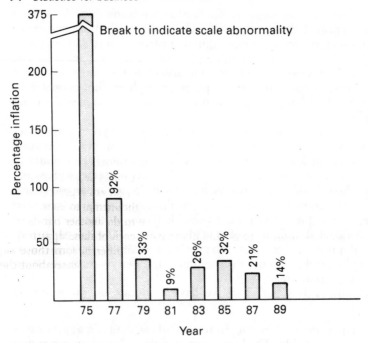

Fig 6.4 Inflation in Chile, 1975–89 (source: World Bank)

1 cm = £250 then 'Groceries' requires

$$\frac{£1750}{£250} \text{ cm} = 7 \text{ cm}$$

c *Horizontal or vertical* Bar charts may be drawn either horizontally or vertically and a choice must be made as to which is more appropriate. In Fig 6.4 inflation rises and falls over the years, and vertical presentation was adopted.

d *Shading or colouring* Colour, or cross-hatching, can be helpful in differentiating between the bars.

a Positive and negative bar charts

Bar charts can also be used to illustrate a positive or negative effect where this is required by indicating a scale above and below zero. In Fig 6.5 on page 75 the United Kingdom balance of payments figures are illustrated. Each year has three bars, which may be positive or negative. The bar with cross-hatching shows the figure for visible trade. The white bar shows the figure for invisible earnings (insurance, tourism, etc.). The bar with double-hatching shows the net result of overseas earnings on current account. Where all earnings are positive (eg 1981), it will be the sum of the visible and invisible earnings. Where visible

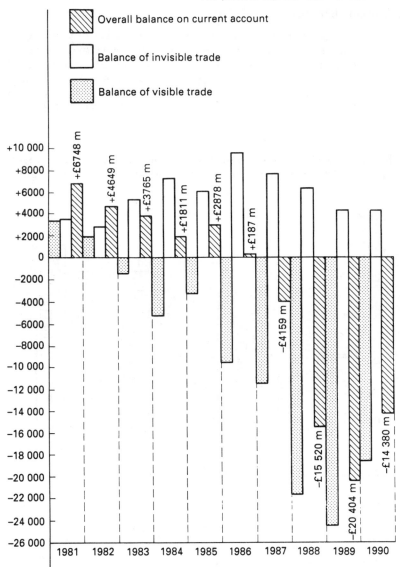

Fig 6.5 United Kingdom balance of payments on current account 1981–90 (source: *The Pink Book*)

earnings are negative and invisible earnings are positive, the balance of payments on current account will be the difference between the two. It may be negative, as in 1987–90, or positive, as in 1983–6. Some of the very serious deficits of 1987–90 were offset by capital movements into the UK from foreign investors. The diagram shows only the current account figures (ie the trading figures for goods and services in the year named).

b Multiple bar charts

If we wish to compare a number of items over a number of years we can draw a multiple bar chart, showing how each item varied over the period. In Fig 6.6 the indexes of retail prices for four years are shown, year 0 being the base year of 100. There are no figures for year 1 as the choice of a new base year presented problems in collection. The figures shown are therefore for years 2, 3, 4 and 5, for food, housing, fuel and clothing.

c Component bar charts

Where a set of data combines to form a total of some sort it is possible to draw a component bar chart which shows the total as the length of

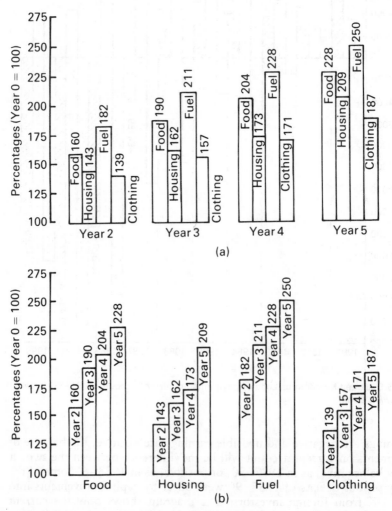

Fig 6.6 Multiple bar charts: *a* comparing the indexes one with another and *b* comparing each index over time (source: *Monthly Digest of Statistics*)

the bar, each component being shown as a shaded section of the bar. Consider the data shown in Table 6.1.

Choosing a scale of 1 cm to each £100 000, the component bar charts would appear as shown in Fig 6.7. (*Note*: Because of photographic adjustment the textbook illustration may not be to scale – although designed by the artist to the scale suggested.)

Table 6.1   Sales (in £'000)

Sales	Year 1	Year 2
Furniture	486	515
Furnishings	78	92
Electrical appliances	225	214
Computers and electronics	39	139
Fine art and ceramics	44	67
Total	872	1027

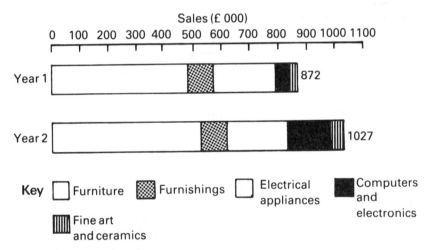

Fig 6.7 Component bar charts

d Percentage bar charts

Another way to display data which are components of a whole set of statistics is to show them in the form of a percentage bar chart. The entire set of statistics is shown as 100%, and the component data are calculated as percentage parts of the whole. A typical example is the illustration in Fig 6.8, which shows the use made of proportions of 'profit' earned by an organisation. In this illustration 'profit' means value-added as a result of the firm's activities, before paying wages and salaries.

e Three-dimensional bar charts

Many published charts and diagrams today show three-dimensional views of bar charts and other pictorial methods of presentation. While

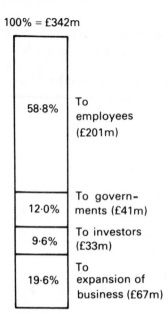

100% = £342m

58·8% — To employees (£201m)

12·0% — To governments (£41m)

9·6% — To investors (£33m)

19·6% — To expansion of business (£67m)

Fig 6.8 A percentage bar chart

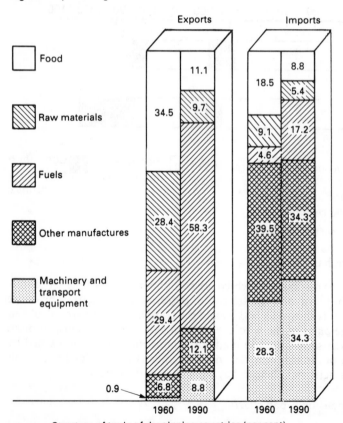

Exports   Imports

Food

Raw materials

Fuels

Other manufactures

Machinery and transport equipment

Exports:
1960: 34.5, 28.4, 29.4, 6.8, 0.9
1990: 11.1, 9.7, 58.3, 12.1, 8.8

Imports:
1960: 18.5, 9.1, 4.6, 39.5, 28.3
1990: 8.8, 5.4, 17.2, 34.3, 34.3

1960   1990   1960   1990

Structure of trade of developing countries (per cent)

Fig 6.9 A three-dimensional bar chart (source: UNCTAD)

this adds to the visual impression and the aesthetic appreciation of the information it does very little for the statistics – it may even confuse the issue giving more than one line to look at for a given set of data. In any case, it is an art in its own right, which not all of us have mastered, and it takes time to draw. In an examination there is no time to draw three-dimensional views, and a student not trained in graphical communication may distort the visual image to no real purpose, while making no improvement at all in the statistical presentation. In Fig 6.9 a simple example is reproduced which does not distort the data in any way, and might seem harmless, but in an examination the time wasted getting the three dimensional effect, for example, would be better spent proceeding with the next question.

Exercises on bar charts

1 Sales in a department store during a year are as follows: furniture, £7.48 million; fashions, £11.89 million; domestic and garden appliances, £5.88 million; soft furnishings, £3.23 million; restaurant, £1.78 million; menswear, £7.33 million; electronics, £12.44 million. Correct these figures to the nearest tenth of a million and draw a bar chart presenting the data.

2 A multinational company sells its products in the following regions in two successive years as shown. All figures are given in US$, to the nearest million. Draw a multiple bar chart to present this data.

Region	Year 1	Year 2
Europe	8 258	9 149
Asia	11 246	15 168
Africa	2 785	3 258
North America	16 356	18 252
South and Central America	5 495	3 958
Australasia and Oceania	4 725	3 584

3 Growth rates (changes in the national output) of a certain country were as follows in a 10 year cycle:

Year 1	1.5%	Year 6	− 1.5%
Year 2	2.0%	Year 7	− 2.3%
Year 3	3.7%	Year 8	− 0.5%
Year 4	4.2%	Year 9	1.1%
Year 5	8.3%	Year 10	3.2%

Illustrate these changes in growth rate with a bar chart that shows positive and negative changes.

4 Using the figures in Exercise 1 above draw a percentage bar chart showing the departmental shares in the total sales of the store.

5 Sales in successive years by a manufacturer of electrical goods were:

Product	Year 1	Year 2
Vacuum cleaners	20 850	23 555
Hair dryers	18 560	27 580
Toasters	14 250	16 385
Blow-heaters	11 380	13 590
Electric fires	34 960	43 890
Total	100 000	125 000

Draw component bar charts to show the sales for the two years.

6.4 Pie charts

One of the commonest concepts in economics is the concept of the 'national cake'. The output of the nation is conceived as a large cake, which can be sliced up and allocated to the various groups within the community. The same idea is used in statistics, though the name applied to the diagram is a pie chart. Any total may be conceived as a round pie, which is divided into slices according to the size of the component parts which make up the total.

Consider the data supplied in Table 6.2. When drawn as a pie chart both parts of the table can be presented as a circular pie, with the component parts shown as slices of the pie. The 360° in a circle must be shared in the same proportion as the parts of the table bear to the total. This is simple enough, especially if an electronic calculator is used. Thus the slice of the pie to be allocated to basic materials in the case of imports is:

$$\frac{3311}{53\,427} \times 360° = 22.3°$$

When drawn the pie chart appears as shown in Fig 6.10. To help students, the number of degrees for each slice of pie has been shown but

Table 6.2 United Kingdom visible imports and exports, 19– (£m)

(Item)	Imports	Exports
Food, beverages and tobacco	6 606	3 924
Basic materials	3 311	1 355
Minerals, fuels and lubricants	7 091	11 193
Semi-manufactured goods	12 967	14 112
Finished manufactures	21 905	23 221
Unclassified items	1 547	1 741
Total	53 427	55 546

(Source: *The Pink Book*)

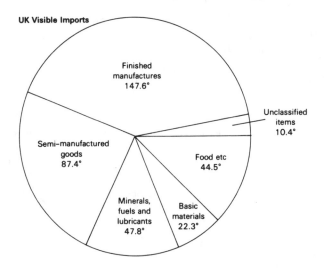

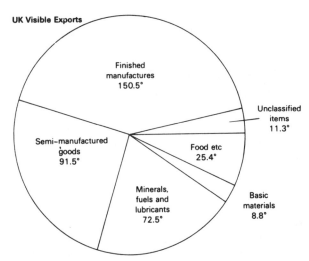

Fig 6.10 United Kingdom visible imports and exports, as pie charts (source: *The Pink Book*)

Notes
  i The pies are divided into slices in proportion as the figure for the class of imports or exports bears to the total figure.
 ii The number of degrees in each slice need not be shown on the final diagram, they are put in here to assist the reader.
iii A three-dimensional view should not be attempted in an examination, but Fig 6.11 on page 82 shows such a presentation from a business publication. The reader will note that the three-dimensional effect adds nothing to the information supplied by the diagram

Total Sales 19__ (£ million)

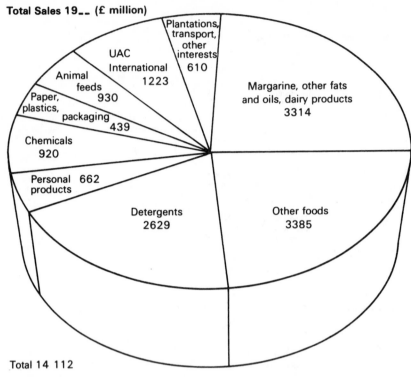

Fig 6.11 Sales for the year 19— (courtesy of Unilever PLC)

of course these figures would not appear in a diagram for use in a business report since they are of no interest to anyone other than the person drawing the diagram.

6.5 Gantt charts

A Gantt chart relates actual performance to planned performance. The chart consists of a layout of equally spaced columns, each of which represents a week (or month). Although the columns are equal in width the planned performances are not necessarily the same, but may be adjusted to suit seasonal variations. Thus a salesman's annual target of £48 000 sales need not be divided into 12 equal monthly targets of £4000, for in some months it might be quite impossible to achieve sales of £4000, while in other months the target would be passed in a few days. After discussion with the employee, and in line with the manager's knowledge of seasonal variations in sales, realistic targets will be set for each month. Table 6.3 shows targets for a 6-monthly period and the results actually achieved in the first 5 months. Each actual figure is then expressed as a percentage of the target figure. Thus in month 1 the achievement was:

$$\frac{3400}{4000} \times 100\% = 85\%$$

Table 6.3   Planned sales and actual sales

Month	Planned sales (£)	Actual sales (£)
1	4000	3400
2	4500	4250
3	3250	3800
4	4000	4750
5	5000	6250
6	8000	

In month 4 the percentage was:

$$\frac{4750}{4000} \times 100 = 118.75\%$$

The chart is completed as shown in Fig 6.12.

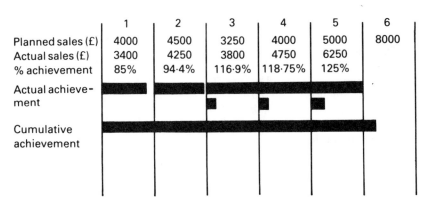

	1	2	3	4	5	6
Planned sales (£)	4000	4500	3250	4000	5000	8000
Actual sales (£)	3400	4250	3800	4750	6250	
% achievement	85%	94·4%	116·9%	118·75%	125%	

Actual achievement

Cumulative achievement

Fig 6.12 A Gantt chart

Notes

i Planned sales are written in on the top line of the chart, in advance.

ii Actual sales are filled in from month to month as the figures become available.

iii The percentage achieved is calculated and written in, but to bring out the result diagrammatically a bar diagram is completed showing the percentage achieved as a bar line across the column. If 100% of the plan is achieved the bar will completely cross the column. If less than 100% is achieved the discrepancy will be obvious, while if more than 100% is achieved a second bar is started (as in months 3, 4 and 5).

iv Finally a cumulative bar shows the extent to which the target has been achieved overall. In the figure above the actual excess over target is £1700. This means that by the end of month 5 £1700 of the planned sales for month 6 have already been achieved. The fraction is 1700/8000 = 21.25%. This portion of month 6 is therefore already completed on the sixth column.

Exercises on pie charts and Gantt charts

1 Invisible exports are made up as follows:

Item	£m
General government earnings	435
Sea transport	3565
Civil aviation	2471
Travel and tourism	3184
Financial services (net)	2145
Other services	5782

(Source *The Pink Book*)

The word (net) on financial services implies that this is the earnings left after imported financial services had been set off against earnings. Ignore this for the purposes of the present exercise. Draw a pie diagram to illustrate these statistics.

2 A multinational company has sales totalling £800 million in the year. The details are:

Product	£m
Dairy products	160
Other foods	240
Detergents	180
Hygiene products	80
Chemicals	72
Paper, plastics	12
Animal feedstuffs	56

Draw a pie diagram to illustrate the data.

3 According to its Central Bank, the country of Caribia has total debts of $11 200 million. This is made up as follows:

Debtor	$m
Civil Service borrowing	6981
Central Bank borrowing	696
Banking sector debt	426
Commercial firm indebtedness	1433
Private borrowing	1664

Draw a pie chart to illustrate the data.

4 A United Kingdom firm sells 46% of its goods to Europe, 13% to the USA, 18% to African countries, 12% to India, 7% to Pakistan and the balance to Australia. Draw a pie chart to show its distribution to overseas territories.

5   A salesman's target for the 6 months shown below differ considerably from the actual results. Draw a Gantt chart to illustrate this information.

Month	Target (£'000)	Actual (£'000)
1	5	2.5
2	6	3.5
3	8	6.5
4	10	8.0
5	14	10.5
6	6	9.5

Include in your chart a cumulative sales line covering the full period.

6   Production targets at Beltpackers Ltd are as follows in the 4-week period shown.

Week	Target
1	60 000
2	80 000
3	55 000
4	90 000

Actual results were: week 1, 50 000; week 2, 75 000; week 3, 75 000; week 4, 80 000. Draw a Gantt chart on both a weekly and a cumulative basis to illustrate these results.

6.6   Histograms

A histogram is a diagram which displays a frequency distribution as a series of adjacent rectangles, each of which represents one class interval. It is sometimes called a block frequency diagram. Because the blocks stand alongside one another, they show the pattern of the distribution. It might, for example, be symmetrical, rising to a peak and then falling away. It may be more erratic, with a number of peaks separated by ranges where the frequency is much smaller.

The basic principle is that the *area* of each block is proportional to the data. The class intervals are measured along the horizontal axis, and if these intervals are all equal the height of the blocks is proportional to the frequency but this does not change the basic principle that the areas are proportional to the frequencies displayed.

If the data are arranged in equal class intervals the width chosen for the blocks is immaterial and may be selected to suit the space available. A simple illustration referring to Table 4.3 on page 47 is shown in Fig 6.13 on page 86. Where the class intervals are not equal it is necessary to adjust the height of the blocks to take account of the frequency density. This is defined as the frequency per standard unit of class

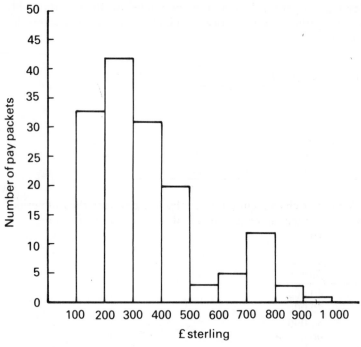

Fig 6.13 A histogram: monthly take-home pay

Notes
 i The data (see Table 4.3 on page 47) are in equal class intervals except that in the first class interval the frequency is 0 as no one has a monthly take-home pay of less than £100.
 ii The class intervals are marked along the horizontal axis, using a scale appropriate to the space available.
 iii The frequencies are marked up the vertical axis. In this case, since the widths used for each block are the same, the height of the blocks varies with the frequency.
 iv Using the midpoint of the class interval, mark in a height above the horizontal axis which is proportional to the frequency. Draw a horizontal line at this point equal to the width of the class interval. Now join up the sides of the rectangle. The result is as shown. Note that the pattern of take-home pay is clearly shown, with a large grouping in the lower pay ranges and much fewer people earning a large pay packet.

interval. The frequency given in the data has to be reduced to take account of the extra width of those class intervals which are larger than the rest. It is found by the formula:

$$\text{Frequency density} = \frac{\text{frequency (area)}}{\text{number of standard units in the class interval}}$$

This is shown in Fig 6.14 on page 87.

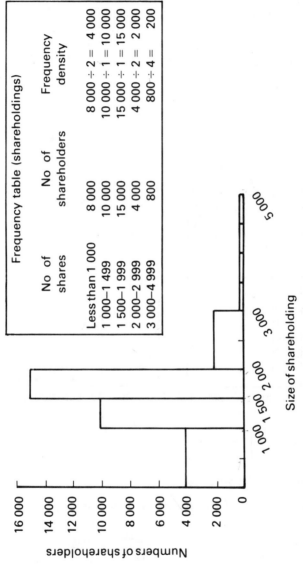

Frequency table (shareholdings)		
No of shares	No of shareholders	Frequency density
Less than 1 000	8 000	8 000 ÷ 2 = 4 000
1 000—1 499	10 000	10 000 ÷ 1 = 10 000
1 500—1 999	15 000	15 000 ÷ 1 = 15 000
2 000—2 999	4 000	4 000 ÷ 2 = 2 000
3 000—4 999	800	800 ÷ 4 = 200

Fig 6.14 Histogram with unequal class intervals (referred to on pages 85—86)

A frequency polygon

A frequency polygon can be drawn on a histogram by joining the mid-points of the tops of the blocks. It will have the same area as the blocks themselves, each line joining two midpoints forming two congruent triangles, one of which is included in the polygon and the other is discarded from the block diagram. This is illustrated in Fig 6.15.

Alternatively the polygon can be drawn without the histogram by plotting the frequencies as if they occurred at the midpoints of the class interval. Such polygons are only correct where the class intervals are the same size.

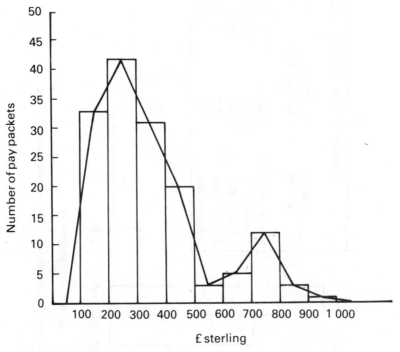

Fig 6.15 A frequency polygon

Exercises on histograms

1   Houses are on offer in Newtown as follows:

Price range (£)	Number on offer
Under 20 000	18
20 000 and under 40 000	38
40 000 and under 60 000	198
60 000 and under 80 000	270
80 000 and under 100 000	86

Draw a histogram to present this data diagrammatically.

2   Commercial property in a city is available as follows:

Rentals (£ per annum)	Number on offer
Under 2 000	12
2 000 and under 4 000	16
4 000 and under 6 000	24
6 000 and under 8 000	20
8 000 and under 10 000	8
10 000 and under 12 000	2
12 000 and under 20 000	8

Draw a histogram to present this data diagrammatically.

3   A survey of wages in an industrial town shows the following results for the first week in the financial year.

Class range (£)	Number in class
25 and under 50	438
50 and under 75	850
75 and under 100	1350
100 and under 125	820
125 and under 150	460
150 and under 175	320
175 and under 200	240

Draw a histogram to present this data diagrammatically.

4   Using the data of Exercise 1 draw a frequency polygon to show the same information as a histogram.

5   Using the data of Exercise 3 draw the histogram and a frequency polygon superimposed upon it.

7 The pictorial representation of data, 2: graphs

7.1 The nature of graphs

Graphs are pictorial representations of data which show the relationship between two variables. Two lines called axes are drawn at right angles to one another on special graph paper which is ruled up in squares. The squares assist the 'plotting' of the data, because the eye can follow the rulings easily to locate any point on the chart. In any pair of variables there is usually one variable which is dependent on the other – the **independent variable**. Thus if we are plotting the temperature of a patient in intensive care, taking the readings every 2 hours, the time is the independent variable and the temperature is the **dependent variable** – what the patient's temperature will be depends upon the time you take it, as the disease progresses. Figure 7.1 below and the notes on page 91 explain the basic features of a graph.

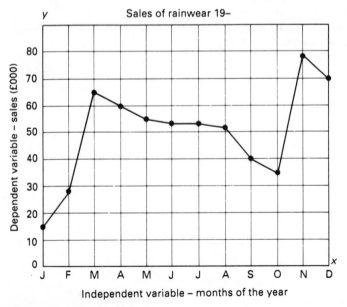

Fig 7.1 Constructing a graph

Notes to Fig 7.1 (see page 90)

i The two axes are called the coordinates of the graph. The horizontal axis is called the abscissa, or *x* axis. It is used to plot the independent variable − in the case shown the months of the year, January, February, etc.

ii The vertical axis is called the ordinate, or *y* axis. It is used to plot the dependent variable − in the case shown sales for the month.

iii A scale is chosen which enables the data to be shown on the graph. In the case shown the largest monthly sale was £79 000 so that the scale used enabled this to be shown easily. Had the largest monthly sale been £179 000 the scale used would have been inappropriate, since £179 000 could not have been shown on the graph. We could only show it by changing the scale to, say, 20, 40, 60, 80, 100, 120, 140, 160, 180 on the *y* axis. The point where the two axes meet, and from which the scales start, is called the origin, and is labelled 0.

iv Points are plotted by making a tiny dot, or perhaps a tiny cross, on the space available between the two axes − for example, if sales in August were £52 000 this gives a unique point on the graph, marked with a tiny dot as shown.

v The points can then be joined by a curve (even if the lines are straight it is convenient to refer to them as a curve). The curve may be continuous, as in Fig 7.1, or discontinuous. Discontinuous lines show up the actual plotting points more easily. (See Fig 7.5 on page 94.)

vi The axes of the graph should be clearly labelled to show what the variable is and if necessary the units used (for example, £'000 on the vertical axis).

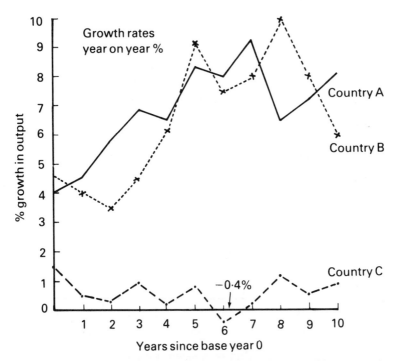

Fig 7.2 Several sets of data plotted to show comparative achievements (source: *Finance and Development*)

Notes to Fig 7.2 (see page 91)
  i Every graph should carry a caption showing what it is about.
 ii The source of the data should be given wherever possible.
iii The axes should be labelled with the name of the variable, and the scales used.
iv The vertical scale should start at zero. If the data are remote from zero the axis
      should still start at zero, but be broken above the zero mark (see Fig 7.3 below
      for an example) continuing with the scale at the upper levels.
  v Three-dimensional effects are *not* desirable in examinations, though they may
      be used in house magazines, etc, where the aim is communication rather than
      statistical clarity.
iv If more than one line is shown they should be varied by dots, dashes, etc.

7.2 Simple graphs

For simple graphs the intention is to display the data and there is no
attempt to use the graph to make predictions. The use of graphs in this
way is explained below (see Section 7.4). For comparison purposes it is
possible to put two or more lines on the same graph, differentiating
between them by using different patterns for the lines. Thus we could use
a dotted line, a line of interrupted dashes, a mixture of dots and dashes,
etc. Such a graph is shown in Fig 7.2 on page 91.

Where the data to be displayed are large, and yet the variations are
only small, it is best to use a graph with an interrupted vertical scale as
shown in Fig 7.3 below. The data compare the circulation of two
national daily papers, each of which sells over 3 million copies. It would

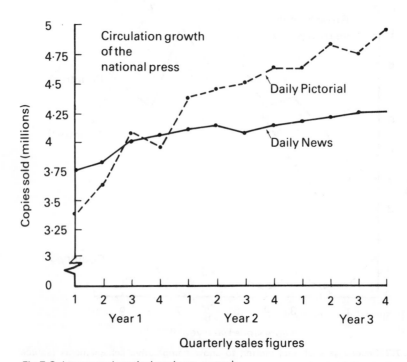

Fig 7.3 Interrupted vertical scale on a graph

waste much of the paper to show the full scale, but the origin must still be shown, with the interruption slightly above it.

Some sets of data consist of component parts of a grand total. For example, the sales of a firm are made up of the individual department sales figures, which add up in a series of layers to give a multilayer total. In Fig. 7.4 the official reserves of the United Kingdom are shown in a layer graph. The data are given in Table 7.1.

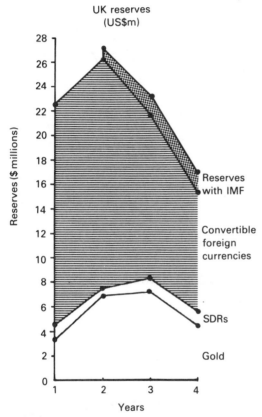

Fig 7.4 A layer graph (source: *The Pink Book*)

Table 7.1   United Kingdom official reserves, year 19—

Reserve	Year 1 ($m)	Year 2 ($m)	Year 3 ($m)	Year 4 ($m)
Reserves deposited with the IMF	—	1 308	1 513	1 568
Convertible currencies at Bank of England, etc	18 034	18 621	13 457	9 634
IMF special drawing rights	1 245	560	1 043	1 233
Gold	3 259	6 987	7 334	4 562
Total	22 538	27 476	23 347	16 997

(Source: *The Pink Book*)

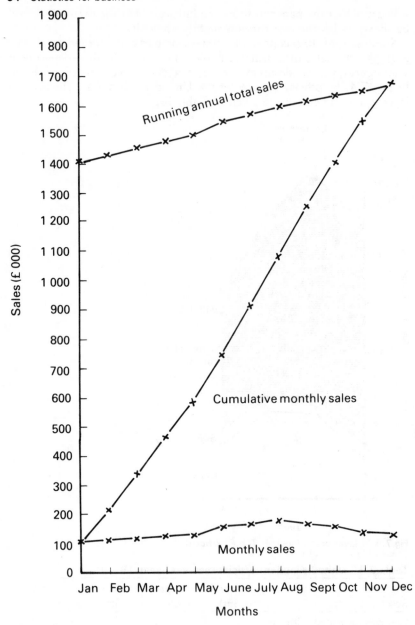

Fig 7.5 A sales Z chart

To plot such a layer graph we start with one set of data. As gold is heavy we will show it as the bottom layer. We first plot this layer and label it. The second layer – IMF special drawing rights – has to be superimposed on the gold layer and should therefore be plotted at the total of these, ie the figures will be 4504 for year 1, 7547 for year 2, etc.

The third layer will be plotted at 22 538, 26 168, 21 834 and 15 429, respectively (adding up the three sets of figures), while for the fourth layer the figures to be plotted will be the total reserves. Note that in year 1 there was no fourth layer.

7.3   Z charts

A Z chart is one which is frequently used in selling organisations or productive situations to plot current figures, cumulative figures and annual figures. The result finishes up at the end of the year as a rather erratically shaped Z.

Consider the sales figures shown in Table 7.2. The Z chart to illustrate this data would be as shown in Fig 7.5. The running annual total starts at 1408 (1387 − 85 (previous January figure) + 106 (current January figure); each month last year's figure is discarded and this year's figure is included). The Z must join up at the end of the year because in December both the cumulative total and the running annual total are the same.

Table 7.2   Sales (£'000)

Month	Previous year	Current year
January	85	106
February	88	110
March	95	119
April	103	125
May	106	128
June	118	158
July	134	168
August	152	174
September	146	164
October	131	153
November	128	139
December	101	128
Total	1387	1672

Exercises on simple graphs

1   A firm deals wholesale in three main areas – furniture, electronics and domestic electrical appliances. Sales in the year 19— were as shown on page 96 in the 13 (4-weekly) 'months'. Plot these sales on a single graph, using distinctive lines to differentiate the three classes.

Sales (£'000)

'Month'	Furniture	Electronics	Electrical goods
1	84	17	46
2	92	24	43
3	86	26	41
4	84	29	37
5	79	33	42
6	82	35	43
7	77	37	38
8	76	35	35
9	75	41	33
10	83	43	36
11	84	45	32
12	73	41	31
13	71	47	28

2 Foreign aid to Latin American countries in the 10 years shown below is made up as follows:

Foreign aid (US$m)

Type of aid	Years									
	1	2	3	4	5	6	7	8	9	10
USA official	33	42	47	51	82	94	106	120	111	128
USA private	84	72	36	24	16	86	88	94	120	108
World Bank, etc	17	24	27	32	35	56	74	29	59	84
Comecon (estimated)	14	32	38	46	36	22	88	92	60	66
Other	7	3	8	11	15	4	36	24	3	12

Plot these figures in the form of a layer graph, to show the total aid in each year.

3 Your firm validates circulations of magazines for advertising revenue purposes. Two rival magazines *Freedom* and *Liberty* have circulations as follows, in millions:

Year	Quarter	*Freedom*	*Liberty*
1	1	3.8	3.3
1	2	3.9	3.4
1	3	4.1	3.6
1	4	4.2	3.9
2	1	4.4	4.0
2	2	4.5	4.3
2	3	4.6	4.8
2	4	4.7	4.9
3	1	5.0	4.8
3	2	5.2	4.7
3	3	5.3	5.2
3	4	5.6	5.8

Draw a graph to illustrate these sales (*hint*: be careful not to waste any paper).

4   Imports of electric shavers (thousands) are as follows:

Month	Year 1	Year 2
January	27	24
February	26	22
March	26	48
April	34	48
May	34	52
June	28	34
July	28	55
August	29	40
September	45	46
October	50	68
November	48	58
December	28	53

(Source: departmental records)

Draw a Z chart for year 2, using the data given above.

5   National expenditure figures over the years 1963–88 in the country of Europa were made up as follows:

Form of expenditure	1963 (%)	1968 (%)	1973 (%)	1978 (%)	1983 (%)	1988 (%)
Private expenditure	71	68	66	60	56	64
Public expenditure (goods and services)	15	16	16	17	19	21
Public expenditure (welfare)	6	8	9	10	12	15
Public expenditure (debt interest)	4	4	5	9	10	14
Public expenditure (investment)	4	4	4	4	3	5

Draw the figures as a layer graph, showing the way national expenditure varied over the 20-year period.

6   a Briefly outline the uses of the Z chart.
     b Draw a Z chart for the sales of the XYZ Co Ltd in year 2 below.

Sales of XYZ Co Ltd (£'000)
(Source: departmental records)

Month	Year 1	Year 2
January	27	31
February	36	37
March	35	40
April	42	44
May	44	47
June	46	53
July	51	62
August	53	71
September	52	70
October	36	49
November	33	46
December	30	45

7.4 Straight-line graphs

Many simple graphs which represent data of sales, production, etc, rise and fall as the figures change from month to month or year to year. Other graphs where the variables are in a constant relationship with one another are **straight-line graphs**. Frequently, straight-line graphs go through the origin. For example, if a particular machine sells at £40 the income arising from the sale of machines is in a constant relationship with the number sold. The sale of one machine brings in £40, two machines earn £80, three bring in £120, etc. No machines earn no money, so the graph will pass through the origin. Such a graph is shown in Fig 7.6.

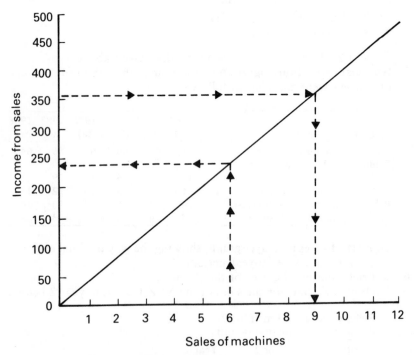

Fig 7.6 A straight-line graph through the origin

Notes

  i Strictly speaking, all we need to draw up such a straight-line graph is one plotting point and the origin of the graph. Twelve machines earn £480 and a line joining this point to the origin of the graph will pass through all the other 'income received' points.

 ii From such a graph we can read off the income from any volume of sales by **interpolation**. A vertical line from point 6 on the horizontal axis intercepts the graph as shown. A horizontal line from this point to the y axis shows that six machines earn £240.

iii The reverse process will answer the question 'How many machines must we sell to earn £360?' This time we start from the y axis and finish up at the x axis.

Obviously the example chosen is a very simple one but such ready-reckoner graphs may be very useful to some businesses. The process of *interpolation* is one where we find the value within the framework of the graph as drawn. If we **extrapolate** we extend the graph beyond the present boundaries. This is used particularly to extrapolate from a given **trend** in certain types of data, such as sales data. We must remember though that in doing so caution is necessary. It does not follow that because 10 machines can be sold for £400 we can earn £400 000 from selling 10 000 of them. To make the extra sales we may have to lower prices.

7.5   Graphs of simple functions

Many variable quantities have a constant relationship to other quantities and may be expressed in terms of them. Thus if we say $y = 2x$ we mean that the quantity y always varies as x varies and is always double the value of x. It follows that the value of y depends upon the value of x and is said to be a **function** of x. So:

if $x = 0$, $y =$ twice $0 = 0$
if $x = 1$, $y = 2$
if $x = 2$, $y = 4$, etc

Such simple relationships always come out on a graph as a straight line. They are usually expressed in the general formula:

$$y = a + bx$$

where y is the dependent variable (depending on the value of x), x is the independent variable and a and b are constants – in other words, numbers. To plot such a graph we need a small table. We will suppose $a = 1$ and $b = \frac{1}{2}$. The values of y will then be:

$x =$	0	1	2	3	4	5	6	7	8	9 etc
$bx = \frac{1}{2}x =$	0	$\frac{1}{2}$	1	$1\frac{1}{2}$	2	$2\frac{1}{2}$	3	$3\frac{1}{2}$	4	$4\frac{1}{2}$ etc
$a =$	1	1	1	1	1	1	1	1	1	1 etc
$y = a + bx =$	1	$1\frac{1}{2}$	2	$2\frac{1}{2}$	3	$3\frac{1}{2}$	4	$4\frac{1}{2}$	5	$5\frac{1}{2}$ etc

When plotted this gives a straight-line graph, as in Fig. 7.7.

7.6   Break-even charts

Figure 7.8 on page 101 shows two break-even charts which illustrate the effect of pricing policy on profitability and safety of the firm from competition, etc. In every production situation there are certain 'fixed' costs – that is costs which have to be borne anyway before we even start to make and sell our product. We must have land and buildings, we must have a management structure, we must have performed certain research and development work to develop and test our product before

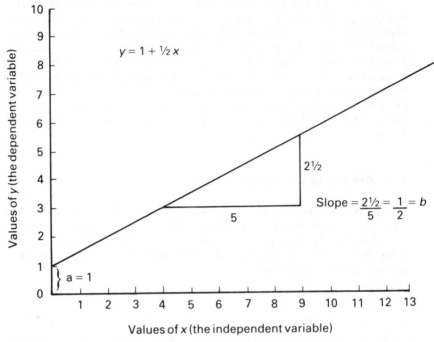

Fig 7.7 A graph of a simple mathematical function

Notes

i Where a function has a constant term (*a* in the expression $y = a + bx$) the graph does not pass through the origin. Instead the constant term decides the intercept on the *y* axis. This is because when $x = 0$ the term $bx = 0$, but the constant term will not be affected and will still be 1 in the case shown. The graph therefore meets the *y* axis at 1.

ii The other constant *b* decides the slope of the graph (often called the gradient of the graph). By slope or gradient we mean the increase in *y* for each unit of *x*. In this figure *y* increases by one half of a unit (ie 0.5) for every unit of *x*.

production really starts. It follows that these costs have to be eventually recovered from the sale of the product. Once production starts we also have **variable costs** – so called because they vary with output. If we make 10 units we need 10 lots of material and labour to work on it. If we sell 100 units we need 100 lots of material and more labour. These costs have also to be recovered by the sales of the product.

In Fig 7.8 fixed costs are £1000 and variable costs are £2 per unit. Variable costs start above £1000 and rise by £2 per unit. This gives a total cost line as shown. In Fig. 7.8*a* the selling price is fixed at £4 per unit. The sales revenue starts at the origin of the graph (no sales, no revenue) and rises by £4 for every unit sold. Consider the situation when 200 have been sold – sales revenue is £800, which does not even cover fixed costs of £1000. We are in a loss situation for total costs are £1400 (£1000 fixed and £400 variable costs). At sales of 500 units we are at break-even point, and the sales revenue line crosses the total cost line.

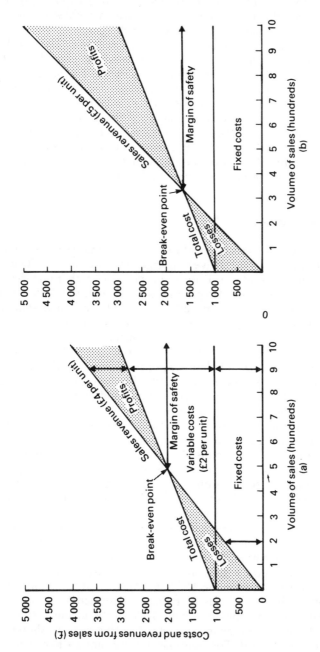

Fig 7.8 Break-even charts

Revenue is £2000, and costs are £2000 (£1000 fixed, £1000 variable). At sales of 900 units the revenue is £3600, covering all the fixed costs (£1000), all the variable costs (£1800) and yielding £800 of profit. The **margin of safety** (the margin of profitability which enables a firm to meet competition from other firms) is shown on the graph.

In Fig 7.8*b* the price has been fixed at £5 per unit. The break-even point now occurs earlier (at sales of 333⅓ units). At every level of production the loss/profit situation is more favourable. The *margin of safety* is extended and management is to that extent more confident – for example, suppose competition forced prices down from £5 to £3.50 per unit, the break-even point would at once move to the right as the gradient of the sales revenue line decreased, and the margin of safety would be seriously reduced. If competition forced prices down to £3 per unit the margin of safety would be eliminated altogether at an output of 1000 units, and the firm would only be breaking even.

7.7 Lorenz curves

A Lorenz curve is a statistical method of displaying variables in such a way as to bring out their relative importance to one another. The object is to bring out the significant features in the data, so that understanding is enhanced. For example, a report some years ago, the Bolton Report, which drew attention to the problems of small firms, had some interesting statistics about the concentration of British industry. Ninety-four per cent of the firms in manufacturing industry produced only 16% of the output. The other 6%, of large firms, produced 84% of the output.

A commonly used set of data in political circles is the data about income distribution – how is the wealth of a nation shared (Fig 7.9 on page 103)? Are there a few very rich people and numerous poor, or is there a more egalitarian division of wealth?

Consider the data given in Table 7.3 on page 103. It relates to a country with 10 million inhabitants and a national income of US$1000 million. In order to display this data as a Lorenz curve we need to insert some extra columns. These will tell us the percentage of the population in each social group, and the percentage of the national income they enjoy – before and after tax. When we do these calculations we find the percentages to be as shown in Table 7.4 on page 104. Note that cumulative percentages have also been given, starting from the bottom. This is to enable us to plot the percentages of population against the percentages of national income accruing to them. The notes below the diagram explain the details shown, but the basic idea is to show the extent of the diversion from the 45° line, which is called the **line of equal distribution**. This is the locus of points where income is equally distributed, 10% of the population have 10% of the income, 20% of the population have 20% of the income, etc. The true facts, as shown in the table, are far from ideal. For example social group 14 has 30% of the population but altogether they only have 6% of the income before tax and 8.6% after tax has redistributed income to them. The bottom 93% of the population have only 37.3% of the national income. By contrast the final 7% of the population in social groups 1–7 have 62.7% of the national income.

Table 7.3   Income distribution: Asiania

Social group	Number in social group	Total income *before tax* ($m)	Total income *after tax* ($m)
1	1 000	250	220
2	3 000	100	90
3	66 000	58	55
4	100 000	50	48
5	130 000	58.5	55
6	150 000	60	60
7	250 000	50	50
8	350 000	52.5	52.5
9	750 000	75	75
10	800 000	40	40
11	900 000	36	36
12	1 000 000	35	38
13	2 500 000	75	95
14	3 000 000	60	85.5
Total	10 000 000	1000	1000

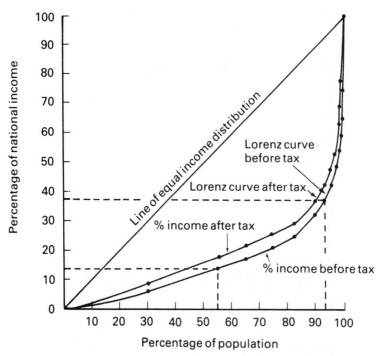

Fig 7.9 Lorenz curves

Table 7.4 Income distribution in percentages: Asiania

Social group	% of population	Cumulative %	% of income before tax	Cumulative %	% of income after tax	Cumulative %
1	0.01	100.0	25.0	100.0	22.0	100.0
2	0.03	99.99	10.0	75.0	9.0	78.0
3	0.66	99.96	5.8	65.0	5.5	69.0
4	1.0	99.3	5.0	59.2	4.8	63.5
5	1.3	98.3	5.9	54.2	5.5	58.7
6	1.5	97.0	6.0	48.3	6.0	53.2
7	2.5	95.5	5.0	42.3	5.0	47.2
8	3.5	93.0	5.2	37.3	5.2	42.2
9	7.5	89.5	7.5	32.1	7.5	37.0
10	8.0	82.0	4.0	24.6	4.0	29.5
11	9.0	74.0	3.6	20.6	3.6	25.5
12	10.0	65.0	3.5	17.0	3.8	21.9
13	25.0	55.0	7.5	13.5	9.5	18.1
14	30.0	30.0	6.0	6.0	8.6	8.6

When we plot this data as a Lorenz curve (see Fig 7.9 on page 103) we note the following:

i The line of equal income distribution shows the path of points if income was equally distributed, with 10% of the population having 10% of the income, 20% having 20% of the income, etc.

ii Divergence from this line indicates an unequal distribution of income. We can read off the percentage of income accruing to each percentage group by drawing in perpendiculars to the Lorenz curve, as has been done at 55% of the population (only 13% of the income) and 93% of the population (37% of the income). A few very rich people have over 60% of the Asianian income. Asiania is of course an imaginary country.

Exercises on graphs

1   Draw a graph of the function $y = 3 + 2x$.
2   Draw a graph of the function $y = 1.5 + 0.4x$.
3   A firm estimates the costs of a particular product as follows:

Fixed costs and development costs   £30 000
Variable costs   £5 per unit

It proposes to charge £12 per unit to customers, with an initial output of 10 000 units. Draw a break-even chart and hence determine *a* the break-even point and *b* the point to which competition would have to reduce prices before the 10 000 units ceased to be profitable.

4   A firm has fixed costs of £20 000 and variable costs of £10 per unit of output. Each unit is sold for £20. Draw a graph of costs and sales in steps of 1000 up to 5000 units of output. Where is the break-even point?

5   *a* Explain the purposes of presenting information in the form of a Lorenz curve.

   b The following figures show trade union membership by size of union in Ruritania, in the year 19—:

Size of union (members)	Number of trade unions	Number of members (thousands)
Under 1 000	319	225
1 000 and under 10 000	72	375
10 000 and under 25 000	41	450
25 000 and under 50 000	32	1 125
50 000 and under 100 000	10	675
100 000 and under 250 000	12	1 500
250 000 and under 500 000	5	1 800
500 000 and under 1 000 000	4	2 100
1 000 000 and under 2 000 000	5	6 750
Total	500	15 000

Construct a Lorenz curve for the above data and comment on your results.

6 The following table shows 10% bands of percentages of income earners in the population of an economically advanced country with a well-developed tax system, together with the share of incomes of each band, before and after tax. You are required to draw Lorenz curves for *a* income before tax and *b* income after tax and social benefits. Comment on the resulting graphs.

Percentage of total income earners	Percentage of total income before tax adjustments	Percentage of total income after tax and welfare benefits
Top 10	28	19
11–20	16	14
21–30	12	11
31–40	10	10
41–50	9	10
51–60	7	9
61–70	6	8
71–80	5	7
81–90	4	6
Bottom 10	3	6

8   Index numbers

8.1   Simple index numbers

Index numbers provide another means of interpreting data. Quite often
in statistics we seek to reduce a jumble of facts or information to a single
item of data so that we can readily characterise the system and identify
changes over time. Index numbers allow us to express different standards
of measures in one figure and make possible the comparison of information over time.

We are all familiar with the Retail Price Index (RPI) which measures
the cost of living. This is the sum of the costs of a weighted basket of
items that an average family buys and is normally expressed relative to
a base year. For example, the price index might be 134.1 for 1991 compared with a base of 100 in 1987. In other words the price index has
risen 34% since 1987.

*An index number may be defined as a statistic which indicates the level
of prices, wages, outputs and other variables at given dates, relative to
their level at an earlier date which is taken as the base or standard.*

Consider the price and quantity information given in Table 8.1 on
page 108. If we take year 1 as the base year a simple price index, I_p, is
calculated as:

$$I_p = \frac{P_n}{P_o} \times 100$$

where P_n is the price in the year of interest to us (n for now) and P_o is
the price in the base year (o for origin). Thus:

$$I_p = \frac{70}{40} \times 100 = 175 \qquad \text{(for eggs the price index is 175)}$$

$$I_p = \frac{50}{35} \times 100 = 142.9 \qquad \text{(for bread the price index is 142.9)}$$

$$I_p = \frac{17}{12} \times 100 = 141.7 \qquad \text{(for milk the price index is 141.7)}$$

These figures are often referred to as **price relatives** since they show how
the price changes over time, relative to the price at the base date.
A simple quantity index is calculated as:

$$I_q = \frac{Q_n}{Q_o} \times 100$$

Table 8.1 Prices and consumption of milk, eggs and bread

Commodity	Units	Price (pence) Year 1, P_o	Price (pence) Year 4, P_n	Quantity consumed (per capita per month) Year 1, Q_o	Quantity consumed (per capita per month) Year 4, Q_n
Eggs	1 dozen	40	70	1.4	1.3
Bread	$\frac{1}{2}$ kg loaf	35	50	3.6	3.5
Milk	1 pint	12	17	20	23

where Q refers to the quantity of goods consumed. The quantity index for the data shown in Table 8.1 is therefore:

$$I_q = \frac{1.3}{1.4} \times 100 = 92.9 \text{ for eggs}$$

$$I_q = \frac{3.5}{3.6} \times 100 = 97.2 \text{ for bread}$$

$$I_q = \frac{23}{20} \times 100 = 115.0 \text{ for milk}$$

These figures are called **quantity relatives**.

An index for the value of the commodities, defined as price multiplied by quantity, is calculated as:

$$I_v = \frac{P_n Q_n}{P_o Q_o} \times 100$$

using the data in Table 8.1 again the indexes for value for eggs, bread and milk would be:

$$I_v = \frac{70 \times 1.3}{40 \times 1.4} \times 100 = 162.5 \text{ for eggs}$$

$$I_v = \frac{50 \times 3.5}{35 \times 3.6} \times 100 = 138.9 \text{ for bread}$$

$$I_v = \frac{17 \times 23}{12 \times 20} \times 100 = 162.9 \text{ for milk}$$

Thus these simple indexes show that the price of eggs, bread and milk have risen. The simple quantity indexes show that the consumption of eggs and bread have fallen and the consumption of milk has risen. However, in terms of value, the value indexes show that the values of all three items have risen since the base year.

The index in a year before base year

We must note that in a period of rising prices if we select a base year from which the index is to be calculated, the years prior to that base year will be less than 100. For example, in Table 8.1 suppose the year 0 price for eggs (the price of eggs in the year before year 1) had been 36 pence the index for year 0 would have been $36/40 \times 100 = 90$.

Exercises on simple indexes

1   Over a 10-year period the price of a certain article of domestic furniture rose as follows: year 1, £38; year 2, £40; year 3, £43; year 4, £48; year 5, £57; year 6, £65; year 7, £82; year 8, £89; year 9, £95; year 10, £102.50. Calculate a price index for the article in question with year 1 as the base year (calculations correct to one decimal place).

2 Over a 5-year period the price of a share on the London Stock Exchange rose as follows: year 1, £1.98; year 2, £2.07; year 3, £4.21; year 4, £4.37; year 5, £4.93. The sudden rise in price in year 3 was due to the company's successful strike of oil in the coastal waters of the Republic of China. Using year 2 as the base year, calculate a price index for the share for the five years concerned (calculations correct to one decimal place).

3 The price of Arabica coffee on the London coffee market is quoted in dollars per 50 kg. The basic contract is 5850 kg. The price of a basic contract of 5850 kg in January is $3300, in February $3250, in March $3850, in April $3925, in May $3950, in June $4250, in July $3850. Work out a price index for coffee based on the January price (calculations correct to one decimal place).

4 The price of wheat on the London markets is quoted in pounds sterling per tonne. The prices for January onwards are quoted as follows: January, £97.50; February, £99.10; March, £99.85; April, £105.35. Using January as the base month calculate a price index for wheat for the four-month period (calculations correct to one decimal place).

5 Wages for a particular class of employee rose as follows in the 10-year period shown. The rate concerned is the payment per hour. The wage index was calculated with year 4 as the base year, after a national wages agreement had taken effect with a sharp increase in the rate payable.

Year 1	£1.25	Year 6	£2.72
Year 2	£1.35	Year 7	£2.78
Year 3	£1.55	Year 8	£2.98
Year 4	£2.50	Year 9	£3.05
Year 5	£2.65	Year 10	£3.12

Calculate the wages index for the 10 years with year 4 as the base year.

8.2 Aggregate price indexes

By an aggregate price index we mean one that deals with a basket of goods. It is usual to select those items that feature in the expenditure of most ordinary people. Thus ocean going yachts may rise in price, but it will not affect the RPI because ordinary people do not buy this type of transport.

To obtain an aggregate price index, the price of several items or commodities could simply be summed at a given moment and compared with the price of the same basket of goods at the base period. Such an index would be an *unweighted* price index. However, an unweighted index, in general, is not particularly useful because the implicit weight of each item depends on the units upon which the prices are based. For example, if the price of milk is reported per hectolitre as against per litre then the price would make a much greater contribution to an unweighted price index for a group of commodities which includes milk. Because of this difficulty aggregate price indexes are generally weighted according to the quantities, q, of commodities. Different aggregate price relatives can be obtained when different period quantities are used. This is unsatisfactory and we would therefore measure the quantity being used by the average household in the base year and use this quantity again in the year that interests us, to isolate the price index from changes in quantity. This common index is called *Laspeyres' index* in which prices are weighted by the quantities associated with the base year before being summed, as follows:

$$I(L) = \frac{\Sigma \ P_n Q_o}{\Sigma \ P_o Q_o} \times 100$$

Some typical data are shown in Table 8.2.

From the summed combinations of P and Q shown in Table 8.2, the Laspeyres' index is calculated as:

$$I(L) = \frac{618}{422} \times 100 = 146.4$$

Instead of using the base-year quantities as weights, the given year quantities can be used. This is termed the *Paasche's index* and is calculated as:

$$I(P) = \frac{\Sigma \ P_n Q_n}{\Sigma \ P_o Q_n}$$

Consider Table 8.3 for the commodity data. The Paasche's index is therefore calculated as:

$$I(P) = \frac{657}{450.5} \times 100 = 145.8$$

Both the Laspeyres and Paasche indexes can be described as **weighted aggregate price indexes**.

The two systems give different results, but the differences are not great. If the Laspeyres (base weighting) system is used, the weighting stays the same as long as the index is in use, which assists comparability from year to year. We are able to compare over the years the cost of a particular basket of goods, and there is no need to re-sample the use of goods to discover changes in the basket of goods in use. The disadvantage is that changes in the pattern of purchases are not taken into account. With the Paasche index the relative importance of the items making up the units is continuously changing. Changes in the prices of goods naturally affect the demand for them – cheaper products may be substituted – and therefore if prices change the weights should really change too. Therefore the Paasche index is, strictly speaking, more accurate but also more expensive to produce as annual usage samples are required.

For example, consider the following data. A company uses three materials in its manufacturing processes, which admit of small variations in use should one of the products become scarce. Details of prices and

Table 8.2 Price and commodity information for calculation of Laspeyres' index

Commodity	P_o (pence)	Q_o	P_oQ_o (product)	P_n	Q_o	P_nQ_o (product)
Eggs	40	1.4	56	70	1.4	98
Bread	35	3.6	126	50	3.6	180
Milk	12	20.0	240	17	20.0	340
Totals			ΣP_oQ_o 422			ΣP_nQ_o 618

Table 8.3 Price and commodity information for calculation of Paasche's index
Source: Freunde Williams, Modern Business Statistics

Commodity	P_o (pence)	Q_n	P_oQ_n (product)	P_n	Q_n	P_nQ_n (product)
Eggs	40	1.3	52.0	70	1.3	91
Bread	35	3.5	122.5	50	3.5	175
Milk	12	23.0	276.0	17	23.0	391
Totals			ΣP_oQ_n 450.5			ΣP_nQ_n 657

usage are given as follows:

Materials	Year 1		Year 5	
	Quantity (tonnes)	Price (£) per tonne	Quantity (tonnes)	Price (£) per tonne
A	15	3600	12	4800
B	12	5200	10	5400
C	8	2300	13	2400

Calculate an index for prices for year 5, with year 1 as the base year:

a base year weighted for usage
b current year weighted for usage

a Base year weighted (Laspeyres)

Material	Q_1	P_1	$Q_1 P_1$	Q_1	P_5	$Q_1 P_5$
A	15	3600	54 000	15	4800	72 000
B	12	5200	62 400	12	5400	64 800
C	8	2300	18 400	8	2400	19 200
			134 800			156 000

$$\text{Index} = \frac{156\ 000}{134\ 800} \times 100 = 115.7$$

The index rose from 100 in year 1 to 115.7 in year 5.

b Current year weighted (Paasche)

Material	Q_5	P_1	$Q_5 P_1$	Q_5	P_5	$Q_5 P_5$
A	12	3600	43 200	12	4800	57 600
B	10	5200	52 000	10	5400	54 000
C	13	2300	29 900	13	2400	31 200
			125 100			142 800

$$\text{Index} = \frac{142\ 800}{125\ 100} \times 100 = 114.1$$

The index rose from 100 in year 1 to 114.1 in year 5.

Conclusion: By rearranging the usage of materials the manufacturers have had a small effect on the cost of materials used.

An alternative approach uses the simple price index for each commodity but it is weighted by the value figure *PQ*. This gives the *weighted average of price relatives* and is calculated using the formula:

$$I_p = \frac{\sum \left(\frac{P_n}{P_o} \times 100 \right) \times \text{weighting}}{\sum \text{weighting}}$$

For a base weighted price relative index:

$$I_p = \frac{\sum \left(\frac{P_n}{P_o} \times 100\right)(P_o Q_o)}{\sum P_o Q_o}$$

For a current weighted price relative index:

$$I_p = \frac{\sum \left(\frac{P_n}{P_o} \times 100\right)(P_n Q_n)}{\sum P_n Q_n}$$

These weighted price relative indexes are commonly used since the simple price index for each commodity is calculated first before aggregating them to produce the weighted index.

In simple terms the aggregate price index of such a group of price relatives should contain that portion of each price relative that its weighting bears to the sum of the weightings.

Example: Calculate a general index of materials prices for a firm which uses our materials, in the portions shown below.

Material	Base year price (£)	Current year price (£)	Weight
A	36	52	25
B	185	225	30
C	84	76	35
D	125	323	10
			100

The calculation is as follows:

Material	Base year price (£)	Current year price (£)	One-item price relative	Weight	Price relative × weight
A	36	52	144.4	25	3 610
B	185	225	121.6	30	3 648
C	84	76	90.5	35	3 167.5
D	125	323	258.4	10	2 584
				100	13 009.5

Therefore aggregate price index $= \dfrac{13\ 009.5}{100} = 130.1$

Or we could calculate each part separately. The final index should have:

$$\left(\frac{25}{100} \times 144.4\right) + \left(\frac{30}{100} \times 121.6\right) + \left(\frac{35}{100} \times 90.5\right)$$

$$+ \left(\frac{10}{100} \times 258.4\right) = 130.1$$

Exercises on aggregate price indexes

1 Calculate the general index of retail prices for all items in December, year 4, given that the following data are available. The index was started in January, year 1, when the index was taken as 100 (answer correct to one decimal place).

Group	Weights	Price relatives December, year 4	
Food	206	299.8	61758.8
Alcoholic drink	77	332.1	25571.7
Tobacco	41	399.1	16363.1
Housing	144	345.6	49766.4
Fuel and light	62	410.2	
Durable household goods	64	242.8	
Clothing and footwear	77	209.6	
Transport and vehicles	154	330.0	
Miscellaneous goods	72	317.8	
Services	65	328.0	
Meals bought and consumed outside home	38	334.2	
Total	1000		

2 Calculate the general index of retail prices in March, year 9, if the following data are available. The index in January, year 1, was 100 (answer correct to one decimal place).

Group	Weights	Price relatives March, year 9
Food	210	321.6
Alcoholic drink	79	330.5
Tobacco	44	284.5
Housing	132	250.6
Fuel and light	62	268.7
Durable household goods	71	219.6
Clothing and footwear	70	199.5
Transport and vehicles	144	238.7
Miscellaneous goods	82	272.6
Services	63	322.4
Meals bought and consumed outside home	43	284.0
Total	1000	

3 a Distinguish between a base year and a current year quantity weighted index number. Give an example to illustrate the difference.
b The table below shows the quantities of four raw materials used

by a manufacturing company annually, and the prices payable per
unit (US$), at the start of year 1 and the end of year 5.

Commodity	Year 1		Year 5	
	Quantity	Price	Quantity	Price
A	15	28	18	47
B	8	16	10	38
C	2	30	2	36
D	7	15	8	56

Calculate an index number for prices for year 5 with year 1 as a base
year *i* base year weighted and *ii* current year weighted (answers
correct to one decimal place).

4 The table below shows the weights of various metals used by an
engineering company in years 1 and 8 of its activities, all quantities
being in metric tonnes. Prices of the metals are in pounds sterling per
tonne.

Metal	Year 1		Year 8	
	Quantity	Price	Quantity	Price
Copper	36	880	32	1340
Tin	15	1920	12	1210
Lead	4	1640	7	1400
Zinc	12	850	17	1360

Calculate an index number for prices for year 8 with year 1 as the
base year *i* base year weighted and *ii* current year weighted (answers
correct to one decimal place). Comment on your results.

5 *a* Briefly explain the advantages and disadvantages of Laspeyres and
Paasche price index numbers.
b Calculate Laspeyres and Paasche price index numbers with year
1 = 100 as base year (answers correct to one decimal place).

Share	Year 1		Year 6	
	Price (p)	Quantity (q)	Price (p)	Quantity (q)
A	85	400	210	200
B	64	250	88	450
C	285	350	435	550

6 The average price of wheat, maize and oats per tonne is given in the
table below.

Cereal grain prices (£ per tonne)

Crop	Year 1	Year 2	Year 3
Wheat	85	88.50	94
Maize	68	73	75.50
Oats	66	73	84

If a manufacturer of breakfast cereals uses them in the ratio of $5:8:2$ (using most maize and least oats) calculate a price index for cereals (with year 1 as 100) over the three-year period (answers correct to one decimal place.)

8.3 Changing the base of an index

Quite often it is necessary to change the base of an index. This may be necessary to keep the index relevant to current conditions. There would be little point making the base year of the RPI 1920, since the RPI would be in the order of thousands. Consider the following price index series based on year 1:

Year	1	2	3	4	5	6	7
Index	100	104	108	109	112	120	125

Suppose we wish to change the base year to year 5. Each index must be recalculated by expressing it as a percentage of the value in year 5. Thus:

Year 1 $\dfrac{100}{112} \times 100 = 89.3$

Year 2 $\dfrac{104}{112} \times 100 = 92.9$

and so on to:

Year 5 $\dfrac{112}{112} \times 100 = 100.0$ (the new base year)

Year 6 $\dfrac{120}{112} \times 100 = 107.1$

Year 7 $\dfrac{125}{112} \times 100 = 111.6$

Note that when changing the base year of an index it is quite a common practice to update the weights which have been used in preparing a general index such as the RPI. Changes of taste and fashion do occur, and changes in the representative basket of goods and services used by the average household are also affected by technological advances and changes in income distribution. To keep the index relevant we must alter the weights to keep in touch with current economic and social patterns of behaviour. The difficulty with such changes is that the figures cease to be strictly comparable with one another, because they represent a changed pattern of expenditure.

8.4 Chain-based indexes

A chain-based index is derived by using the previous period as the base for calculating the next index. This has some advantages over a fixed-base index. It is a good way of showing the rate of change occurring, ie whether prices are falling, rising or remaining constant.

It is also possible to incorporate new items into this kind of index without recalculating the whole of the previous period's figures. Consider the data used in the previous section. The chain index is calculated as follows:

Year	Single-price index	Chain index
1	100	100
2	104	$\dfrac{104}{100} \times 100 = 104$
3	108	$\dfrac{108}{104} \times 100 = 103.8$
4	109	$\dfrac{109}{108} \times 100 = 100.9$
5	112	$\dfrac{112}{109} \times 100 = 102.8$
6	120	$\dfrac{120}{112} \times 100 = 107.1$
7	125	$\dfrac{125}{120} \times 100 = 104.2$

From the chain index we can see that the index is falling at certain times despite the general increase in the single-price index. The chain index brings out the 'rate of change' of prices.

It is also possible to construct a chain index which accounts for more than one product, and which can be weighted. Table 8.4 illustrates this. The procedure is to list the commodities, their prices and their quantities or weights. The single chain indexes are calculated for each commodity and the indexes are multiplied by the weights and summed. The summed index is then divided by the sum of the weights to find the final weighted chain index.

Table 8.4 Finding a weighted chain index of prices for commodities

Commodity	Weight	Year 1 Price (pence per kg)	Base	Year 2 Price (pence per kg)	Calculation	Index no × weight	Year 3 Price (pence per kg)	Calculation	Index no × weight
Wheat	5	32	100	35	$\frac{35}{32} \times 100 \times 5$	546.9	38	$\frac{38}{35} \times 100 \times 5$	542.9
Sugar	3	40	100	43	$\frac{43}{40} \times 100 \times 3$	322.5	48	$\frac{48}{43} \times 100 \times 3$	334.9
Caramel	2	54	100	60	$\frac{60}{54} \times 100 \times 2$	222.2	55	$\frac{55}{60} \times 100 \times 2$	183.3
Total	10					1091.6			1061.1

1091.6 ÷ 10 = 109.2
on base of year 1

1061.1 ÷ 10 = 106.1
on base of year 2

The index for all commodities is thus 100, 109.2 and 106.1 over the period.

Exercises on chain-based index numbers

1 The price of bulk sugar to manufacturers of confectionery rose in a 5-year period as follows:

Year	Price per tonne (£)
1	170
2	175
3	185
4	195
5	198

  a Calculate an ordinary price index for bulk sugar based on year 1 as 100.
  b Calculate a chain-based index number based on year 1 as 100 and all succeeding years based on the previous year as 100 (calculations correct to one decimal place).

2 The price of petrol at the pump increased as follows:

Year	Price per litre (pence)
1	32
2	35
3	37
4	40
5	42

  a Calculate an ordinary price index for petrol based on year 1 as 100.
  b Calculate to 1 decimal place a chain-based index for petrol based on year 1 as 100 and all subsequent years related to the previous year as 100. What is the particular merit of a chain-based index?

3 A manufacturer produces household domestic cleaning material which makes use of four products. They are combined in the ratio shown below under 'weights'. The price changes over a period of 3 years are as shown. Calculate a weighted chain index for the cleaning product over the three-year period (correct to one decimal place).

Product	Weight	Price (in pence per litre)		
		Year 1	Year 2	Year 3
A	5	8	9	10
B	3	5	9	13
C	2	4	5	6
D	1	3	3	2

4 The information tabulated below refers to three commodities used

by the manufacturer of a breakfast cereal. The weighting and the price changes for a three-year period are shown. Calculate a weighted chain index for the breakfast product over the three-year period (correct to one decimal place).

Commodity	Weight	Year 1 (£)	Year 2 (£)	Year 3 (£)
A	4	1.20	1.50	1.85
B	2	2.35	2.55	3.25
C	2	2.45	2.35	2.25

8.5   Use of indexes in deflating time series

When assessing investment decisions or comparing the costs and profits of businesses it is often important to allow for inflation. By doing this we compare the 'real' value or cost of sales, imports, wages, assets, etc. To *deflate* a time series we divide each observation by the current value of a suitable price index, and multiply the result by the base rate value of 100.

Consider the data shown in Table 8.5. It is clear from the data that the average employee, although appearing to be drawing higher and higher wages is in fact receiving a real cut in living standards, since the income received is not keeping pace with inflation. The £225 received in year 6 only has the purchasing power of £125.70 in year 1 when the wage had been £154.

Another example of allowing for inflation is to use interest rates to assess capital expenditure or future profits. A business could put its investment money in a bank and just leave it there to accumulate interest.

Table 8.5   Deflating a time series

Year	Average weekly earnings (£)	Retail Price Index	Calculation	'Real' earnings (£ at year 1 values)
1	154	100		154
2	175	116.5	$\dfrac{175}{116.5} \times 100 =$	150.21
3	195	135	$\dfrac{195}{135} \times 100 =$	144.44
4	205	146	$\dfrac{205}{146} \times 100 =$	140.41
5	215	165	$\dfrac{215}{165} \times 100 =$	130.30
6	225	179	$\dfrac{225}{179} \times 100 =$	125.70

Table 8.6 Interest rate index used to deflate profit figures

(i) Year	(ii) Interest rate index	(iii) Expected profits (£'000)	Calculation	(iv) 'Real' profits after deflation (£'000)
1	100	6		5.000
2	111	15	$\left(\dfrac{15}{111} \times 100\right)$ (other calculations are similar)	13.514
3	123.21	37		30.030
4	136.76	100		73.121
5	151.81	165		108.688
6	168.51	180		106.819
7	187.05	250		133.654
8	207.62	340		163.761
Total				634.587

Notes

i The accumulating effect of interest rates gives an index (column (ii)) which can be used to deflate the expected profits (column (iii)) and reduce them to the value they would have had in year 1. For example, looking at year 2 the profits of £15 000 – 1 year late – would have only been £13 514 in year 1.

ii Similarly in year 3 £37 000 – 2 years late – is only the same as £30 030 in year 1. Thus the expected profits shown in the table can be deflated to give the profits in real terms. This is called **discounted cash flow**; we discount the likely proceeds from the investment in plant, machinery, etc, to reduce them to the value they would have had in year 1 had they been received then.

iii These profits may be summed and compared with the initial capital expenditure. If the capital expenditure is less than £635 000 then the profits will exceed the capital expenditure, making the investment worthwhile. Needless to say, since interest rates fluctuate over the years and there are difficulties associated with forecasting profits, capital investment decisions are often difficult to make.

Suppose the interest rate is 11%, then over an eight-year period every £100 in the bank accumulates as shown in Table 8.6, column (ii). The money saved in this way more than doubles in 8 years. The notes below Table 8.6 explain how this helps us to judge capital expenditure, and whether it will be profitable.

8.6 The Retail Price Index and the Tax and Price Index

There are many types of indexes and these two United Kingdom indexes are of great interest. *The Retail Price Index (RPI)* is the best known index of all, and is widely used as an indicator for such matters as price fixing, wage claims, etc. It is a weighted average of price relatives index, and is particularly suited to value, rather than volume, weighting.

a Calculating a weighted average price relatives index

The index is calculated from the price relatives referred to earlier, which are essentially one-item price relatives. Thus if the price of tomatoes in the base year was 25 pence per kilogram and their price today is 50 pence per kilogram the one-item price index is 200 now, compared with the base year when it was 100. In order to know which items to include in our collection of price relatives we must do a survey of the prices of goods and services purchased by the average household at the start of the base year. This is a fairly daunting task, involving a large sample of households from all parts of the country, and the result is a typical 'basket' of goods and services purchased by the average household. Items included in this basket will be individual items whose prices are to be recorded month by month, and for which individual price relatives are to be calculated, on the simple formula:

$$\frac{P_1}{P_0} \times 100$$

Thus the tomato prices referred to earlier give:

$$\frac{50}{25} \times 100 = 200$$

200 is the index number for tomatoes in the current month.

We now have to arrange these price relatives to find the general RPI. We cannot of course take a simple average; we have to weight the average with the relative importance of each item in the 'basket' of goods and services used by the average family. Thus if 'housing' takes one-fifth of all the expenditure in the average family the element of the current month's housing index to be included in the general price index is one-fifth. Because the basket of goods and services includes many items the list of weights is divided into 1000 parts, and weighting are allotted to

Table 8.7 Weights for the general RPI
(*Source: Monthly Digest of Statistics*)

Group of items	Weights
1 Food	154
2 Alcoholic drink	83
3 Tobacco	36
4 Housing	175
5 Fuel and light	54
6 Durable household goods	71
7 Clothing and footwear	73
8 Transport and vehicles	151
9 Miscellaneous goods	73
10 Services	81
11 Meals outside the home	49
All items	1000

the individual items as part of this 1000. These weights are adjusted annually as the pattern of household expenditure changes, and appear in the publication *Monthly Digest of Statistics*, at the head of the table. The index for each year is based on the weightings discovered for the previous year, so this weighting survey has to be virtually continuous to keep the data representative of the true state of affairs. In the most recent year available these figures were as shown in Table 8.7. Of course, each of these groups is really made up of a number of other items which have entered into the weighting applied to the group. Thus the clothing and footwear weighting of 77 was made up as shown in Table 8.8.

In order to calculate the general RPI from the single-item indexes the individual indexes are multiplied by the weights and the resulting products are summed to give a grand total. When divided by the sum of the weights (ie 1000) we have the general price index. We should get exactly the same result if we treated each index separately and summed the results,

$$\text{Food} = \frac{113.5 \times 154}{1000} = 17.479$$

We would thus be including that fraction of the current food index that ought to go into the RPI to reflect the weighting of food in the average household's basket of purchases. The full calculation is shown in Table 8.9. When divided by 1000 this gives us the general index of 119.1 correct to one decimal place.

The RPI is published in detail each month in the *Monthly Digest of Statistics*. It frequently happens that figures are adjusted slightly over the months as new data corrects minor errors in earlier figures.

An abbreviated presentation is shown in Table 8.10 on page 126.

b The Tax and Price index

The Tax and Price Index (TPI) is a development from the RPI in that it takes into account changes in taxation (in the United Kingdom this means not only income tax but also National Insurance contributions), as well as changes in retail prices. It is, perhaps, an illustration of political influence at work on the Central Statistical Office, in that the call for the new index came from the Conservative Government rather than from the Statistical Office itself. It was felt that the RPI took account only of the inflation of prices, and not of the ability of the public to meet these

Table 8.8 Weighting of the group 'clothing and footwear'

Items	Weights
1 Men's outer clothing	14
2 Women's outer clothing	22
3 Children's clothing	9
4 Other clothing, underwear, hose, haberdashery and hats	13
5 Footwear	15
Total	73

Table 8.9 Calculation of RPI

Group	Single-item index	Weight	Products (index × weight)
Food	113.5	154	17 479.0
Alcoholic drink	115.4	83	9 578.2
Tobacco	108.1	36	3 891.6
Housing	143.9	175	25 182.5
Fuel and light	109.7	54	5 923.8
Durable household goods	111.8	71	7 937.8
Clothing and footwear	113.0	73	8 249.0
Transport and vehicles	115.3	151	17 410.3
Miscellaneous goods	110.9	73	8 095.7
Services	117.5	81	9 489.2
Meals outside the home	119.5	49	5 855.5
Total		1000	119 092.6

Note: When divided by 1000 this gives us the general index of 119.1.

increases because taxation had been reduced to assist them. Whilst it may well be true that the traditional index had not reflected current social conditions the fact remains that the body charged with the duty of presenting reliable statistics for the nation had not noticed the problem, and was only dragooned into producing the new index by the politicians. The index was first issued in August 1979 and has now been calculated back to 1974. A comparison between inflation rates under both indexes is given below. First, consider the index itself, which is updated monthly in the *Monthly Digest of Statistics* (Table 8.11 on page 127).

c Calculating the rate of inflation

The rate of inflation in an economy is calculated in the following way:

$$\frac{\text{current index}}{\text{index at the same time last year}} \times 100.$$ Then deduct 100 to find the increase in the year.

Calculating the rate of inflation by both indexes, using the December 1990 indexes we have:

Inflation rate according to the RPI:

$\frac{129.9}{118.8} \times 100 = 109.3.$ Subtracting 100, we have:

an inflation rate of 9.3 for the year to December 1990.

Inflation rate according to the TPI:

$\frac{123.3}{113.1} \times 100 = 109.0.$ Subtracting 100, we have:

an inflation rate of 9.0 for the year to December 1990.

Table 8.10a The general RPI (prices at January 1974 = 100)
(*Source: Employment Gazette*)

Year	Jan.	Feb.	Mar.	Apr.	May	June	July	Aug.	Sept.	Oct.	Nov.	Dec.
1974	100.0	101.7	102.6	106.1	107.6	108.7	109.7	109.8	111.0	113.2	115.2	116.9
1975	119.9	121.9	124.3	129.1	134.5	137.1	138.5	139.3	140.5	142.5	144.2	146.0
1976	147.9	149.8	150.6	153.5	155.2	156.0	156.3	158.5	160.6	163.5	165.8	168.0
1977	172.4	174.1	175.8	180.3	181.7	183.6	183.8	184.7	185.7	186.5	187.4	188.4
1978	189.5	190.6	191.8	194.6	195.7	197.2	198.1	199.4	200.2	201.1	202.5	204.2
1979	207.2	208.9	210.6	214.2	215.9	219.6	229.1	230.9	233.2	235.6	237.7	239.4
1980	245.3	248.8	252.2	260.8	263.2	265.7	267.9	268.5	270.2	271.9	274.1	275.6
1981	277.3	279.8	284.0	292.2	294.1	295.8	297.1	299.3	301.0	303.7	306.9	308.8
1982	310.6	310.7	313.4	319.7	322.0	322.9	323.0	323.1	322.9	324.5	326.1	325.5
1983	325.9	327.3	327.9	332.5	333.9	334.7	336.5	338.0	339.5	340.7	341.9	342.8
1984	342.6	344.0	345.1	349.7	351.0	351.9	351.5	354.8	355.5	357.7	358.8	358.5
1985	359.8	362.7	366.1	373.9	375.6	376.4	375.7	376.7	376.5	377.1	378.4	378.9
1986	379.7	381.1	381.6	385.3	386.0	385.8	384.7	385.9	387.8	388.4	391.7	393.0
1987	394.5	396.1	396.9	401.6	402.0	402.0	401.6	402.8	404.0	405.9	407.9	407.5

Table 8.10b General Index of Retail Prices recalculated to a new base year (Prices at January 1987 = 100)

Year	Jan.	Feb.	Mar.	Apr.	May	June	July	Aug.	Sept.	Oct.	Nov.	Dec.
1987	100.0	100.4	100.6	101.8	101.9	101.9	101.8	102.1	102.4	102.9	103.4	103.3
1988	103.3	103.7	104.1	105.8	106.2	106.6	106.7	107.9	108.4	109.5	110.0	110.3
1989	111.0	111.8	112.3	114.3	115.0	115.4	115.5	115.8	116.6	117.5	118.5	118.8
1990	119.5	120.2	121.4	125.1	126.2	126.7	126.8	128.1	129.3	130.3	130.0	129.9
1991	130.2	130.9	131.4	133.4	133.5	134.1	133.8	134.1	134.6	135.1	135.6	135.7

Table 8.11a The Tax and Price Index (January 1978 = 100)
(Source: Monthly Digest of Statistics)

Year	Jan.	Feb.	Mar.	Apr.	May	June	July	Aug.	Sept.	Oct.	Nov.	Dec.
1974	50.2	51.2	51.7	54.3	55.2	55.9	56.5	56.8	57.6	58.9	60.1	61.2
1975	63.0	64.3	65.8	68.5	71.9	73.5	74.4	74.9	75.7	77.0	78.0	79.2
1976	80.4	81.6	82.2	82.9	84.0	84.5	84.7	86.1	87.5	89.4	90.9	92.4
1977	95.3	96.4	97.5	96.4	97.3	98.5	98.6	99.2	99.9	100.4	98.7	99.3
1978	100.0	100.7	101.5	98.4	99.1	100.0	100.5	101.3	101.8	102.4	103.2	104.3
1979	106.1	107.2	108.2	110.5	111.6	113.8	113.8	114.9	116.2	117.6	118.8	119.8
1980	123.2	125.3	127.2	130.8	132.2	133.6	134.9	135.3	136.3	137.3	138.5	139.4
1981	140.4	141.9	144.3	151.3	152.4	153.5	154.2	155.5	156.6	158.2	160.1	161.2
1982	162.3	162.4	164.0	166.0	167.4	168.0	169.0	169.0	168.9	169.9	170.9	170.5
1983	170.7	171.6	171.9	171.8	172.7	173.2	174.3	175.1	176.0	176.7	177.5	178.0
1984	177.9	178.8	179.4	178.8	179.6	180.1	179.9	181.8	182.2	183.5	184.1	183.9
1985	184.7	186.4	188.4	190.2	191.2	191.7	191.3	191.8	191.7	191.4	192.1	192.4
1986	192.9	193.7	194.0	192.5	192.9	192.8	192.1	192.9	194.0	194.3	196.3	197.1
1987	198.0	198.9	199.4	197.4	197.6	197.6	197.4	198.0	198.8	199.8	201.0	200.8

Table 8.11b Tax and Price Index (TPI) recalculated to a new base year (January 1987 = 100)

Year	Jan.	Feb.	Mar.	Apr.	May	June	July	Aug.	Sept.	Oct.	Nov.	Dec.
1987	100.0	100.5	100.7	99.7	99.8	99.8	99.7	100.0	100.4	100.9	101.5	101.4
1988	101.4	101.8	102.3	101.4	101.9	102.3	102.4	103.7	104.3	105.4	106.0	106.3
1989	107.1	108.0	108.5	109.8	110.5	110.9	111.1	111.4	112.2	111.7	112.8	113.1
1990	113.9	114.7	115.9	118.2	119.4	119.9	120.0	121.4	122.7	123.8	123.4	123.3
1991	123.6	124.3	124.9	125.4	125.8	126.5	126.2	126.5	127.0	127.5	128.1	128.2

Note
It is important to note that this index only reflects the increases in inflation for *taxpayers*, since non-taxpaying citizens do not get any benefits from reductions in tax. Even among taxpayers the index is not directly applicable to higher income groups, who are affected by taxation rather differently than those paying 'normal' rates of tax.

The reduction of the inflation rate from 9.3 to 9.0 for taxpayers may seem a worth-while reduction to an inflation-conscious politician seeking to prove a point. To the unemployed or the poor non-taxpaying citizen it may be less satisfactory, and – rather unfairly to the statisticians – may even lead to claims that 'you can prove anything by statistics'.

Other indexes

Index numbers are widely used, both officially and in business. Besides the indexes named above the *Monthly Digest of Statistics* includes references to the following indexes: the Index of Producer Prices of Agricultural Products; the Index of Wholesale Prices; the Index of Average Earnings; the Index of Sales Volumes of Engineering Products; the Value and Volume Indexes of Imports and Exports; the Index of Road Transport; and the Index of Industrial Production. Other index numbers are used on the commodity markets (*The Economist* publishes a Commodity Price Index) and on the Stock Exchange, while many trade associations draw up index numbers relative to their own industries.

8.7 Practical problems with index numbers

Index numbers are used in many fields besides prices. There are indexes of industrial production, import and export trade, share prices, unemployment rates, wages rates and in many other areas. The construction of an index is not easy and involves problems of definition, the choice of items to be included, the choice of a base period, etc. Some of these problems must now be considered.

a The purpose of the index

In devising any index there is a useful purpose to be served. We have a problem, and we feel that if we collect data systematically over a long period it will help us to understand the problem. We shall be able to find out how the situation is changing, and if we apply a particular policy we shall be able to see whether it has the desired effect or not. If not, perhaps we can see why, and modify the policy to correct the defect. Almost always we shall get off to a better start if we define the problem and the purpose of the index. This will suggest what influences have a bearing on the problem, and what areas should be examined in order to throw light upon it.

b The choice of a base period

The natural inclination is to take the current year as the base year for a new index, so that the index in the future relates back to the time we started the inquiry. This may often be quite satisfactory, but we must remember that any year may be subject to random events which affect the data. If an abnormal year is chosen as a base year the related data in subsequent years will be affected by this abnormal base. Thus in a year when industrial production was beset by many strikes, the lowered figure for output would create a false impression in subsequent 'normal' years when it might appear that a 'normal' year was a very good year relative to the low output figure in the base year. Ideally, a base year should be one as close to a trend output as possible. If the current year is an abnormal year it would be better to relate back to a recent year which was generally agreed to be 'normal'.

c The choice of items

The items to be included in an index must be selected with a view to achieving the purposes listed in our consideration of *a* above. This is where definitions are so important. For example, if the RPI is about the purchases made by an 'average family' the definition of an average family may be crucial to the decisions about the items. Does the 'average family' eat bread, drink milk, wear business suits, or buy perambulators? Perhaps it does all these things. Does it play golf, go water skiing, parascend or fly microlight aircraft? Which of these items merits inclusion in our observation of prices year by year? Perhaps none of them. We cannot include all the thousands of items on sales in an advanced market economy. Comprehensiveness must be sacrificed to economy in the collection of data, yet those items to be observed must be representative of purchases generally. The Stock Exchange deals in several thousand different shares, which may be arranged in many categories. For a share price index we have to choose a reasonable number which are representative of the rest.

d The choice of weights

Some items used in an index will be more important than others, and should be given added weight. Decisions on the weighting to be applied must be made at the very start of an index, and it may be necessary to hold a preliminary survey to discover the desirable weighting to be applied to a particular item. These weightings must then be kept in review, and changed as the pattern of expenditure, output, etc, alters. We have already referred to the weightings applied in preparing the RPI, which are updated every year to allow for changes in the public's pattern of expenditure. Weighting may be **volume orientated** – we change the weighting as the quantity of the item used is changed – but it is sometimes better to use **value weighting**, since the volume used may not change but the value of the item may change considerably. Basic commodities are subject to fluctuations in price which reflect natural events and business expectations as much as demand for the product. Such an index may be more affected by the value than the volume of the commodity used.

e The monitoring of the data

Data cannot be obtained out of thin air. They have to be collected by a team of observers who know what is required, how to obtain the information (compulsory powers may be necessary), how to assemble, assess and interpret it and how to feed it into the index so that it is taken into proper account. This requires training, experience and regular review by supervisory personnel. The index becomes of use only when it is published in an authoritative way – so that publication deadlines must be met. A handbook relating to the index should be available, giving definitions and explanatory notes, so that a full understanding of the conception, preparation and development of the index is available to potential users.

Summary

1   Index numbers enable us to express changing data over the years in a series of figures related to a base year, which is designated as 100. If the volumes or values of the data have increased over the years the index will rise above 100. If they have declined over the years the index will fall below 100.
2   The RPI is the best example of an index in regular use in the United Kingdom. It is a weighted average of price relatives for goods purchased by the average household. First a price relative is calculated for each good or service included in the average family's basket of requirements. Then these price relatives are averaged on the basis of weightings which give proper emphasis to each item according to its importance in the basket of goods.
3   A simple price relative takes account of price changes and is calculated with the formula $P_n/P_o \times 100$, where n means the year under consideration and o means the original year (ie the base year).
4   A simple quantity relative is calculated on the formula $Q_n/Q_o \times 100$.
5   A value index takes account of both price and quantity and may be calculated on the formula $I_v = P_nQ_n/P_oQ_o \times 100$.
6   To isolate a price index from the quantity factor it is usual, in drawing up an aggregate price index (one that relates to a basket of goods), to use Laspeyres' index. This uses the formula:

$$I(L) = \frac{\Sigma\ P_nQ_o}{\Sigma\ P_oQ_o} \times 100$$

The index is therefore related to the quantities in use in the base year.
7   An alternative is to use the Paasche index, which uses current year quantities and the formula:

$$I(P) = \frac{\Sigma\ P_nQ_n}{\Sigma\ P_oQ_n} \times 100$$

8   A chain-based index is one where the index is recalculated every year with the previous year used as a new base year. It shows the *rate* of change occurring.
9   Indexes may be used to deflate a time series, so that comparisons between periods may be made in 'real' terms which ignore changes

in the value of money in the interval between the two periods. This idea may also be used to discount expected cash flow, so that a true comparison may be made between the capital cost of an investment and estimates of its yield in the years ahead.

10 The RPI is a weighted average of price relatives based upon the purchases of an average household in the previous year. The weightings used sum to 1000 and are divided into 11 main groups of items: food, alcoholic drink, tobacco, housing, etc. Each item included in the index is sampled for price monthly, and a price relative to the base year is calculated. These price relatives are then merged as a weighted average of goods and services, which is the RPI.

11 The inflation rate for a given period can be calculated by the formula:

$$\frac{\text{Current RPI}}{\text{RPI at start of period}} \times 100$$

It is used to calculate the rate of inflation every month over the previous 12 months.

12 The TPI reflects the impact of inflation upon normal taxpayers, by taking into account the level of taxation imposed as well as the changes in prices. It is not meaningful to non-taxpayers or those with very large incomes, who are taxed at abnormal rates.

13 When preparing index numbers it is essential to define the purpose of the index, the method of arriving at the index and to anticipate problems of collection, collation and interpretation of data. The base period should be one as close to the trend as possible – an abnormal base year distorts the index in subsequent years. The items to be included must be carefully selected as representative of all relevant items and the weighting to be accorded to each must be carefully considered. For the correct calculation of official indexes it may be necessary to compel firms to provide accurate data.

More exercises on index numbers

1 *a* Discuss the uses and limitation of index numbers.
   b The wages paid to manual workers of a company in years 1 and 5 are given below

	Year 1		Year 5	
	Average wage	Numbers employed	Average wage	Numbers employed
Skilled	80	80	160	50
Semiskilled	60	160	120	180
Unskilled	45	40	100	50

Calculate an index number for wages for year 5 with year 1 = 100 with *i* base year weighted for the numbers employed and *ii* current year weighted for the numbers employed. Comment on your results.

2 Describe the construction and use of *either* the General Index of Retail Prices or the Index of Industrial Production.

3 What is meant by 'the inflation rate'? How is it calculated?

4 What indexes are available to measure the degree of price inflation in a community? Give examples of the methods used in a country of your choice and outline the calculations required.

5 The Index of Net National Production in a certain country is based on year 1 when the index stood at 100 and the net national product was US$39 375 million.

  a Calculate the index for year 5 – when the net national product was US$43 405 million.

  b Calculate the index for year 10 when the net national product was US$52 156 million (answers correct to one decimal place).

6 Explain the terms *i* weights and *ii* price relatives used in index-number construction.

  b Figures for the Index of Production of Engineering and Allied Industries, year 5 (year 1 = 100) were:

Industry	Weights	Index
Mechanical engineering	110	130
Instrument engineering	15	85
Electrical engineering	82	144
Marine engineering	15	62
Motor vehicles	84	112
Other allied industries	44	103

  i Find an index of all engineering and allied industries for year 5.
  ii Comment on your results.

7 *a* Figures for the Index of Industrial Production in Westland for year 6 (year 1 = 100) were:

Group	Weights	Index
Mining and quarrying	41	322
Manufacturing:		
Food, drink and tobacco	77	154
Chemicals	66	130
Metal manufacture	47	122
Engineering	298	117
Textiles	67	108
Other	142	153
Construction	182	88
Gas, electricity and water	80	185

Calculate the Index of Industrial Production for year 6 *i* for all industries, *ii* for all industries except mining and quarrying and *iii* for manufacturing industries only.

b Comment on your results.

8 The Index of Agricultural Prices, based on year 1 = 100, is as follows for year 5 for cereals:

Cereal	Weights	Index numbers
Wheat	50	138
Barley	46	122
Oats	4	96

Calculate an overall index number for cereals for year 5.

9 Published statistics

9.1 The development of official statistics

The enumeration of populations is as old as civilisation itself. One early African king who was migrating with his tribe to new lands in southern Africa required everyone who successfully crossed a certain river to deposit a stone on the far side. The stones were counted when all were safely over the river to give the king a complete census of his people. The hill of stones is still available, but the people are not so easily identified. The Christian story explains the birth of Christ at Bethlehem as the result of a census ordered by the Roman Emperor Augustus, which required people to return to their original cities. The United Kingdom Census of Population began in 1801, and takes place every 10 years in the first year of the decade. It requires a considerable amount of preparatory work, with forms being designed to establish not only the names, addresses and nationalities of every person resident in the United Kingdom on census night, but also more detailed facts which are prepared from a 10% sample of the population. This requires the heads of selected households to answer a more detailed survey about the social situation of the household – such questions as whether they have a telephone, a car, a television set, etc. Besides such routine records a particular survey might feature a current problem, and hold an in-depth inquiry into it. To assist those heads of households who are not particularly sophisticated in statistical matters temporary staff are taken on as interviewers to assist in the completion of these more detailed census forms.

Apart from the census, statistical records were not collected systematically until very recent times. Such detailed inquiries as were conducted were privately funded by charitable bodies seeking to know the true facts of economic and social conditions. Politicians and economists frequently made pronouncements which had the most enduring impact upon society on the basis of the slimmest evidence, frequently biased by their own situation and their own apprehension of the state of affairs – entirely uncorroborated by evidence of any sort. The most famous example is the Malthusian doctrine, which held that the population increased in geometric ratio, 2, 4, 8, 16, etc, while agricultural production only increased arithmetically, 2, 4, 6, 8, etc. Therefore the world was doomed to see mass starvation unless something was done about it, and the 'appetite of the sexes' could be restrained. Malthus argued that the numbers of the labouring classes could only be held in check by diseases, wars, famines, etc, which thus became tools of the Almighty to keep the balance between man and nature. This idea became the basis on which the 'workhouse' system of poor relief was established – poor people were forced into institutions called workhouses where the sexes were segregated and relief was reduced to a minimum level. The resulting misery left an enduring mark upon British society, yet the original idea was totally without solid statistical foundation, and even though the 1 billion human beings of Malthus's times have now increased to 6 billions, we have not yet experienced the mass starvation he predicted.

Early statistical inquiries included Charles Booth's Victorian inquiry into the *Labour and Life of the People of London*, and Rowntree's study of poverty among the working classes of York, where his chocolate factory still provides a major source of employment. Such inquiries apart, detailed statistics about the economy and the wider social organisation were simply not available. It was not until the Second World War required the full mobilisation not only of the armed forces of the nation but all its other resources as well, that the Central Statistical Office was established as a special branch of the Cabinet Office. This proved over the years to be a less than satisfactory arrangement, and the Central Statistical Office has now become a separate department in its own right. One junior recruit to the CSO, who left shortly after the incident, related to one of the authors of this book how he was asked to draw a graph of some data for a Cabinet Minister. When he presented it he was told by a rather irritated Minister, 'Oh, but we didn't want it to look like that; we hoped it would look like this' – indicating a very different curve. His refusal to change the graph was not favourably received.

Another example of bias was one celebrated occasion when the *Retail Price Index* (RPI) was proving that the public had been adversely affected by government policies. Therefore, a new index was prepared alongside the RPI, called the Tax and Price Index (TPI), which established that when tax changes were taken into account, people had in fact benefitted. This may have been politically satisfying, but it ignored the fact that many poorer people, who pay no taxes anyway, were still suffering from the increases in retail prices.

The decision to remove the Central Statistical Office from the Cabinet Office is almost certainly a sound one, for it is *prima facie* undesirable to have such a close link between the centre of political power and an organisation which must essentially be unbiased in all its activities. Regular users of official statistics cannot fail to notice subtle changes of influence over the years. One hopes that this does not amount to political bias, but only to an influence over the types of problems that should be investigated. Senior statisticians in such official organisations certainly have to preserve their independence from political pressures, and must not allow their work to be subverted in the interests of any particular government.

In the United Kingdom the best reference book on published statistics is the *Guide to Official Statistics*, published by the Central Statistical Office and available in most public libraries, or from Her Majesty's Stationery Office (HMSO). Those requiring regular copies of several publications can open an account with HMSO at their postal address, Nine Elms Publications Centre, 51 Nine Elms Lane, London SW8 5DR. Payment arrangements vary, but for private citizens payment by direct debit is often used. HMSO has a bookshop in several major cities apart from London, and has accredited agents in about 50 large towns. They also operate a telephone ordering service on 071-873 9090 which will dispatch publications at once, against payment by credit card. The advantage here is that the clerk will at once check the availability of the title requested and will only accept the order if the publication is in print.

9.2   The Guide to Official Statistics

This is a comprehensive guide to the official statistics that are available. It has over 400 closely printed pages, and sets out to give the user a broad indication of whether the statistics required have been compiled and, if so, where they may be found in published form. It cannot always pinpoint a source of particular statistics, but it will then give a general indication that a certain publication may possibly have the required information.

The guide is set out in 16 main subject areas, which are listed in a Subject List on the Contents page at the front of the book. The 16 areas are (1) General; (2) Area, climate, environment; (3) Population, vital statistics (these are statistics about births and deaths); (4) Social statistics; (5) Labour; (6) Agriculture; (7) Production industries; (8) Transport; (9) Distribution and other services; (10) Public services; (11) Prices; (12) The economy – national income and expenditure; (13) General and public finance; (14) Financial and business institutions; (15) Overseas transactions; (16) Isle of Man.

Each subject area is then broken down into subsidiary areas. As an example we have:

8. *Transport.* 8.1 General sources of transport statistics; 8.2 Railways; 8.3 Road transport; 8.4 Sea transport; 8.5 Seaports; 8.6 Air transport; 8.7 Other transport; 8.8 Communications; ...

When dealing with each of these subsidiary areas the information is broken down into *regular sources* and *occasional sources*, so that the user can locate not only regular sources which update statistics on a monthly or annual basis but also the details of recent publications which feature particular surveys made to meet a particular need. Thus a National Travel Survey conducted a few years earlier may be of considerable interest to those contemplating a local survey in their own home area, even though the actual data would not be up to date.

9.3   The Monthly Digest of Statistics

This digest provides the latest collection of up-to-date statistics available in the United Kingdom. It consists of calendar monthly data, or monthly averages, on a huge range of data collected by government departments, nationalised industries and trade associations. The January issue each year includes a *Supplement of Definitions and Explanatory Notes* which gives detailed definitions of all the terms and units used in the *Digest*.

The *Monthly Digest* is available in most libraries and should certainly be available in all United Kingdom colleges and universities.

9.4 The Annual Abstract of Statistics

As its name implies, this publication gives annual figures for most of the data published on a monthly basis in the *Monthly Digest*. It also gives figures going back over a period of 10 years. It is therefore possible to find the long-term trend in many sets of data, which may be helpful to business managers seeking to determine likely markets in the future, the pattern of expenditure in a field they are proposing to enter, and so on.

The areas covered include most of those mentioned in the *Official Guide* (see Section 9.2) but an extra section headed Banking, Insurance, etc, covers banking, insurance companies and insolvency.

9.5 National income and expenditure – The Blue Book

This book is published annually about August and gives estimates of the national product, income and expenditure of the United Kingdom to the end of the previous year. The data are given for a 21-year period, giving a very long-time series of data. This book will be familiar to every student of economics, for it is the basis of a whole field of economic study. What is the wealth of the nation? How is it created and shared? These are fundamental questions for economists. A unique feature of these tables is that the data are arrived at in three ways; the gross national product of all the industries in the nation is the same as the gross national income earned by all the producers (either as rents, wages, interest or profits), then the expenditure they all indulge in, together with the capital formation achieved in the period, is again the same total as the other figures. This is not an economics textbook but any data about national income and expenditure is obviously of interest to businessmen making decisions about marketing, potential market share, etc.

The data are analysed into sectors, including the personal sector, the output of limited companies and financial institutions, the public corporations and central and local authorities. There is a special section on capital formation. A *glossary of main terms* at the back of the book gives the definitions used in collecting data together on such an enormous range of headings as the national income and expenditure.

9.6 United Kingdom balance of payments – The Pink Book

This is another publication appearing each year in August or September giving figures for the United Kingdom balance of payments up to 31 December of the previous year. It consists of a very long series of data – spread over the previous 21 years – showing the trade figures in their two main headings of visible trade and invisible trade. Visible trade is trade in goods, which can be seen physically entering or leaving the

United Kingdom through its ports and airports. Invisible trade is trade in services, banking, insurance, carriage, communications, etc. While these cannot be seen physically entering or leaving the country they are enormously important in helping to pay for the imports the country requires. Before the advent of North Sea oil there was almost always a deficit on United Kingdom visible trade which was made up by a surplus on invisible services. Today the situation (until North Sea oil is exhausted) is much healthier and balance-of-payments crises have become rarer events than formerly, for this (and other) reasons.

9.7 United Kingdom Census Report

This report appears as a set of volumes prepared by the Office of Population Censuses and Surveys, within about two years of the Census held in the first year of every decade, ie 1971, 1981, etc. The terms used in the Report are explained in detail in a 'General definitions' volume issued shortly after the Census. The current one is called *Census 1981, Definitions, Great Britain* (HMSO). The 1991 definitions should appear within another year or so. The report begins by emphasising that no census can be completely accurate since it is difficult to identify every property in a district, and every family in a multi-occupation property. Some properties appear empty or it may be impossible to locate the owner or occupier, while human error or deliberate deception leads to wrong data being accepted by the Office of Population and Censuses. The results given are very detailed – the 1981 Report gives the United Kingdom population on Census night as 54 285 422. This compares which 53 978 538 in 1971 and 51 283 392 in 1961. Such a Report – Part 1 alone has nearly 300 pages of detailed statistics and there are about ten other parts equally large – obviously contains a wealth of data, all collected on one night in 1981.

9.8 Economic Trends

This is a monthly journal which brings together all the main economic indicators. Data are given in three main ways – as 'latest developments', 'five year or so movements' and 'movements over longer periods'. Interesting and informative reviews of trends in national accounts appear in the January, April, July and October issues.

9.9 Social Trends

This monthly publication presents carefully selected social data to give a rounded picture of trends and patterns in society. There are about 200 tables and charts on social topics, and each issue features articles on selected topics, current problems, etc. The areas covered are population, households and families, employment, leisure, personal income and

wealth, personal expenditure, health, education, housing, the environment, public safety, civil administration and resources.

9.10 Regional Trends

This publication is issued from time to time and brings together a wide
range of official statistics on the regions of the United Kingdom. There
is a descriptive profile of each region, its local authorities, population,
health, housing, education, employment, energy resources and uses and
every other aspect of life in the region. It is of great interest to market
researchers, industrialists and others seeking a local viewpoint rather
than a national picture of the economy.

9.11 The Bank of England Quarterly Bulletin

This is the best, most up-to-date collection of financial statistics available
in the United Kingdom. The statistics appear as an annex in a quarterly
volume which is otherwise devoted to articles about the Bank's view of
the economy and current problems in world and domestic banking. The
helpful thing from the student's point of view is that a series of
'Additional Notes to the Tables' appears at the back of each issue
drawing attention to salient features of the current quarter's figures and
where necessary giving cross-references to earlier explanatory articles.
The tables include details of (1) Bank of England assets and liabilities,
(2) liabilities of the monetary authorities, (3) assets and liabilities of
banks in the United Kingdom, (4) the discount market, (5) details of
advances made in sterling and foreign currency, (6) the United Kingdom
monetary sector, (7) the central government borrowing requirement and
its financing, (8) an analysis of government debt, etc. Interesting figures
for economics students are the money supply figures, private-sector
liquidity, the PSBR figures (public-sector borrowing requirement – the
extent to which government expenditure fails to be met by tax revenues),
official reserves, interest rates in various sectors and the rates of exchange
of international currencies.

The *Bulletin* is available in most libraries, or may be purchased by the
submission of a standing order to the Bank of England on a yearly basis.

9.12 Year Book of Labour Statistics

This publication of the International Labour Office in Geneva presents
a summary of the principal labour statistics of approximately 180
countries, drawn from official publications or official statistical services
in the countries concerned. The data are presented in eight chapters.
These are (1) total and economically active population, (2) employment,
(3) unemployment, (4) hours of work, (5) wages, (6) consumer prices,
(7) occupational injuries and (8) industrial disputes.

9.13   Euro-statistics

The volume of data being made available from the European Community is so enormous that it is difficult to keep track of it. An official publication *Euro-statistics: data for short-term economic analysis* contains a
wealth of data in two sections – community tables and country tables.
The community tables are in ten parts: national accounts, employment/
unemployment, Index of Industrial Production, opinions in industry,
output, external trade, prices, financial statistics and balance of payments. Full particular of *Euro-statistics* may be obtained from the
Statistical Office of the European Community, Batiment Jean Monnet,
Plateau de Kicheberg, Boite Postale 1907, Luxembourg.

9.14   World Bank publications

The World Bank publishes a wealth of data about every country in the
world, and has particularly good coverage of Third World countries.
One of the best sources is the annual publication *World Tables*. These
tables allocate four A4 sides to each country in the world, giving all the
major statistics, population, gross national product, balance of payments, etc over a 20-year period. World Bank publications are available
in the United Kingdom from Microinfo Ltd, PO Box 3, Omega Park,
Alton, Hampshire, GU34 2PG, Tel 0420 86848.

Exercises on published statistics

1   Describe in detail one of the following: *a* the *Monthly Digest of Statistics* or *b* the *Annual Abstract of Statistics*.
2   What is a census? What problems does a full census present to the
organisers? How are the results of the United Kingdom Census
presented to the public?
3   Describe briefly *one* of the following: *a The Blue Book on National
Income and Expenditure* or *b The Pink Book on the Balance of
Payments*.
4   What is the *Guide to Official Statistics?* How does it guide us to the
statistics we require?

10 Measures of central tendency

10.1 Averages in statistics

It is frequently difficult to describe a set of data. Any mass of statistics consists of a huge range of information from which we have to draw conclusions, yet a reference to any one statistic may be quite inappropriate because it may be unrepresentative. We have to see if there is any pattern in the data, and one of the best ways to start is to find an average. *An average is a point within a group of data which is central to the group, and around which the other values are distributed.* It is therefore a **measure of central tendency** – a measure which starts to summarise the data by fixing one point, the centre. The position of the central item fixes the location of the distribution and averages are therefore sometimes called *measures of location*.

Unfortunately, there are several possible 'centres' or 'averages', which we must list and look at in turn. Before we do so let us notice the common feature to them all; that they stress the middle items in the set and reduce the significance of the extreme values. If we take the simplest average of production in a factory which turns out 27, 25, 3 and 46 units of product in a 4-week period – the third week's production having been affected by a strike, compensated by overtime working in the fourth week – we find that the average is $101 \div 4 = 25.25$ units per week. This average figure replaces the extreme values 3 and 46 by an average figure much closer to the two 'normal' weeks. This average figure does not coincide with any of the actual figures in the series, nor is it in fact an actual number of whole units, but it does describe a week's typical production more clearly than any of the four actual figures, and much more accurately than either of the extremes.

The four types of average may be listed as follows:

a the arithmetic average – often called the arithmetic mean
b the geometric average – or geometric mean
c the median – or central item
d the mode – or most fashionable item

10.2 The arithmetic mean

The arithmetic mean is the most commonly used average, and is often referred to simply as 'the mean'. It is found by adding together the individual values and dividing by the number of items. Thus consider a batsman in cricket who scores as follows in a five-match series: 168, 27, 52, 1 , 17, 0, 256, 88, 19, 22 – there being two innings in each match. The total runs scored are 650. Dividing by 10, the average score is 65. Note that none of the original scores was 65, so that every original score was really unrepresentative of the batsman's ability. The most extreme scores, 0 and 256, were very unrepresentative, but they have contributed to the calculation of 65 as the average score. Note also that the centrality of 65 as an average can be proved by showing how much the other numbers varied from 65. We can set this out as:

Scores below average	Variation from mean	Arithmetic mean	Variation from mean	Scores above average
27	– 38	65	+ 103	168
52	– 13	65	+ 191	256
1	– 64	65	+ 23	88
17	– 48	65		
0	– 65	65		
19	– 46	65		
22	– 43	65		
Total	– 317		+ 317	

The variations above and below the average are equal, and 65 is therefore central to the distribution.

Such simple average calculations are very elementary. Variations on them are as follows.

a Weighted average calculations

Where a particular item occurs a number of times it is said to weight the statistics in its favour. Thus consider the average wage of the employees in the factory of the X Co Ltd shown below. There are five rates of pay:

Weekly wages (£)	Number of employees	Total pay (£)
135	30	4 050
150	62	9 300
175	25	4 375
190	40	7 600
230	30	6 900
Total	187	32 225

To find the arithmetic mean we must multiply each rate of pay by the number of employees receiving that rate (this is the weighting) to give a total pay at each rate. Then we must divide the grand total not by 5, but by the sum of the frequencies (ie the number of employees). The result is:

$$\frac{£32\ 225}{187} = £172.33 \text{ (correct to the nearest penny)}$$

b The arithmetic mean of a grouped frequency distribution

Many statistics are given in the form of grouped frequency distributions, such as the one given in Table 10.1.

Note that in this type of grouped distribution we have no idea what the individual outputs of the operatives were. Seven operatives produced between 21 and 30 units in the 4-week period but whether they produced 22, 23, 27 or 29 is not known. We can only find an average if we make some sensible assumption about the actual outputs. The assumption is that they are evenly distributed throughout the band of 21–30, which is the same as saying that the average within that particular band is the midpoint of the band. Since there are an even number of items in the band (21–30 inclusive is ten items) we assume that the midpoint is halfway between 25 and 26, ie 25.5 (a quick method of fixing the midpoints is to add up the extreme items 21 and 30 and divide by 2 = 25.5). The midpoints of all the classes are found in the same way, as shown in Table 10.2. We now multiply this midpoint figure for each class by the frequency (the number of operatives whose output came within that band). The resulting products are entered in the end column and totalled. We now divide this total by the number of operatives (ie the sum of the frequencies = 45):

$$\text{Average output per operative} = \frac{1\ 977.5}{45}$$

$$= 43.9 \text{ (correct to one decimal place)}$$

Some statistics textbooks at this stage introduce short-cut methods which are helpful to students who do not have calculators, because the short-cut methods keep the figures smaller. Since the calculator has made such laborious calculations unnecessary, it is assumed all students will use one and short-cut methods are therefore not included here.

Table 10.1 Output of operatives: weeks 1–4 inclusive

Output in units	Number of operatives
21–30	7
31–40	11
41–50	14
51–60	8
61–70	5
Total	45

Table 10.2   Output of operatives: weeks 1–4 inclusive

Output in units (a)	Midpoints (b)	Number of operatives (c)	Output of groups (b) × (c) (d)
21–30	25.5	7	178.5
31–40	35.5	11	390.5
41–50	45.5	14	637.0
51–60	55.5	8	444.0
61–70	65.5	5	327.5
Total		45	1977.5

How to deal with open-ended distributions   There can be a difficulty where the end groups of a grouped frequency distribution are open ended. In such cases we have to make an assumption about the size of the open-ended classes. We usually assume that the end group is twice as large as the other groups, but some other assumption might be made in certain circumstances. Whatever the assumption it may mean that an error is creeping into the calculation, especially if there are a large number of items in the group.

Thus suppose the figures given in Table 10.1 had had an open-ended group as shown in Table 10.3. We should assume that this group is twice as large as the other groups, so we treat it as 61–80. This makes the midpoint of the group 70.5 (instead of 65.5) and accordingly the calculation of the average output per operative would be as shown in Table 10.4.

$$\text{Average output per operative} = \frac{2002.5}{45}$$

$$= 44.5$$

Formulae for the arithmetic mean   This book attempts to teach statistics without undue emphasis on mathematical formulae, but statistics is a branch of mathematics, and some of the concepts are easier to understand if the student has a nodding acquaintance with the use of symbols to express ideas. If you are clear how to find the averages you will have

Table 10.3   Output of operative: weeks 1–4 inclusive

Output in units	Number of operatives
21–30	7
31–40	11
41–50	14
51–60	8
61 and over	5
Total	45

Table 10.4 Output of operatives: weeks 1–4 inclusive

Output in units (a)	Midpoints (b)	Number of operatives (c)	Output of groups (b) × (c) (d)
21–30	25.5	7	178.5
31–40	35.5	11	390.5
41–50	45.5	14	637.0
51–60	55.5	8	444.0
61	70.5	5	352.5
Total		45	2002.5

no difficulty in following the symbols which express the methods being used. These are:

$\bar{x}$ for arithmetic mean
Σ (capital sigma) meaning 'the sum of'
f for frequencies
x for the individual items of data
n for the total frequencies – so n has the same meaning as Σf

Using these symbols we have the following formulae:

For a simple series:

$$\bar{x} = \frac{\Sigma x}{n} \quad \text{or} \quad AM = \frac{\text{sum of the individual items}}{\text{number of items}}$$

For a weighted average:

$$\bar{x} = \frac{\Sigma fx}{\Sigma f} \quad \text{or}$$

$$AM = \frac{\text{sum of the products (individual items} \times \text{frequency)}}{\text{sum of the frequencies}}$$

For a grouped frequency distribution:

$$\bar{x} = \frac{\Sigma fx}{\Sigma f}$$

(Note that here x means the midpoint value of each class in the display and f means the number of items in the class concerned.)

Features of the arithmetic mean   The main characteristic of the arithmetic mean is that in calculating it all the values in any distribution are used and exert an influence on the size of the mean. This seems only right, but it may in fact be a disadvantage, as where an octogenarian joins an evening class of 16-year-olds. The 'average' age may be raised considerably when 80 years are added on for this member, and may distort our description of the age distribution of the class.

The mean is simple to calculate and susceptible to mathematical manipulation (for example, the mean × frequency gives the aggregate value of the distribution). At the same time the mean of grouped distributions, especially open-ended ones, can only be calculated on the basis of assumptions made about the position of items within the group and the size of open-ended groups.

Exercises on the arithmetic mean

1 Students attending a certain evening course are aged as follows:

17, 17, 17, 18, 19, 19, 19, 19, 21, 22, 23, 23, 35, 37, 38, 44

What is the mean age?

2 In a certain factory gas consumption per month is as follows:

Month	Therms consumed	Month	Therms consumed
January	17 318	July	10 725
February	14 924	August	11 846
March	15 618	September	14 925
April	14 212	October	18 203
May	13 168	November	19 214
June	12 849	December	21 174

What is the mean consumption per month?

3 Theatre tickets are sold as follows: 386 front stalls at £8.50; 436 rear stalls at £6.50; 86 dress circle at £7.50; 240 upper circle at £5; 296 gallery at £3.50. What is the mean price of a ticket (answer correct to nearest penny)?

4 Mass-produced cylinder blocks have internal diameters as follows: 8 blocks are 9.456 cm, 7 are 9.457 cm, 3 are 9.458 cm, 12 are 9.459 cm. What is the mean diameter (answer correct to 3 decimal places)?

5 What is the average of 48 016, 48 156 and 48 176?

6 What is the average of 28 385, 29 268, 28 721 and 28 522?

7 Sales by representatives employed by a toy wholesaler are as follows:

Sales (£'000)	No of representatives
Under 10	3
10 and under 20	8
20 and under 30	16
30 and under 40	15
40 and under 50	8
50 and under 60	4

Calculate the mean sales (*answer correct to the nearest £100*).

8 The weekly incomes of families in a certain industrial town are

found to be as follows:

Weekly income (£)	No of incomes
Under 120	36
120 and under 150	68
150 and under 180	93
180 and under 210	85
210 and under 240	71
240 and under 270	60
270 and under 300	42
Over 300	45

Note
Both the first group and the last group are
open-ended and should be treated as twice
the size of other groups.

Calculate the mean wage (answer to the nearest £).

9 Students admitted to university for undergraduate courses were
found to have the following ages:

Age	Males	Females
16	1	4
17	2	—
18	87	75
19	96	85
20	54	65
21	42	51
22	17	19
35	1	—
55	—	1
Total	300	300

a Find the arithmetic mean age for males and females separately.
b How may these means be combined to give the mean age for all
students?

10 Three hundred light bulbs are tested to extinction for quality
control purposes. The results are as follows:

Lifetime (hours)	Frequency
Under 500	36
500– 749.9	52
750– 999.9	64
1000–1249.9	72
1250–1499.9	52
1500 and over	24

    a Find the arithmetic mean lifetime of a bulb (answer correct to the nearest hour).

    b Explain what assumptions you made when doing this calculation.

10.3 The geometric mean

Although the geometric mean is listed second in the choice of averages available in statistics, its chief use is in the preparation of index numbers where, for theoretical reasons beyond the scope of this book, the geometric mean is sometimes preferred to the arithmetic mean. Here it is sufficient to note the method of calculation and the difference from the arithmetic mean. The arithmetic mean is found by adding the values and dividing by the number of values. So the average of 4, 6 and $9 = 19/3 = 6.33$ (correct to two decimal places).

The geometric mean is found by multiplying the numbers and finding the appropriate root of the answer. Thus the geometric mean of 4, 6 and $9 = \sqrt[3]{4 \times 6 \times 9} = \sqrt[3]{216} = 6$. The answer is slightly different from the arithmetic mean. The appropriate root is the same root as there are numbers – so if we had 5 numbers we would take the 5th root and if there were 10 numbers we would need the 10th root. In mathematical terms we define the geometric mean as the nth root of the product of n numbers.

Most scientific calculators have a key (labelled 2nd F) which will find the xth power of any number, and in its reverse (second) function the xth root of any number. This key is usually labelled y^x and above the key the second function is shown as $\sqrt[x]{y}$. We can therefore find the geometric mean of a set of numbers as follows.

What is the geometric mean of 248, 292, 336, and 505?

First, multiply the numbers $248 \times 292 \times 336 \times 505$

Now touch the 2nd F key and the $\sqrt[x]{y}$ key, which readies the calculator to do a 'square root' calculation.

Now touch the 4 key to tell the calculator you want the 4th root, and the = 'equals' key, and the answer 332.9 appears.

This mean is slightly different from the arithmetic mean, which comes to 345.25. Practice finding roots of a number with the following simple cases.

Number to be used	Root to be found	Answer expected
32	5	2
343	3	7
16 777 216	6	16
125	3	5
14 641	4	11

Exercises on the geometric mean

1 Find the geometric mean of the groups of numbers given below (answers correct to one decimal place):
   a 27, 32, 59, 84
   b 312, 429, 346
   c 79, 85, 69, 78, 99
   d 27, 32, 64, 75, 86
   e 127, 429, 316, 518

10.4 The median

The median is a very simple average to find. All we do is arrange the data as an array (ie in increasing order of size) and take the middle item. For example, the average output of 11 operatives is given as follows in units per week:

27 29 13 14 12 48 37 25 32 19 23

Rearranged as an array we have:

12 13 14 19 23 25 27 29 32 37 48

The median item is the middle item of the array which is 25. The median separates the array into halves – in this case with the weaker performers on the left and the better performers on the right:

$(12, 13, 14, 19, 23)$ 25 $(27, 29, 32, 37, 48)$

The formulae for the median

To find the median item we use the formula:

$$\text{Median} = \frac{n+1}{2}$$

Thus with 11 items the median item is $(11+1)/2 = 6$th item. In the example given above the median item is 25, which has 5 items below it (making it the 6th item) and 5 items above it, to give 11 items in all. Where the number of items is even we find that the formula results in a figure ending in $\frac{1}{2}$. Looking back to Table 4.2 (see page 47) we find there were 150 items in the array. The median item in the array is $(150+1)/2 = 75\frac{1}{2}$ item. We cannot have a $75\frac{1}{2}$th item so the median must be the average of the two items at the centre of the array – which means the average of the 75th and 76th items. We find that the 75th item was £297 take-home pay and the 76th item was £314 take-home pay. The average of these is:

$$\frac{£297 + £314}{2} = \frac{£611}{2} = £305.50$$

The median figure for take-home pay is £305.50. This illustrates a very common student error which is to confuse the median with the median item. Thus many students would state in examination answers that the median in the above example is $75\frac{1}{2}$, whereas of course it is £305.50. *The median is defined as the* **value** *of the central item in an array.*

b The median of grouped data

Where data are grouped, as in Table 10.1 on page 143, we cannot find an exact median, because the individual values within the groups are not available. As with the arithmetic mean we must make an assumption – that the items are spread evenly within the group. We cannot of course know this – they might all be bunched at the top of the group, or towards the bottom of the group – we can only assume they are evenly spread.

We have to decide where the median item is, and to do this we rearrange the table, with a cumulative frequency column added. This is done in Table 10.5.

There are 45 items, so what is the median item? Here we must learn a rather tricky point. The median item in a group distribution is found by the formula $n/2$ not $(n+1)/2$. The reason for this is that in assuming that the items are evenly spread throughout the group we imagine a number of subdivisions, each with 1 in it. The formula $(n+1)/2$ finds the upper end of a subdivision, not the middle of it, and we must drop back $\frac{1}{2}$ division to $n/2$. This formula gives $45/2 = 22\frac{1}{2}$. We therefore need to find the $22\frac{1}{2}$th item in the distribution. This is clearly in the 41–50 group and is the $4\frac{1}{2}$th item out of the 14 in the group. The value of the median output is therefore:

$$40 + \left(\frac{4\frac{1}{2}}{14} \times 10\right) \text{ units} = 40 + \frac{90}{28}$$

$$= 40 + 3.21$$

$$= 43.21 \text{ units}$$

To the nearest whole unit this is 43 units. Remember that as the median is the central item of a distribution it will be an actual item, and it is most sensible to give the answer as a round number.

c Finding the median by interpolation

For any given grouped frequency distribution we can draw a cumulative frequency curve (called an ogive because of its similarity to the shape of

Table 10.5 Output of operatives: weeks 1–4 inclusive

Output in units	Number of operatives	Cumulative frequency
21–30	7	7
31–40	11	18
41–50	14	32
51–60	8	40
61–70	5	45

a Gothic arch of the same name). To draw an ogive we plot the cumulative frequencies against the upper limit of the class intervals. Thus in Table 10.5 we plot the 7 operatives against the output of 30 units (so that we may say 7 operatives do not produce more than 30 units, 18 operatives do not produce more than 40 units, etc). The resulting curve is as shown in Figure 10.1.

Quartiles and deciles

Although quartiles and deciles are not strictly speaking averages – and should therefore be more appropriately discussed in the chapter on dispersion (see Chapter 11) – it is convenient to discuss them here because they are found by the same method as the median. The median has been defined as the value of the central item in an array. The quartiles divide the series into four equal parts, in other words each quartile is the midpoint of the halves of the series marked off by the median. The lower

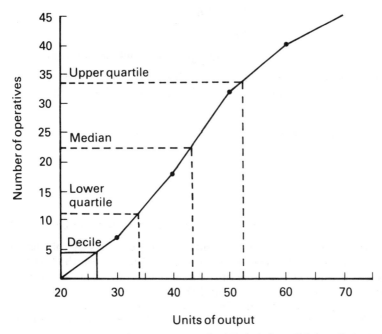

Fig 10.1 A cumulative frequency curve for interpolation of the median

Notes
  i The classes of data are plotted along the *x* axis and the cumulative frequencies along the *y* axis.
 ii The joining of the points by straight lines recognises that we are assuming the data are distributed evenly throughout the group.
iii The median item is the $22\frac{1}{2}$ item, which gives on interpolation a value of just over 43 units of output. This is the same result as we obtained by calculation.
iv Two other interpolations have been made to find the lower and upper quartiles of distribution. These are explained above. The first decile has also been found. This is also explained above.

quartile of grouped data is found by the formula $n/4$ and the upper quartile is found by the formula $3n/4$. We thus have the following series of formulae for grouped data:

The lower quartile is the value of the $n/4$th item. The median is the value of the $n/2$nd item
The upper quartile is the value of the $3n/4$th item

For the distribution in Table 10.5 the calculations are:

a   Lower quartile $= 45/4$ item $= 11\frac{1}{4}$ item. Since there are 7 items in the first group the quartile item is the $4\frac{1}{4}$th item of the second group. Its value is therefore:

$$\text{Value of lower quartile} = 30 + \left(\frac{4\frac{1}{4}}{11} \times 10\right) \text{ units}$$

$$= 30 + \left(\frac{17}{44} \times 10\right)$$

$$= 30 + 3.86$$

$$= 33.86$$

$$= 34 \text{ units (to nearest whole number)}$$

b   Upper quartile $= (3 \times 45)/4$ item $= 135/4 = 33\frac{3}{4}$ item. Since there are 32 items in the third group the median is the $1\frac{3}{4}$th item in the fourth group:

$$\text{Value of upper quartile} = 50 + \left(\frac{1\frac{3}{4}}{8} \times 10\right) \text{ units}$$

$$= 50 + \left(\frac{7}{32} \times 10\right)$$

$$= 50 + 2.19$$

$$= 52 \text{ units (to nearest whole number)}$$

The whole distribution could be divided into ten parts by calculating the ten deciles – of which the median is of course the fifth ($5/10$). A decile is defined as the value of the item lying $1/10$, $2/10$, etc, up the distribution. The formulae to find the deciles would be successively the $n/10$th, $n/5$th, $3n/10$th, $2n/5$th, etc, item.

In Table 10.5 the decile would be the $4\frac{1}{2}$th item. This would be in the first group. The calculation is:

$$\text{Value of decile} = 4\frac{1}{2}\text{th item}$$

$$= 20 + \left(\frac{4\frac{1}{2}}{7} \times 10\right)$$

$$= 20 + \frac{90}{14}$$

$$= 20 + 6.43$$

$$= 26.4 = 26 \text{ units (to nearest whole number)}$$

Both the quartiles and the deciles can of course be read off from the ogive by interpolation, as explained in Fig. 10.1 for finding the median value. They have been marked in on the ogive in Fig. 10.1 and give values for the quartiles and deciles which are the same as we found by calculation above.

10.5 Features of the median

The median lies at the centre of the distribution, with half the data on one side of it and half on the other side. Where the position of the centre is important the median can therefore be a useful average.

Where the data contain extreme items which distort the picture the median pays no attention to them and gives a more correct picture. Thus if 20 students in a class are aged 18 but two mature students are, respectively, 60 and 64 years of age, the median declares the average age to be 18, and ignores the extreme values. The mean, by contrast, gives an average age of 22 which really distorts the picture.

The disadvantage of the median is that it is unsuitable for mathematical calculation. It is the value of a central item in an array. This does not mean that it can be put to mathematical use – for example, the arithmetic mean × frequency gives the aggregate value of all the items in a set of data, but the median × frequency does not give any such result.

Exercises on the median

1 Children using a die to play a board game throw successively as follows:

1, 6, 3, 4, 1, 2, 5, 6, 4, 3, 2, 5, 3, 1, 4

What was the score of the median throw?

2 A soccer team in successive matches scores as follows:

1, 3, 7, 2, 1, 0, 5, 1, 2, 3, 0, 0, 2, 0, 4, 4, 3, 0
What is the median score?

3 In an examination the marks obtained by 140 pupils (rounded to the nearest whole number) are as follows. What is the median score?

Marks	Frequencies
0– 9	3
10–19	7
20–29	11
30–39	14
40–49	29
50–59	31
60–69	17
70–79	11
80–89	9
90 and over	8
Total	140

4 The following monthly take-home pay of employees in a company was recorded for January 19—. Find the median take-home pay.

Earning (£)	Number of employees
260 and under 280	31
280 and under 300	47
300 and under 320	83
320 and under 340	185
340 and under 360	106
360 and over	48

5 Construction costs and selling prices of new houses in the city of Newtown were as follows in the year 19—

Cost per house (£)	Selling price per house (£)	Number of houses
Less than 15 000	Less than 40 000	181
15 000–19 999	40 000–49 999	326
20 000–24 999	50 000–59 999	284
25 000–29 999	60 000–69 999	135

Find *a* the median cost of houses and *b* the median selling price of houses in Newtown (answers correct to the nearest £1).

6 A stock exchange broker drew up a table to illustrate the profitability of his dealings in the year 19— as following:

Profit (£'000)	Number of deals
Less than 1	18
1 and less than 2	27
2 and less than 3	5
3 and less than 4	3
4 and less than 5	7

Calculate the median value of profit per deal from this table (answer correct to the nearest £1).

7 Percentage distribution of weight for adult males is as follows:

Weight (kg)	Percentage of males
Up to 60	4
60.1– 70.0	7
70.1– 80.0	24
80.1– 90.0	29
90.1–100.0	13
100.1–110.0	15
110.1–120.0	7
Over 120	1
Total	100

Construct a cumulative percentage frequency curve and determine
a the median, *b* the lower-quartile, *c* the upper-quartile and *d* the
decile weights (answers to the nearest kg).

8   Distribution of total income after tax and welfare benefits in the
United Kingdom is as follows:

Income (£)	Percentage
Under 5 000	11.7
5 000 and under 7 500	27.5
7 500 and under 10 000	26.8
10 000 and under 12 500	12.3
12 500 and under 15 000	8.9
15 000 and under 17 500	7.4
17 500 and over	5.4
Total	100

Draw a cumulative frequency curve and hence determine *a* the
median income, *b* the upper-quartile income and *c* the lower-
quartile income (answers correct to the nearest £1).

9   In an 'office methods' investigation of clerical work it was found that
the time taken by a clerk to find, make an entry on and refile a
record card varied as follows:

Time in seconds – motor records section

48	42	47	41	39	65	48	49	56	78
37	50	62	79	57	48	70	51	46	53
44	63	72	36	47	49	65	38	73	65
60	45	58	80	44	39	32	49	42	71
54	71	46	67	58	48	66	59	55	31

You are required:
a To draw up a grouped frequency distribution (in 10 groups of 5
seconds each).
b To draw a histogram and an ogive (cumulative frequency curve)
from the data.
c To find the median, and the upper and lower quartiles from the
ogive curve (not by calculation).

10 In a 'work study' exercise components being assembled by a group
of operatives are timed as follows:

Component assembly times (seconds)

55	60	67	58	73	68	72	75	67	79
78	56	75	88	95	73	96	65	73	85
62	76	97	52	68	78	69	73	86	65
82	77	76	77	71	87	53	89	62	74
93	83	85	64	79	72	59	66	74	51

    a Draw up a grouped frequency distribution in 10 equal classes.
    b Draw a histogram and a frequency polygon to represent the data.
    c Find the median, the lower quartile and the upper quartile from the data.

10.6 The mode

Sometimes neither the mean nor the median give the best description of a set of data. The mean takes account of all the values in a set of data but does not draw any attention to extreme items which may be of great significance. The median is the value of the central item and divides the set of data into halves, but in many cases this item may be quite unrepresentative. For example, there are about $1\frac{1}{2}$ million businesses in the United Kingdom, of which $1\frac{1}{4}$ million are very small, while the 500 largest are of such importance that they employ more capital and more people than all the rest put together. The median item in this array of $1\frac{1}{2}$ million businesses is quite insignificant.

Statements are frequently made which use the word 'average' in a different sense from either the mean or the median. For example, a statement 'The average family with young children enjoys a visit to the circus' means that the vast majority of families with young children find a visit to the circus an enjoyable and memorable occasion. This type of 'average' draws attention to the value which is most frequent within a distribution. It is called the 'mode' – a word which has some link with the world of fashion – and the concept of the 'modal' item as the most popular, or fashionable may help the reader to remember this average. *The mode is defined as that value which occurs most frequently in a distribution.*

The mode is most helpful and its value may be very obvious where the set of data consists of discrete items. Thus the modal number of legs for human beings is two, although one occasionally sees people who have lost a leg, or even both legs. The number of bedrooms in houses is a common feature of advertisements, and the numbers are discrete. We can have 1, 2, 3, 4 and 5 bedrooms, etc, but we cannot have a house with 1.87 bedrooms, or 3.45 bedrooms. Suppose the accommodation available in a town consists of 2000 houses made up as follows:

Accommodation in Anytown

Number of bedrooms	1	2	3	4	5
Frequencies	32	484	963	434	87

Clearly the modal type of house is a 3-bedroomed house, for its frequency is greatest. The 3-bedroomed house best describes the average accommodation available in Anytown.

a Bimodal and multimodal series

Sometimes, especially where there are a large variety of items in the distribution, we may have two or more items which are equally popular.

Thus if a team of 11 cricketers score as follows:

69, 36, 27, 14, 9, 36, 4, 14, 3, 1, 0

we have a bimodal series – two batsmen scored 36 and two scored 14. If the scores had been:

69, 36, 27, 14, 9, 36, 9, 14, 3, 1, 0

we should have had a multimodal series with 36, 14 and 9 runs being scored by two batsmen each.

It is of course possible to have a series with no modal frequency as where all the scores are different and each value occurs only once.

b The mode of a grouped distribution

If data are in the form of a grouped distribution it is not possible to state the modal value accurately. Consider the data in Table 10.6. We cannot know where the mode is – for example, if all 6 of the representatives in the final group had sold £32 000 of goods in the month, and no other group had a similar concentration of results, the mode would be £32 000. We have no way of knowing this unless the full data are available elsewhere.

When asked to give the mode of a grouped distribution we therefore have to make some assumptions. These are:

a that the mode lies in the group with the highest frequency – in Table 10.6 this is the second group
b that the frequencies in all the groups are evenly spread within the group

This does not mean that we would place the modal item at the mid-point of the second group in Table 10.6, because the pattern of the whole distribution influences our idea of where the mode should be. Since there are more representatives achieving sales in group 3 than in group 1 we would expect that the mode should come above the midpoint of group 2. Had the position been reversed – with more representatives achieving sales in the group below the modal group than in the one above it – we should have expected the mode to be below the midpoint of its group.

Table 10.6   Sales by representatives, October—

Sales (£'000)	Number of representatives
10 and under 15	10
15 and under 20	36
20 and under 25	28
25 and under 30	10
30 and under 35	6
Total	90

We can find out where the mode is in two ways:

a by calculation
b by interpolation on a histogram

Looking at this visually first, the histogram method is shown in Fig 10.2. Study this carefully now.

By calculation we must use the formula:

$$\text{Mode} = L + \frac{f_m - f_l}{(f_m - f_l) + (f_m - f_h)} \times \text{CI}$$

Here L is the lower limit of the modal group (£15), f_m is the frequency of the modal group, f_l is the frequency of the lower group, f_h is the frequency of the higher group and CI is the class interval.

Substituting the values from Table 10.6 we have:

$$\text{Mode} = 15 + \frac{36 - 10}{(36 - 10) + (36 - 28)} \times 5 \text{ £'000}$$

$$= 15 + \frac{26}{26 + 8} \times 5 \text{ £'000}$$

$$= 15 + 3.82 \text{ £'000}$$

$$= \text{£18 820}$$

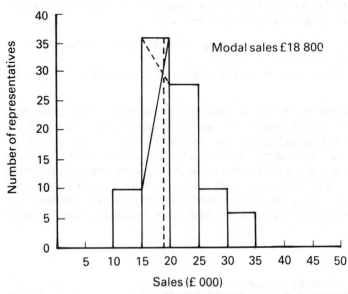

Fig 10.2 Finding the mode by interpolation

Notes

i The histogram is drawn in the usual way.

ii A line is then drawn from the top left-hand corner of the modal class (the tallest rectangle) to the top left-hand corner of the next group, as shown.

iii Similarly a line is drawn from the top right-hand corner of the modal class to the top right hand corner of the group below.

iv Where these lines intersect a vertical line is dropped to the *x* axis to find the modal sales figure – £19 000.

(*Note*: This formula is not the only one that has been proposed but it takes account of the proportion of influence exerted on the mode by the spread of the distribution on either side of the modal class. An absolute value for the mode cannot really be determined and is to some extent illusory.)

To conclude, the mode is most useful when discussing discrete variables, where it is an actual item, and therefore more meaningful.

Exercises on the mode

1 Four bowlers have the following records of success in a series of 10 matches. What is the modal performance of each bowler for wickets taken?

Bowler A	2	4	4	3	1	0	4	4	3	4
Bowler B	3	1	1	0	1	0	3	2	5	1
Bowler C	7	3	2	1	4	5	2	1	6	8
Bowler D	3	2	3	4	3	2	4	3	4	4

2 Houses in Seaville have the following numbers of bedrooms:

Number of rooms	1	2	3	4	5	6	7
Frequency	387	542	483	172	39	28	4

How many bedrooms has the modal-sized house?

3 A survey of shoe sizes in a college of higher education shows the following frequencies of shoe sizes:

Size of shoes (male)	5	6	7	8	9	10	11	12			
Frequency	3	23	284	301	139	60	22	8			
Size of shoes (female)	3	$3\frac{1}{2}$	4	$4\frac{1}{2}$	5	$5\frac{1}{2}$	6	$6\frac{1}{2}$	7	$7\frac{1}{2}$	8
Frequency	47	88	195	163	195	142	83	47	27	8	5

What is the modal size of shoes for *a* males and *b* females?

4 The following data relates to the salaries of civil servants in certain categories. Draw a histogram of the data and hence estimate the modal earnings before tax.

Earnings before tax (£)	Number
7 500 but under 8 000	200
8 000 but under 8 500	450
8 500 but under 9 000	800
9 000 but under 9 500	650
9 500 but under 10 000	320
10 000 but under 10 500	180

5 Draw a histogram to represent the following data. Then use the histogram to find the modal output.

Output of operatives in units	Number of operatives
500–509	46
510–519	84
520–529	284
530–539	362
540–549	72
550–559	38
560–569	14

Summary

1 To describe a statistical distribution we begin by defining its centre. This locates the heart of the distribution – later we shall explain how it is spread around this centre.
2 The measures of central tendency, or measures of location, are all averages of one sort or another. They are the arithmetic mean, the median and the mode. Two others are the geometric mean and the harmonic mean, but they are not discussed fully in this book.
3 The arithmetic mean is the commonest average used. The various formulae are:

a for a simple series

$$\bar{x} = \Sigma \frac{x}{n}$$

b for a weighted average

$$\bar{x} = \frac{\Sigma fx}{\Sigma f}$$

c for a grouped frequency distribution

$$\bar{x} = \frac{\Sigma fx}{\Sigma f}$$

(with x meaning the midpoints of the groups).
4 The median is the value of the middle item in an array. It is found by the formula $(n+1)/2$ for a simple series. For a grouped frequency distribution it is found by $n/2$. We can also find the median by interpolation from a cumulative frequency curve (ogive).
5 The mode is the value which occurs most frequently in a distribution. Where the data consist of discrete items the mode is easily found. With grouped data the mode is assumed to lie in the group with the greatest frequency, but its position in that group may be influenced

by the size of the groups on either side. It is usually found by drawing a histogram and interpolating the modal position from lines joining the modal group to the groups on either side.

6   To compare the averages we may say that the most useful average is the arithmetic mean, which is influenced by all the data. If for some reason the mean is unsatisfactory – as where it is unduly influenced by abnormal extreme items or where it is unrealistic (like the statement that an average horse has 3.98 legs) – the median is usually the best alternative. The mode is appropriate for some purposes, but has the disadvantage that it is possible to have no-modal and multimodal series.

11 Measures of dispersion and skewness

11.1 The concepts of dispersion and skewness

The purpose of statistics is to promote understanding of some business or human situation, so that we know what that situation is and can make business decisions or social decisions which will advance the aims of our organisation or our society. We have seen that an adequate description of any situation starts with taking a measure of its central tendency – an average which places the central point in the array of data, around which the rest of the data are grouped. Such an average, whether it is a mean, a median or a mode is only helpful if the rest of the items really are grouped around it – if they are equally spread along the whole range of data an average would not really advance our knowledge very much. We need to know how the rest of the data are spread around the central item – in other words we need to have a **measure of dispersion**. Consider the two sets of data given in Tables 11.1 and 11.2, each of which has a mean of 40 years.

It is clear that the dispersion of these sets of data around the mean of 40 is very different. In Laburnum Close the head of households are all close to the average age of 40 – the youngest is 36 years old and the oldest is only 42 years old. In Lilac Close the spread is much greater, from 21 years for the youngest head of household to 74 years for the oldest.

Measuring from the start to the finish of a set of data is called the **range** of the data. Our description of the set of data is often greatly helped by knowing the range – for example, the description of the two sets of data given in Tables 11.1 and 11.2 would be:

Laburnum Close: average age 40 years range 36–42 years
Lilac Close: average age 40 years range 21–74 years

We can see at once that these are very different sets of data. Unfortunately there is a major disadvantage in the range – a single extreme item will distort the description of the data. Suppose one head of house-

Table 11.1 Ages of heads of households (Laburnum Close)

36	39	39	40	40	40	41	41	42	42

Table 11.2 Ages of heads of households (Lilac Close)

21	23	24	24	26	28	45	62	73	74

hold in Laburnum Close had been a very old person, aged 102. This would have raised the average to 46 and changed the range to 36–102 years. This makes both the mean and the range unrepresentative of the data as a whole.

The range of 36–102 years also makes it clear that the range tells us nothing about the way the data are distributed *within* the range, and therefore it is not all that helpful as a measure of dispersion. What we need are measures which describe the distribution of the intermediate items around the central point, and summarise the whole series for comparative purposes. Such measures will help us understand how sets of data vary, and are often called **measures of variation**. They are of two chief types, **measures of dispersion** and **measures of skewness**. To understand these terms we must consider a variety of dispersions.

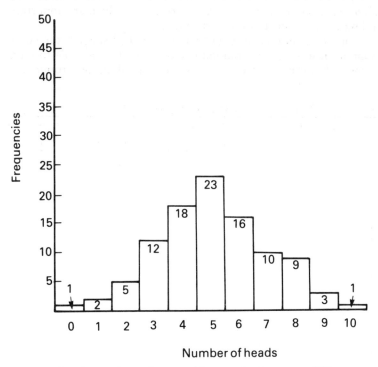

Fig 11.1 One hundred experiments with ten coins (*see page 164*)

Notes
  i The general pattern of the histogram is that it rises to a peak in the centre and falls away to nothing at either end.
  ii As we have only done 100 experiments the result is rather erratic – the smoothness of the pattern can be achieved only if very large numbers of experiments are performed.
  iii The smoothness of the histogram could be improved in another way – by increasing the number of coins tossed. For example, if we had tossed 100 coins each time, and carried out the experiment 1000 times, we could have had 101 rectangles in the histogram, ranging from 0–100. Now return to the text on page 164.

11.2 Symmetrical frequency distributions

First consider an experiment in which 10 coins are tossed into the air. If they are all true coins, equally balanced, we would expect the normal result to be 5 heads and 5 tails, but on any particular experiment we might have some other combination – 6 and 4, or 7 and 3, etc. Just occasionally we might have 10 heads and no tails, or 10 tails and no heads, but these would be fairly rare events. Suppose we carry out 100 experiments we might achieve results as shown in Table 11.3. This could be drawn as a histogram, as in Fig 11.1 on page 163.

If, as suggested in the notes to Fig 11.1, the number of coins and the number of experiments had been increased, the result would have been a symmetrical bell-shaped curve, such as the one illustrated in Fig 11.2 below. This is called a *normal distribution curve*, or more simply the *normal curve*. It is only one of several distributions which are important in sampling theory, but it is the best known.

The shape of the normal distribution curve is bell shaped, the curve being symmetrical about the midpoint. However, it is possible to have many types of normal curves, because the distributions around the

Table 11.3 One hundred experiments tossing 10 coins

Number of heads	0	1	2	3	4	5	6	7	8	9	10
Frequency		1	2	5	12	18	23	16	10	9	3	1

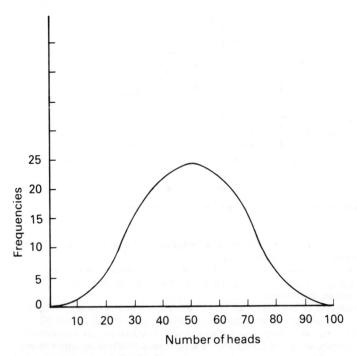

Fig 11.2 The normal distribution curve

central point may be symmetrical and yet the dispersions may differ. For example, the two normal curves in Fig 11.3 below have very different dispersions. In curve *ss* the average deviation of results from the mean is larger than with curve *tt*. Most of the results recorded in the *tt* curve have quite small deviations from the mean – the largest deviation being only about ±17, giving an average deviation from the mean of about ±8.5. With curve *ss* the deviations vary from ±0 to ±50 giving an average deviation of ±25. In describing these two sets of data we can say:

Set *s*:   mean 50   average deviation from the mean 25
Set *t*:   mean 50   average deviation from the mean 8.5

Clearly, the more closely the data are grouped around the mean the higher the peak of the graph, for the frequencies in the narrow band around the mean must be greater.

We shall see later in this chapter that if we calculate the mean of a set of data and then calculate the deviations of the individual items from the mean we can build up a picture of the dispersion of the data around the

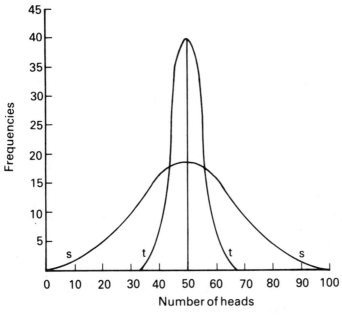

Fig 11.3 Normal curves with different distributions

Notes
  i Both curves are symmetrical about the mean 50.
  ii The dispersion of data around the mean in curve *ss* is much greater than the dispersion of the data around the mean in curve *tt*.
  iii We can therefore describe the two distributions by giving *a* the mean (which is the same in both cases) and *b* the average deviation from the mean – which tells us how spread out the dispersion is.

mean. However, it may not always be normal. When it is not normal (symmetrical) it is said to be skewed.

Position of the mean, median and mode in a normal distribution curve

Before looking at skewed curves it is helpful to make one further point about normal curves. With a normal curve the mean, median and mode are all exactly the same and are positioned centrally. The mode, by definition, is always found at the apex of the curve. In a symmetrical curve the median, the value of the central item, will always be at the apex too, so will the mean, because the various values are symmetrically spread around the mean.

11.3   Skewed frequency distributions

Where a frequency distribution is not symmetrical it is said to be skewed. Figure 11.4 shows two skewed distributions. The dotted line indicates

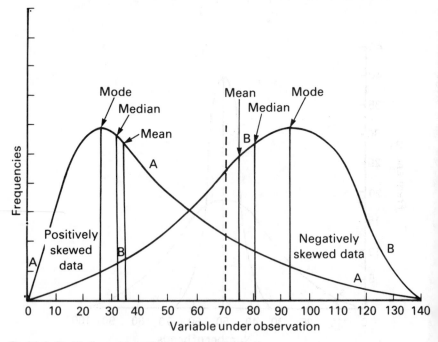

Fig 11.4 Positively and negatively skewed distributions

Notes

i Curve *AAA* is positively skewed. The modal position is to the left of the centre, and the mean is shifted positively (to the right). The median lies between the mode and the mean.

ii Curve *BBB* is negatively skewed, with the mode towards the upper end of the range of observations. The mean is dragged to the left of centre – being dragged down by the smaller values of the non-modal observations. The median again lies between the mean and the mode.

the midpoint of the x axis, where – if the curves were normal and not skewed – the centre of the distribution would lie, with a bell-shaped distribution around it. Curve *AAA* is said to be positively skewed. The majority of the data lies to the left of the centre of the x axis. The reason the data are said to be positively skewed is that the mean is pulled over to the right of the data – being dragged upwards by the few, but large, items above. Thus if we imagine the wage structure of the average nation it tends to be a positively skewed distribution – most of the nation earn relatively low wages – but the few really high income earners drag the average income up disproportionately, away from the modal position where the mass of incomes is situated.

With a negatively skewed distribution the data are skewed so that the majority of the observations are greater than the midpoint of the x axis, and the mean is dragged to the left; to take account of the lower values of the non-modal items. Data related to health are often negatively skewed – for example, more old people tend to wear spectacles, have false teeth or sustain heart attacks than young people.

The relationship between the mean, the median and the mode

As a very rough guide the median will usually be found at one-third of the distance from the mean to the mode. The median lies nearer the mean than the mode – in a ratio of $1:2$. This is only an approximation but it does mean that if we know the values of two of the averages we can find the approximate position of the third. This is discussed further in Section 11.11 on pages 183 to 186.

11.4 The measures of dispersion and skewness

We are now ready to take a detailed look at the various measures of dispersion and skewness. Remember that the purpose of these measures is to amplify the imperfect summary of any distribution which is provided by the three averages in common use, the mean, the median and the mode. These averages are inherently unsatisfactory in that no average can tell us everything about a distribution and the wider the dispersion of data around the average the less satisfactory the average becomes. To improve our understanding we need to know how wide the dispersion is around the average, and whether it is symmetrical or asymmetrical (ie skewed). As explained earlier the first set of measures we need are called measures of dispersion, and the second set measures of skewness.

The measures of dispersion are:

a The range
b the quartile deviation
c the mean deviation
d the standard deviation

The measures of skewness are called Pearson's first coefficient of skewness and Pearson's second coefficient of skewness. There is also Bowley's coefficient of skewness.

We must now look at each of these measures in turn.

11.5 Measures of dispersion, 1: the range

The range has already been referred to in the introductory section of this chapter (see Section 11.1 on pages 162 to 163). *It is defined as the difference between the smallest and largest values in a distribution.* Thus in the case of the two households mentioned in Section 11.1 the range of ages of heads of households in Laburnum Close (youngest 36 years, oldest 42 years) was only 6 years, while in Lilac Close the range was $74 - 21 = 53$ years. Unfortunately we cannot know the range accurately in many sets of data, for there are open-ended classes at both ends of many grouped distributions. In many tables of income distribution the first class will be an open-ended class such as 'less than £3000 per annum', while the last class is open ended in the form '£21 000 and over'. By convention we take the midpoint of the lowest group as the start of the range, which means that £1500 would be the start of the range in the example given above. With the upper class we make the usual assumption that the group interval of the open-ended class is twice as large as the ordinary groups preceding it. We then take the midpoint of the group. Thus if the groups given above were rising by £3000, to reach £21 000, we would regard the '£21 000 and over' group as including salaries from £21 000 to £27 000. The midpoint of this group would therefore be £24 000 and the range $£24 000 - £1500 = £22 500$.

The range is not extensively used because of the disadvantage mentioned earlier that extreme items at either end distort its usefulness. It is of concern to some people, such as market gardeners who are concerned with the range of temperatures likely to be met in their greenhouses and have 'maximum and minimum' thermometers which record the range automatically. It is also used in some sorts of 'quality control' systems since it is a very simple statistic to detect and limits can be specified beyond which a production system must not be allowed to go.

11.6 Measures of dispersion, 2: the quartile deviation or semi-interquartile range

The range is unsatisfactory as a measure of dispersion because it is affected by extreme items which may render it unrepresentative of the majority of the data. A measure of dispersion which does not take any account of the extreme items is the **quartile deviation**, or **semi-interquartile range**.

Quartiles have already been discussed (see Section 10.4 on page 151). They are the boundaries which separate the items in a distribution into quarters. There are therefore three quartiles, the *lower quartile* (at the 25% mark), the *median* (at the 50% mark) and the *upper quartile* (at the 75% mark). To find the quartiles of ungrouped data we use $(n + 1)/4$, $(n + 1)/2$ and $3(n + 1)/4$. If the answer results in an odd number of quarters in the quotient it is usual to express the quartile to the nearest whole number. For grouped data, as we saw in Section 11.4, we use $n/4$, $n/2$ and $3n/4$ to find the quartiles and the median item. Thus in the distribution given in Table 10.5 (see page 150) there were 45 items of which the lower quartile was the 11¼th item, the median was the 22½th item and the upper quartile was the 33¾th item. The actual results are:

Q_1 (lower quartile)   34 units of output
Q_3 (upper quartile)   52 units of output

These figures can be used to describe the dispersion of the set of data. They define for us the **interquartile range** – that is to say the range between the two quartiles. This is clearly $Q_3 - Q_1 = 52 - 34 = 18$ units. This interquartile range has an advantage over the ordinary range in that it only covers the two middle quarters of the data, and therefore is not affected by any extreme items.

However, in describing a dispersion we wish to show how the data are dispersed around the average position. In this case the average we are employing is the median, the value of the central item in the array. To show how the data are dispersed around the median, and ignoring the extreme quarters of the dispersion, we use the quartile deviation – which is the semi-interquartile range. This is found by halving the interquartile range, ie:

$$\text{Quartile deviation} = \frac{Q_3 - Q_1}{2}$$

$$= \frac{52 - 34}{2}$$

$$= \frac{18}{2}$$

$$= 9 \text{ units}$$

We can therefore best describe the distribution in Table 10.5 as having a median value of 43 units and a quartile deviation around the median of 9 units.

Consider the data of Table 11.4, collected by a trade association from a questionnaire completed by member firms. The quartiles are found as

Table 11.4   Profitability of retail grocery outlets, year 19—

Profits made (£)	Frequencies	Cumulative frequency
Less than 10 000	1453	1453
10 000–14 999.99	789	2242
15 000–19 999.99	980	3222
20 000–24 999.99	1325	4547
25 000–29 999.99	1642	6189
30 000–34 999.99	825	7014
35 000–39 999.99	436	7450
40 000 and over	187	7637

follows:

Lower quartile $= \dfrac{7637}{4} = 1909\frac{1}{4}$ item

Median $\qquad = \dfrac{7637}{2} = 3818\frac{1}{2}$ item

Upper quartile $= \dfrac{3 \times 7637}{4} = \dfrac{22\,911}{4} = 5727\frac{3}{4}$ item

Q_1 lies in the second class and is the $456\frac{1}{4}$th item in the class $(1909\frac{1}{4} - 1453$ in the previous class $= 456\frac{1}{4}$:

$$\therefore\ Q_1 = £10\,000 + \left(\frac{456\frac{1}{4}}{789} \times £5000 \right)$$

$$= £10\,000 + £2891.32$$

$$= \underline{£12\,891}\ \text{(correct to the nearest £1)}$$

The median lies in the fourth group and is the $596\frac{1}{2}$th item in the class $(3818\frac{1}{2} - 3222$ in the previous classes $= 596\frac{1}{2}$):

$$\therefore\ \text{Median} = £20\,000 + \left(\frac{596\frac{1}{2}}{1325} \times £5000 \right)$$

$$= £20\,000 + £2250.94$$

$$= £22\,251\ \text{(correct to the nearest £1)}$$

The upper quartile lies in the fifth group and is the $1180\frac{3}{4}$th item in the class $(5727\frac{3}{4} - 4547$ in the previous classes $= 1180\frac{3}{4}$):

$$\therefore\ Q_3 = £25\,000 + \left(\frac{1180\frac{3}{4}}{1642} \times £5000 \right)$$

$$= £25\,000 + £3595.46$$

$$= \underline{£28\,595}\ \text{(correct to the nearest £1)}$$

The interquartile range is therefore:

$$Q_3 - Q_1 = £28\,595 - £12\,891$$

$$= \underline{£15\,704}$$

The quartile deviation (ie the semi-interquartile range) is therefore:

$$\frac{£15\,704}{2} = \underline{£7852}$$

We can therefore best describe this distribution as having a median value of £22 251 and a quartile deviation around this average of £7852.

Finding the quartile deviation by interpolation from the ogive

As explained in Section 10.4 the values of the quartiles can be read off from an ogive (cumulative frequency) curve. Once the quartiles have been found the interquartile range can be determined by subtracting Q_1 from Q_3, and if this is halved we have the quartile deviation.

Exercises on the range and the quartile deviation

1 What is meant by the concept of dispersion? What measures of dispersion are used and what are the merits of each?

2 In a particular week out-workers in the employment of a particular clothing factory make the following garments:

36	21	5	78	39	44	27	15	8	17
29	84	92	51	34	14	39	26	18	63

What is the average output? What is the range of the data?

3 The daily records of output by two employees, one of whom is frequently absent, are as follows for a one month period:

Employee X: units produced					**Employee Y: units produced**				
0	42	56	72	0	28	29	37	29	27
7	63	56	84	0	25	28	46	43	29
0	96	87	0	0	28	38	44	38	37
34	84	98	88	0	38	32	34	36	38

  a What were the total outputs of each employee?
  b What is the range of outputs in each case?
  c A situation has arisen where one employee has to be made redundant. How helpful is this data in assisting management to decide which employee to retain?

4 The following data give the cost of repairs, in pounds sterling, of 20 pieces of equipment repaired under guarantee:

10	12	7	14	21	24	6	18	14	15
19	28	3	15	18	32	16	17	14	8

  a What is the range of the data?
  b Find the median and the quartile values.
  c Find the quartile deviation.

5 A consumer research bureau discovers that a certain kind of meat retails at the following prices in 30 shops throughout the country. The quality of the joints available is deemed to be the same and the prices are given in pence per kilogram.

185	193	177	166	169
148	186	179	164	154
204	199	149	184	183
196	163	185	150	176
158	153	149	176	181
194	186	203	199	202

172 Statistics for business

    a What is the median price?

    b What is the quartile deviation of prices around the median?

6   The following data refer to the annual turnovers of 250 retail outlets in the electronic hardware trades:

Takings (£)	Number of retail outlets
Less than 100 000	47
100 000–149 999.9	33
150 000–199 999.9	33
200 000–249 999.9	35
250 000–299 999.9	29
300 000–349 999.9	29
350 000–399 999.9	18
400 000–449 999.9	14
450 000–499 999.9	12

Find *a* the median turnover (correct to the nearest £1000) and *b* the quartile deviation (correct to the nearest £100). What is the range of the data?

7   Cars waiting to enter a multi-storey car park on a busy shopping day were delayed as follows:

Waiting time (seconds)	Number of cars
Less than 30	142
30– 59	136
60– 89	272
90– 119	254
120–149	262
150–179	174
180–209	154
210–239	106

No car was delayed for more than 4 minutes. Use an ogive curve to find the median and the quartile deviation of this distribution (confirm your results by calculation if you wish).

11.7 Measure of dispersion, 3: the mean deviation

The third measure of dispersion, which leads on to the more important **standard deviation**, is the mean deviation. The deviation measured is the deviation of every item in the distribution from the agreed average (either the arithmetic mean or the median). If we sum these deviations and find the average value we have the mean deviation (a measure of the average tendency of the data to spread themselves out throughout the range – or to cluster near the average position). Because some items will lie below the average and some above the average we shall have negative and positive items. To avoid the deviations summing to zero we ignore the signs, treating them all as positive. This is justified because we are only interested in knowing how the items are spread around the average – not whether they are above or below the average.

Using again the examples used earlier about the ages of the heads of households in Laburnum Close and Lilac Close, we have the deviations shown in Table 11.5. We may therefore describe the two sets of data as follows:

Laburnum Close heads of households are on average 40 years of age, and the dispersion of ages around 40 is very small – on average only 1.2 years away from the mean age.

Lilac Close heads of households also have an average age of 40, but there ages vary much more – the average deviation from the mean age is 18.8 years on either side.

For grouped data the formula for the mean deviation is:

$$MD = \frac{\Sigma f(x - \bar{x})}{\Sigma f}$$

where x is the midpoint of the groups of data, $\bar{x}$ is the arithmetic mean (or other measure of central tendency) and Σf is the total frequency.

A simple example of the calculation of the mean deviation is given in Table 11.6 on page 174. The notes below the table explain it clearly.

Conclusion about the mean deviation

The mean deviation can be used to describe the distribution of data around a central position, but disregarding the signs is a fatal flaw as far as advanced statistical work is concerned and the mean deviation is

Table 11.5 Ages of heads of households

Laburnum Close		Lilac Close	
Ages	Deviation from mean (40)	Ages	Deviation from mean (40)
36	− 4	21	− 19
39	− 1	23	− 17
39	− 1	24	− 16
40	0	24	− 16
40	0	26	− 14
40	0	28	− 12
41	1	45	+ 5
41	1	62	+ 22
42	2	73	+ 33
42	2	74	+ 34
Sum (ignore signs)	12	Sum (ignore signs)	188
Mean deviation	1.2 years	Mean deviation	18.8 years

Table 11.6 Sales by representatives in Nigeria

(i) Classes (N'000)	(ii) Midpoints of class (x)	(iii) Number of salesmen (f)	(iv) fx	(v) Deviation $(x - \bar{x})$	(vi) $f(x - \bar{x})$
6–10	8	3	24	−19.95	−59.85
11–15	13	8	104	−14.95	−119.60
16–20	18	11	198	−9.95	−109.45
21–25	23	17	391	−4.95	−84.15
26–30	28	19	532	+0.05	−0.95
31–35	33	18	594	+5.05	+90.90
36–40	38	16	608	+10.05	+160.80
41–45	43	8	344	+15.05	+120.40
		Σf 100	2795 $\bar{x} = 27.95$		746.10 (ignoring signs)

Notes

i The first 3 columns show the original data, sales being in Nigerian currency – the Naira (N).

ii Column (iv) shows how the arithmetic mean is calculated using the formula:

$$\bar{x} = \frac{\Sigma fx}{\Sigma f} = \frac{2795}{100} = 27.95$$

iii Column (v) shows the deviation of the midpoint of each class from the arithmetic mean of 27.95.

iv Column (vi) shows the product of cols (iii) and (v) – in other words the deviation from the mean multiplied by the number of persons in the class. The sum of this column (when the signs are ignored) gives us the sum of the deviations from the mean, and when divided by the number of salesmen (ie the total frequency in column (iii) gives us the mean deviation (746.1 ÷ 100 = 7.461). Expressed to one decimal place, we have: AM = 28.0 and MD = 7.5.

v We may therefore describe the sales achieved by representatives in Nigeria as on average N28 000 with a mean deviation of N7500.

therefore rarely used. A much more satisfactory concept – the standard deviation – is used instead.

11.8 Measures of dispersion, 4: the standard deviation

The standard deviation is found in a similar way to the mean deviation, but is superior to it in that we are not obliged to disregard the + or − signs (a process which is mathematically unsound). Instead we square the deviations which makes all the data positive. We recall from simple arithmetic that $+4 \times +4 = 16$, and $-4 \times -4 = 16$, so that we eliminate the negative signs when we square the data.

The standard deviation for ungrouped data is found in the following way:

a Find the deviations from the mean, as before when finding the mean deviation. However, note that while the mean deviation can be found using any measures of central tendency, the standard deviation always requires us to use the arithmetic mean as our central measure, since it alone is susceptible to mathematical manipulation. The whole point of the standard deviation is that it is mathematically sound. The deviation from the mean will be either positive or negative.
b Square these deviations, so that all the signs are positive.
c Add the squared deviations.
d Find the average of the squared deviations (this is known as the *variance*).
e Take the square root of this variance.

Put into mathematical terms for ungrouped data, this may be expressed as follows:

$$\sigma = \sqrt{\frac{\Sigma (x - \bar{x})^2}{n}}$$

where σ (lower case sigma) is the sign used for standard deviation, Σ (capital sigma) means 'the sum of', x is the individual items of data, $\bar{x}$ is the arithmetic mean and n is the total number of observations.

Using the figures for Lilac Close and Laburnum Close again we have the data given in Table 11.7 on page 176. Note that the standard deviation gives a slightly larger value for the average deviation than the mean deviation (see Table 11.5 on page 173). This is because the process of squaring gives slightly greater emphasis to the extreme items in the distribution.

a The standard deviation of grouped data using an assumed mean

When data are grouped into a frequency distribution, it is easier to find the standard deviation by using a method known as the 'assumed mean' method. As the figures for grouped data are rather large, and the mean is rarely a whole number, the calculations, particularly the squaring calculations used in finding the standard deviation, become rather

Table 11.7 Ages of heads of households

Laburnum Close			Lilac Close		
Ages	Deviations from mean (40)	Square of deviations	Ages	Deviations from mean (40)	Square of deviations
36	-4	16	21	-19	361
39	-1	1	23	-17	289
39	-1	1	24	-16	256
40	0	0	24	-16	256
40	0	0	26	-14	196
40	0	0	28	-12	144
41	1	1	45	5	25
41	1	1	62	22	484
42	2	4	73	33	1089
42	2	4	74	34	1156
Total		28			4256

Laburnum Close:
Average of squared deviations (variance) = 2.8
Square root of variance, ie standard deviation = ±1.67

Lilac Close:
Average of squared deviations (variance) = 425.6
Square root of variance, ie standard deviation = ±20.63

laborious even with a calculator. In Table 11.8 below we have some data collected about the costs incurred on behalf of accident victims in the casualty departments of hospitals in a particular region. The figures have deliberately been given in the sort of awkward form that they would assume in real life (round numbers rarely turn up in any real-life investigation of data).

Table 11.8 Costs per hospital patient – casualty department

Classes (£)	Number of patients (f)
0– 49.9	87
50– 99.9	127
100–149.9	338
150–199.9	286
200–249.9	134
250–299.9	98
300–349.9	62
350–399.9	41
400–449.9	71
450–499.9	165
500–549.9	42
550–559.9	15
600 and over	38
Total	1504

To find the arithmetic mean we shall have to work from the midpoint of the classes, multiplying the midpoints by the number of patients in each class and then dividing by the total number of patients, 1504. Since the mean, when we find it, actually comes to 240.3590426, and we now have to take each of the midpoints from this to find the variations from the mean, and square the result, the figures become horribly large. We can simplify the whole problem by working from an assumed mean (which will be a convenient round number) and the best number to choose is one of the midpoints. In Table 11.9, where all the figures have been set out for you in tabular form, we chose the midpoint of the 200–249.9 class as the assumed mean, 225. Before studying this table in great detail by reading the notes below it, notice one special point. The end class is open ended and has been assumed to be three times as big as the other classes. This is unusual – we usually assume an open-ended class is twice as big as the other classes. However, accident cases are very expensive to cure and some might be very costly, so we have allowed the class to be three times as large on this occasion. The notes below the data explain the detailed calculations and should be studied carefully (see page 178).

Table 11.9 Costs per hospital patient – casualty department

(i) Classes (£)	(ii) Midpoints of class	(iii) Number of patients (f)	(iv) Deviation (d^1) from mean	(v) Products $f \times d^1$	(vi) Products $f \times d^2$
0– 49.9	25	87	– 4	– 348	+ 1 392
50– 99.9	75	127	– 3	– 381	+ 1 143
100–149.9	125	338	– 2	– 676	+ 1 352
150–199.9	175	286	– 1	– 286	+ 286
200–249.9	225	134	0	0	0
250–299.9	275	98	1	+ 98	+ 98
300–349.9	325	62	2	+ 124	+ 248
350–399.9	375	41	3	+ 123	+ 369
400–449.9	425	71	4	+ 284	+ 1 136
450–499.9	475	165	5	+ 825	+ 4 125
500–549.9	525	42	6	+ 252	+ 1 512
550–599.9	575	15	7	+ 105	+ 735
600 and over	675	38	9	+ 342	+ 3 078
Total		1 504		+ 462	15 474

Notes

i In column (iv) the mean has been assumed to lie at the midpoint of the 200–249.9 class – in other words at £225. The other classes are then shown as being distant from the mean by 1, 2, 3, etc, class intervals of £50. Of course the groups which are smaller than the mean are – 1, – 2, – 3, etc. The exception to the class-interval difference is the final class, which, as explained in the text, has been assumed to be as large as 3 class intervals. The result is that the midpoint (£675) is £450 away from the assumed mean, which is 9 class intervals.

ii Column (v) is the product column which takes the frequency of accidents in each price band into account. It is the product of the frequency and the deviation. The total of this column is important. It is the amount by which the column fails to sum to zero, and therefore tells us how far the assumed mean is from the true mean position. This is used to adjust our results – and is explained on page 179.

iii Finally, column (vi) multiplies the figures in columns (v) by the deviations of column (iv) again. This is effectively squaring the deviations, since $f \times d^1 \times d^1$ is the same as $f d^2$. We thus eliminate the – signs and end up with a full set of positive data – in this case totalling to 15 474. Now return to the main text to follow the calculations.

Calculating the mean and the standard deviation

The calculations of the true mean and the standard deviation are as follows.

The true mean = assumed mean ± an adjustment for the extent to which the figures in column (v) failed to sum to zero. As the result was positive (+462), the true mean is above the assumed mean:

$$\therefore \text{ True mean} = £225 + \frac{462}{1504} \times £50$$

$$= £225 + £15.36$$
$$= £240.36$$

The standard deviation is found by dividing the total of column (vi) by the frequency but the result has to be adjusted by the same figure by which the true mean was adjusted, but this time the adjustment has to be squared. This is done *before* taking the square root, and we must also remember that as this is still in class intervals we have to multiply by the class interval as well, ie £50 in this case.

Showing the variance first (ie the deviation of the squared data):

$$\sigma^2 = \left(\frac{15\,474}{1504}\right) + \left(\frac{462}{1504}\right)^2$$

$$= 10.2886 + 0.0944$$
$$= 10.3830$$
$$\therefore \sigma = \sqrt{10.3830} \times £50$$
$$= 3.222 \times £50$$
$$= £161.10$$

We may therefore describe the distribution as one where the mean cost of treating an accident victim is £240 with a standard deviation of costs from this average of £161.

11.9 A comparison of the measures of dispersion

We may compare the measures of dispersion, as is shown in the table on page 180.

11.10 The coefficient of variation

One disadvantage of all the measures of dispersion is that they are expressed in terms of the units in which the original data were expressed. Our conclusions of the standard deviation of the data in Table 11.9 were in pounds sterling, because the original data were in pounds sterling. It follows that if we have to compare two sets of data, expressed in different units (for example, miles and kilometres), we have to convert one to the other before we can make a comparison. This might also be necessary if the two sets of data were in the same units, but widely separated in

	Range	Quartile deviation	Mean deviation	Standard deviation
1	Simple	Fairly simple	Not simple	Not simple
2	Affected by extreme items	Ignores extreme items	Not unduly affected by extreme items	Not unduly affected by extreme items
3	No indication of distribution throughout the range	Covers only half the items in the range	Is affected by every item in the distribution	Is affected by every item in the distribution
4	Value depends on the two extreme items, ie the limits	Value depends on the two quartiles	Shows the average deviation of all items from the mean or the median	Shows the average deviation of all items from the arithmetic mean (only)
5	Not susceptible to mathematical use	Not susceptible to mathematical use	Not susceptible to mathematical use	Other calculations may be based on it

value. Thus we can only compare a rise in the wages paid to farm labourers with a rise in the incomes of wealthy landowners if we use some relative term, such as a percentage increase. If a television personality is given a rise of £1000.00 per week the studio caretaker is unlikely to be offered the same increase.

To make comparisons of this type between sets of data we can turn the absolute measure of dispersion (the standard deviation) into a relative measure. This measure is called the **coefficient of variation** and *expresses the standard deviation as a percentage of the arithmetic mean*.

The formula for the coefficient of variation (sometimes called the coefficient of dispersion) is:

$$CV = \frac{100\sigma}{\bar{x}}$$

Using the data given in Table 11.8 on pages 177–9 we have:

$$CV = \frac{100 \times £161.10}{£240.36}$$

$$= \underline{67.0\%}$$

Strictly speaking it is not necessary to use the percentage form; we could speak of the coefficient of variation being 0.67 of the mean. Whichever is used, our description of the data would now be that the mean of the data was £240 and the dispersion around the mean was of the order of 67%. The £ signs have of course cancelled out in the calculation, and we are left with a coefficient (a number only) not in any particular units.

Exercises on mean deviation and standard deviation

1 *a* What is the meaning of 'mean deviation'?
   b The ages of the students in a class of mature adults are as follows:

   Ages (years): 22, 19, 36, 48, 32, 19, 25, 35, 46, 47, 33, 32

   i What is the mean age? *ii* What is the mean deviation?
2 Weight of males in the age group 20–29:

Weight (kg)	Percentage of males
Under 50	4
50 and under 55	5
55 and under 60	6
60 and under 65	6
65 and under 70	16
70 and under 75	15
75 and under 80	13
80 and under 85	14
85 and under 90	12
90 and under 95	4
95 and under 100	2
100 and over	3

Making such assumptions about these data as you feel are necessary calculate *a* the mean weight and *b* the mean deviation (answers correct to 0.1 kg).

3 A company takes a random sample of 100 export orders from the order book. The value of the orders was distributed as follows:

Value of order (£)	Number of orders
Under 1000	8
1000 and under 1500	11
1500 and under 2000	13
2000 and under 2500	17
2500 and under 3000	14
3000 and under 3500	14
3500 and under 4000	10
4000 and under 4500	7
4500 and under 5000	4
5000 and over	2
Total	100

a Calculate the mean order value and the mean deviation.

b A second random sample of 100 export orders is found to have a mean order value of £3200. Calculate the mean of the combined samples.

4 *a* What is the meaning of the term 'standard deviation'?

b The following data show the cost (£) of installing a sprinkler system in various warehouses to comply with fire regulations:

4 800	3 600	19 400
5 600	13 400	8 600
7 200	5 800	4 800
8 900	7 200	5 200
7 800	17 200	1 300

Calculate *i* the arithmetic mean and *ii* the standard deviation (answers correct to the nearest £1).

5 The gross rental value of premises (the rent paid by the tenant of each property) for 100 premises is as follows:

Rental value of premises (£)	Percentage of properties
Under 100	11
100 and under 200	32
200 and under 300	36
300 and under 400	8
400 and under 500	8
500 and over	5

  a Calculate the arithmetic mean and the standard deviation.
  b Using your results describe the set of data. What desirable part of any description of a set of data are you unable to supply from these results?
6 One hundred light bulbs are tested to destruction and give the following lifetimes:

Lifetime (hours)	Frequency
Under 250	3
250 and under 500	14
500 and under 750	24
750 and under 1000	37
1000 and under 1250	15
1250 and under 1500	5
1500 and over	2

Find the mean lifetime and the standard deviation.
7 The weights of a group of recruits to the armed forces are as follows:

Weight (kg)	Number of recruits
Under 55	12
55 and under 60	37
60 and under 65	68
65 and under 70	197
70 and under 75	232
75 and under 80	162
80 and under 85	58
85 and over	34

  Calculate the arithmetic mean and the standard deviation.
8 What is a coefficient of variation? What is its advantage over the standard deviation?
9 Using the data of Exercise 7 above calculate the coefficient of variation from your answers to that question (answer correct to one decimal place).

11.11 Measures of skewness

Measures of skewness measure the degree of asymmetry of a distribution; a distribution which is not symmetrical is said to be skewed. In Fig 11.4 on page 166 we saw that the mean, the median and the mode, which in a normal distribution all coincide at the central point, do not coincide in a skewed distribution. Instead the mode – which by definition occurs at the peak of the distribution – is separated from the mean, and the median lies between the other two. It should be possible therefore to develop some measure of skewness from this separation of the three averages. However, with an infinite variety of skewed distributions recorded in a wide range of units a measure expressed in the original units of the data would not be very helpful for comparative purposes. We need a measure which expresses the skewness in relation to the spread of the data in a particular distribution – in other words which expresses the skewness in relative terms, not absolute terms. As with the coefficient of variation mentioned earlier, we need a **coefficient of skewness**.

Such a coefficient, called after its devisor Professor Karl Pearson, is **Pearson's No 1 coefficient of skewness**, the formula for which is:

$$sk = \frac{mean - mode}{\sigma}$$

The mean, the mode and the standard deviation are all expressed in the units of the original data. When the difference between the mean and the mode is calculated as a fraction of the standard deviation (in other words as a fraction of the average spread of the data around the mean) the original units cancel out in the fraction, and we are left with a coefficient only – a coefficient of skewness – a number which tells us the extent of the skewness in the distribution.

Using the data of Table 11.9 on page 178 – the mode of which is found to be £135 – the calculation is as follows:

$$sk = \frac{£240.36 - £135}{£161.10}$$

$$= \frac{£105.36}{£161.10}$$

$$= \underline{0.654}$$

Since a complete absence of skewness, ie a symmetrical distribution, would have a coefficient of skewness of zero, and since the mean was larger than the mode, we have a positive result, the distribution of Table 11.9 is positively skewed to the extent of 65% of the standard deviation.

Unfortunately the mode is difficult to determine precisely in many distributions, and an alternative form of the **Pearson's formula, (No 2)** uses the relationship of the displacement of the median from the mean instead. This was referred to earlier in Section 11.3 as being approximately one-third of the displacement of the other two. We therefore have:

$$sk = \frac{3(mean - median)}{\sigma}$$

In Table 11.9, where the median is found to be £184.97, we have:

$$sk = \frac{3(£240.36 - £184.97)}{£161.10}$$

$$= \frac{3 \times £55.39}{£161.10}$$

$$= \frac{£166.17}{£161.10}$$

$$= \underline{1.03}$$

That these results vary considerably demonstrates the approximate nature of the relationship between the mode, the mean and the median. The second result suggests that the skewness of the distribution is even more positive, and extends to 1.03 of the standard deviation.

A further coefficient of skewness suggested by Professor Bowley takes account of the relative positions of the quartiles to the median. In a symmetrical distribution the quartiles would lie at equal distances on either side of the median. Therefore, we could say:

$$(Q_3 - M) - (M - Q_1) = 0$$

If the distribution is skewed the equation above would not be true. If the distance $(Q_3 - M)$ were greater than the distance $(M - Q_1)$ we should have a positively skewed distribution, while if the distance $(M - Q_1)$ were greater we should have a negatively skewed distribution.

The left-hand side of the equation can be rearranged as follows:

$$Q_3 - M - M + Q_1 = 0 \qquad \text{or} \qquad Q_3 + Q_1 - 2M = 0$$

Unfortunately this measure is in the original units, and is not a coefficient. We must therefore turn it into a coefficient by relating it to the spread of data around the median – in other words the quartile deviation. Therefore this coefficient of skewness is:

$$\mathrm{sk} = \frac{Q_3 + Q_1 - 2M}{\dfrac{Q_3 - Q_1}{2}}$$

$$= \frac{2(Q_3 + Q_1 - 2M)}{Q_3 - Q_1}$$

Using the data of Table 11.9 again, where the median is £184.97, Q_1 is found to be £123.96 and Q_3 is found to be £346.77:

$$\therefore \ \mathrm{sk} = \frac{2(£346.77 + £123.96) - 2(£184.97)}{£346.77 - £123.96}$$

$$= \frac{2(470.73 - £369.94)}{£222.81}$$

$$= \frac{2 \times £100.79}{£222.81}$$

$$= \frac{£201.58}{£222.81}$$

$$= 0.905$$

$$= 0.9$$

This measure of skewness gives a result indicating that the distribution of the data in Table 11.9 is positively skewed to the extent of 0.9 of the quartile deviation. Since this measure relates to the quartile deviation and not the standard deviation it is not strictly speaking comparable with the other measures already described.

Exercises on skewness

1 a What is meant by skewness?
   b What is a coefficient of skewness and how does it help us to describe a set of data?
2 A distribution of data about salesmen's salaries per month is found to have an arithmetic mean of £630, with a standard deviation of £165 and a coefficient of skewness of 0.72. Explain what these terms mean in describing the data.
3 A certain set of data about the weight of female typists in the 20–29 age group gives a mean weight of 51 kg, a standard deviation of 7.5 kg. The median weight is 49.5 kg. What is the coefficient of skewness?
4 The rents of unfurnished dwellings in Hilltown are investigated and found to be as follows:

Rents per annum (£)	Percentage of dwellings
Under 1000	5
1000 and under 1250	8
1250 and under 1500	13
1500 and under 1750	24
1750 and under 2000	27
2000 and under 2250	13
2250 and over	10

By making suitable assumptions about these data find: a the mean, b the standard deviation, c the median and d the coefficient of skewness. What information do these data give you about the distribution of rents in Hilltown?

Summary

1 The dispersion of a set of data is a measure of the extent to which the individual items are spread around the average.
2 A distribution may be normal (with the individual observations grouped around the midpoint in a bell-shaped symmetrical curve) or skewed (with the bulk of the items offset to one side of the average either positively or negatively). Positively skewed data have the bulk of the data to the left of the mean position, while negatively skewed data have the bulk of the data to the right of the mean position.

3   The range is the difference between the smallest and largest values in the distribution. If the distribution is grouped and the first class is larger than the rest we take the midpoint of that group as the start of the range. If the last group is open ended we assume it is twice as large as other groups and take the midpoint of that (ie one extra full class interval) as the end of the range.

4   The quartile deviation is a measure of dispersion which is linked with the median. The quartiles are values which divide the set of data into four equal parts, the lower quartile at the 25% level, the median at halfway and the upper quartile at the 75% level. The difference between the upper quartile and the lower quartile is called the inter-quartile range, and the quartile deviation is half of this range. It therefore tells us to what extent the central half of the data is spread around the median position.

5   The mean deviation is the average deviation of the data from the central point of the distribution. Any measure of central tendency may be used, ie the mean, median or mode, but in finding the deviations from the centre there must be positive and negative items, and they will sum to zero. To avoid this the signs must be ignored, and the mean deviation is the average deviation of the absolute data – regardless of the sign. This is a disadvantage in advanced statistics. For ungrouped data the formula for the mean deviation is $\Sigma(x - \bar{x})/n$: the sum of the deviations from the mean divided by the number of observations. For grouped data the formula is $\Sigma f(x - \bar{x})/\Sigma f$, where x is the midpoint of the group and Σf is the sum of the frequencies in the groups.

6   The standard deviation is a measure of dispersion which is mathematically sound and can therefore be used in advanced statistical work. It measures the extent to which data are spread around the arithmetic mean. It overcomes the difficulty arising from deviations being positive or negative (so that the sum of the deviations is zero) by squaring the deviations, finding the average and taking the square root of the answer. The formula is $\sigma = \sqrt{\Sigma(x - \bar{x})^2/n}$ for ungrouped data. For grouped data it is usual to work from an assumed mean. Typical calculations are given in the text (see page 178).

7   The coefficient of variation expresses the standard deviation as a percentage of the arithmetic mean. The formula is $CV = 100\sigma/\bar{x}$.

8   Coefficients of skewness seek to describe the extent to which a distribution is asymmetrical by expressing the displacement of the three averages from one another in relative terms. In a symmetrical distribution the three averages coincide. In a skewed distribution they must be displaced. There are three formulae: Pearson No. 1 gives the skewness as $sk = (\text{mean} - \text{mode})/\sigma$. Pearson No. 2 uses the median with the formula $sk = 3(\text{mean} - \text{median})/\sigma$. Bowley's formula uses the displacement of the quartiles from the median, and uses the formula $sk = 2(Q_3 + Q_1 - 2M)/(Q_3 - Q_1)$. In revising these it is advisable to re-read the text (Section 11.11, pages 183 to 186).

9   Measures of dispersion and skewness help us to describe a set of data as fully as possible. They enable us to specify the range of the data (from the smallest to the largest). They enable us to say where the

centre of the data is, with a mean or median or mode, and to say how they are spread around the midpoint (with a quartile deviation, a mean deviation or a standard deviation). Finally, they enable us to say to what extent the data is asymmetrical, skewed positively or negatively away from normal.

12 Time series analysis

12.1 Nature of a time series

Many sets of data, such as the frequency distributions discussed in earlier chapters, give information about a situation at a given moment in time. Thus we may have production figures for a particular plant in a particular month or year or we may have the sales of representatives in a particular period. Where data is collected at regular intervals on a standard basis it becomes possible to compare the data from earlier periods with current data and thus establish business or social **trends**. There are many examples of comparisons made over a period of time. We might for example take the data each year for deaths in motor-cycle accidents and compare them over the years. Is the problem getting worse, or is road safety in this respect improving? A motor-cycle manufacturer might be very interested in such a time series, since it might help him to rebut criticisms of the machines being manufactured. Table 12.1 shows a simple time series. The annual total column shows that sales are increasing over the years though the very great increase in year 4 was not maintained in year 5 and sales fell back a little. We also notice that sales in the second and third quarters of the year are always greater than sales in the first and fourth quarters of the year. This means we have a seasonal product to some extent – which is not surprising since peat products are used in gardening and more gardening takes place in the United Kingdom in the summer months than in the winter months. Table 12.1 should be studied, together with the notes, before we analyse the figures in more detail (see page 190).

The purpose of time series analysis

Time series analysis seeks to analyse a time series of data so as to distinguish the underlying trend in the data from the seasonal fluctuations. There are also random variations caused by abnormal events: wars, strikes, natural disasters, economic failures, etc. If we can find out what the underlying trend is for our business, and what the seasonal influences are, we may be able to take advantage of this useful knowledge. We might, for example, save our advertising budget to use it at the most effective time when we know our customers will be especially interested. If we detect a random event which has affected our sales we shall know that it was an unusual interest in our product and not something we should expect to be repeated. Time series analysis should enable us, to some extent, to predict future developments.

The analysis begins with an averaging process over the natural period of the inquiry – for example, we might take a 12-monthly moving average, or a 4-quarterly moving average. With data spread over many years, such as investigations of cyclical activity (booms and slumps), we may have to decide what the cycle seems to be – say an 8-year cycle – and average 8 years at a time. We must now see how a moving average reveals the trend.

Table 12.1 Sales of peat products

Year	Quarter	Sales (£'000)	Annual total (£'000)
1	1	1508	
	2	3852	
	3	2875	
	4	1151	9 386
2	1	1610	
	2	3961	
	3	2936	
	4	1268	9 775
3	1	1725	
	2	4254	
	3	3312	
	4	1386	10 677
4	1	1836	
	2	4954	
	3	4122	
	4	1251	12 163
5	1	1874	
	2	4316	
	3	3425	
	4	1438	11 053
Total			53 054

Notes

 i The sales figures for each quarter of the year have been produced by the sales manager covering the last 5 years. They have also been totalled to give the annual sales figures.

 ii The whole purpose of a time series is to study the figures over the years. For example we can see that sales increased in the first 4 years from year to year, but there was a small set-back in year 5, with sales falling by over a million pounds in value.

 iii Looking at the 1st year we see that the smallest sales were in the 4th quarter of the year and the largest sales were in the 2nd quarter.

 iv Looking at the other years, we see this pattern repeated; in fact we have a regular pattern: 1st quarter = small sales, 2nd quarter = very large sales, 3rd quarter = quite good sales and 4th quarter = smallest sales. This is therefore a seasonal change, with good sales in Spring and Summer and poor sales in Autumn and Winter.

12.2 The trend of data

The trend of a set of data is the long-term pattern underlying the data. We shall see (in Fig 12.1 on page 195 that the data given in Table 12.1 when plotted on a graph show an erratic pattern with very large sales in the 2nd quarter and much lower sales in the 4th quarter.

It is not easy to pick out the underlying trend from such a series of data, but we can see from the general shift of the pattern that there is a slight rise overall from left to right. The technique used to find the trend is called the moving average. A moving average is an average that moves down the line of data. For example consider the year 1 figures of Table 12.1:

1508
3852
2875
1151

To find the average sales, we must add the 4 figures and divide by 4. This gives us

$$\frac{9386}{4} = 2346.5$$

If we write this average against the 4 quarterly figures we have

1508
3852
      2346.5
2875
1151

(Note that we have to spread the figures out to put the average in its correct position – halfway between the second quarter and the third quarter.)

Now to continue our moving average we move one-quarter down the column data in Table 12.1, taking 4 quarters again, but this time we drop the sales figure for the 1st quarter of year 1 and pick up the 1st quarter in year 2. This gives us:

3852
2875
1151
1610

This totals to $9488 \div 4 = 2372$. Added in to our table we now have

1508
3852
      2346.5
2875
      2372.0
<u>1151</u>
1610

Table 12.2 Analysing sales to discover the trend

(i) Year	(ii) Quarter	(iii) Sales (£'000)	(iv) Four-quarterly moving average	(v) Centred trend	(vi) Variation of the actual from the centred trend
1	1	1508			
	2	3852			
			2346.50		
	3	2875		2359.25	+ 515.75
			2372.0		
	4	1151		2385.625	− 1234.625
			2399.25		
2	1	1610		2406.875	− 796.875
			2414.50		
	2	3961		2429.125	+ 1531.875
			2443.75		
	3	2936		2458.125	+ 477.875
			2472.50		
	4	1268		2509.125	− 1241.125
			2545.75		
3	1	1725		2592.75	− 867.75
			2639.75		
	2	4254		2654.50	+ 1599.50
			2669.25		
	3	3312		2683.125	+ 628.875
			2697.00		
	4	1386		2784.50	− 1398.50

		(iii)	(iv)	(v)	(vi)
4	1	1836		2973.25	− 1137.25
			2872.00		
	2	4954		3057.625	+ 1896.375
			3074.50		
	3	4122		3045.50	+ 1076.50
			3040.75		
	4	1251		2970.50	− 1719.50
			3050.25		
5	1	1874		2803.625	− 929.625
			2890.75		
	2	4316		2739.875	+ 1576.125
			2716.50		
	3	3425			
			2763.25		
	4	1438			

Notes

i In column (iii) we have the quarterly totals of sales.

ii In column (iv) the four quarterly totals are added and averaged to give a four-quarterly average. Naturally the first of these averages comes midway between the second and third quarters. For the next figure the first quarter in year 1 is now discarded and the first quarter of year 2 is used instead. The average of these four quarters falls between the third and fourth quarters of year 1. So the moving average follows down the list until we come to the middle of the fifth year, when figures cease to be available for the first quarter of year 6, and the moving average therefore ceases at the midpoint of year 5.

iii Unfortunately the displacement of the moving average by half an interval from the quarterly figures means that we cannot strictly compare the average with the quarterly figures of column (iii). This difficulty is overcome by averaging the averages yet again – taking two at a time. The average of the first two figures in column (iv) becomes the **centred trend** of column (v). It lies midway between the two figures from which it was derived, and hence is at the same level as the original quarterly figures, and can be compared with them.

iv Later we shall see that this enables us to calculate (in column (vi)) the variation of the actual data from the centred trend, which is used to de-seasonalise the data.

v Now return to the main text.

We now have the start of a moving average, which can be continued by dropping off the 2nd quarter of year 1 and picking up the 2nd quarter of year 2, etc.

The calculation of a moving average is shown in stages in Table 12.2 on pages 192 and 193. The stages are most easily followed from the notes below the table, rather than in the body of the text, and the reader should break off to study the calculations of this moving average in Table 12.2.

When working out the moving averages the original data will decide the average to be used. For example, in Table 12.2 we used the four quarterly figures, adding the first four quarters together and dividing by 4. Had we had monthly figures we could have added the 12 months together and divided by 12. Other types of data might conceivably be best served by some other grouping.

a Plotting the trend on a graph

When the centred trend figures have been found the trend can be plotted on a graph, as shown in Fig 12.1. The quarterly figures have been plotted at the midpoints of the quarters and give an erratic picture of sales which rise to a peak in the second quarter (spring in the Northern Hemisphere) and fall away to a trough in the fourth quarter (winter in the Northern Hemisphere). The centred trend has also been plotted at the midpoint of the quarter, but there are no figures for the first two quarters or the last two quarters as explained in the notes to Table 12.2 on page 193. The data are clearly affected by seasonal influences, but these have been averaged out in the trend calculations to give a smooth line showing the growth of the business over the years when the seasonal influences do not distort the picture. It is clear that there is an increase in sales of an unusual nature in year 4, followed by a decline to more normal situations in year 5. This is an example of a **random influence** at work. Was year 4 a long bright summer so that more gardening was done than usual? Did a sudden surge in incomes or house ownership affect the amount of gardening carried on? We do not know the details in this case but in a real-life situation some explanation of this random event would no doubt suggest itself to those using the data.

b Extrapolating from the trend

If we know the trend of a set of data we can use it to predict the likely developments over the years ahead. This is called extrapolation from the trend. We continue the trend along the same pattern as appears to be evident in the trend data, to get the likely trend figures in the year or so ahead. This might have important implications for production. We may need to build new plant to supply the expected demand or to envisage closure of what is likely to be excess capacity if a downward trend continues. We may need to take on and train extra staff or to envisage redundancy programmes as staff will no longer be needed. Random events, like the one in year 4 of our trend data, make this extrapolation

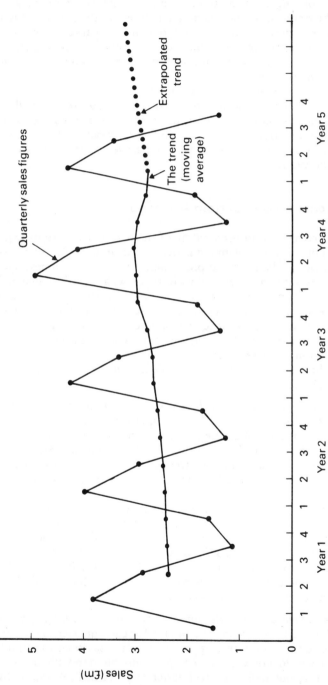

Fig 12.1 The trend in sales of peat products

Notes

i The data are clearly influenced by the seasonal nature of the product, with a peak in the 2nd quarter of the year and a trough in the 4th.

ii The trend takes up a central position (as with any average) but it shows the underlying pattern of sales. These reveal a slow but steady growth over the years, but with a sudden surge in year 4. This is a random event affecting the data.

iii The trend data cease at the midpoint of the 2nd quarter of year 5. We may estimate the future trend – to set production targets, for example – by extrapolating from the trend. This is shown by the dotted line.

more difficult – even the trend is not a simple straight line, it has its humps and hollows.

Reference has already been made to the process of predicting future sales by extrapolating from the trend. Caution is necessary in extrapolating from the trend, since there is no guarantee that the past trend will be continued. All sorts of forces are at work in any market – political, economic and competitive developments may render the predictions inaccurate – and we must watch for such developments and take them into account wherever possible.

Even when we have devised an extrapolated trend which seems to fit the evidence available, actual quarterly sales in the future will still be seasonal. We have to superimpose on the extrapolated trend the likely quarterly variations, so that we can set production targets. This requires us to know the **seasonal variations** over the past few years. Let us look at seasonal variations.

12.3 Seasonal variations from the trend

In seeking to arrive at an understanding of the seasonal variations from the trend we hope to assist planning activities aimed at maximising customer satisfaction, plant utilisation, maintenance programmes, etc. Extrapolating from the trend will allow us to see what the likely demand will be at any time in the near future. We can build stocks ready for a surge in business or reduce stocks to allow for seasonal decline. This may enable us to carry out maintenance programmes at times when the least disruption will be caused, or divert maintenance workers into production if an increased output is required.

There are three stages to the task of calculating seasonal variations. They are as follows:

Stage 1. Calculate the variations between the centred trend and the actual figures over the time series. The first quarter for which we can do this in Table 12.2 is the 3rd quarter of year 1. In column (vi) we can see that the variation is + 515.75. In other words, in that quarter actual sales were £515 750 greater than the trend. In the 4th quarter of year 1 sales were £1 234 625 *less* than the trend; an unfavourable season for peat products.

These variations, whether positive or negative, could obviously be affected by seasonal influences, but random influences of one sort or another might also be involved. In one recent year the eruption of a volcano in the United States produced very adverse weather conditions for a full 12 months and drastically affected garden activities in the Northern Hemisphere. It even produced the proverbial blue moon. How shall we eliminate random variations?

Stage 2. In this stage we eliminate random variations by averaging them away. This is done by averaging the figures for each quarter. Thus, to refer to the 3rd quarter of year 1 again, as far as the seasonal variations are concerned we do not want to compare this quarter with the 4th quarter in year 1, but with the 3rd quarter in years 2, 3, 4 and 5. In column (vi) of Table 12.2 we see that these figures are as follows:

Year 1	+ 515.75
Year 2	+ 477.875
Year 3	+ 628.875
Year 4	+ 1076.50
Year 5	Not available

We can see that in this quarter of the year sales are well above trend figures, and if averaged out we find that on average sales are $2699.0 \div 4 = 674.75$ (£'000) above the trend. To carry out this averaging process we need to set out the data in quarterly tabular form (Table 12.3, below). Study Table 12.3 now.

Stage 3. In this section we make a correction in the seasonal variation. Unfortunately, this averaging calculation is not perfectly accurate – it has not quite eliminated the random variations in the data. This is because any average must be calculated using the data that are available, and this includes the random variations which consequently get reduced – they are divided by 4 – but not eliminated. To eliminate them we need a third stage in the process. *This is a process of correcting the seasonal variation.*

The correction depends upon the fact that the quarterly variations should sum to zero. The figures from which an average has been calculated should be equally spread around the average. Thus the average of 2, 4, 6 and 8 is 5. The variations of the numbers on either side of 5 are

Table 12.3 Seasonal variation (£'000)

Year	Quarter 1	Quarter 2	Quarter 3	Quarter 4
1	—	—	+ 515.75	– 1234.625
2	– 796.875	+ 1531.875	+ 477.875	– 1241.125
3	– 867.75	+ 1599.5	+ 628.875	– 1398.5
4	– 1137.25	+ 1896.375	+ 1076.50	– 1719.5
5	– 929.625	+ 1576.125	—	—
Totals	– 3731.5	+ 6603.875	+ 2699.0	– 5593.75

Average quarterly deviation:

$$\text{Quarter 1} \quad \frac{-3731.5}{4} = -932.875$$

$$\text{Quarter 2} \quad \frac{+6603.875}{4} = +1650.96875$$

$$\text{Quarter 3} \quad \frac{+2699.0}{4} = +674.75$$

$$\text{Quarter 4} \quad \frac{-5593.75}{4} = -1398.4375 \quad \text{(Now return to \textit{Stage 3} above)}$$

198 Statistics for business

as follows:

2:	− 3	
4:	− 1	
6:		+ 1
8:		+ 3
	− 4	+ 4

The various below the average and above the average are the same. This should also happen with our data, but does it?

The means of the quarterly variations are as follows:

− 932.875	+ 1650.96875
− 1398.4375	+ 674.75
− 2331.3125	2325.71875

Clearly, these are not quite the same. Our average figures are slightly wrong. If we correct them by one quarter of the error in each case we shall have the correct figures.

The difference is − 5.59375. This means that each seasonal variation has to be adjusted by + 1.3984375. Working to three decimal places this is + 1.398. This is known as the **correction factor**.

Our adjusted seasonal variations are therefore:

Quarter 1	Quarter 2	Quarter 3	Quarter 4
− 932.875	+ 1650.969	+ 674.75	− 1398.438
+ 1.398	+ 1.398	+ 1.398	+ 1.398
− 931.477	+ 1652.367	+ 676.148	− 1397.040

Check:

− 931.477	+ 1652.367
− 1397.040	+ 676.148
− 2328.517	+ 2328.515

The tiny error is due to rounding. These seasonal variations now sum to zero. Now that we have available a set of corrected seasonal variations we can use these seasonal variations to discover the random variations.

12.4 Random variations

Random variations arise from a wide variety of causes both internal and external to the firm. They may be either positive or negative, and different influences may be at work at the same time. Thus changes in the economic climate, the political climate or natural disasters of one sort or another may be at work simultaneously. Such events can have widespread repercussions on all firms, but usually affect some firms more than others. If a major part of a firm's trading is with an area that becomes politically or economically unstable it may be seriously affected. Similarly, within a firm changes of management policy resulting from takeover bids, or the arrival (or departure) of a particularly strong executive, may have important effects on the company concerned.

The process of arriving at the random variations is described in Table 12.4 on page 200 and the notes on page 201. Study these pages now.

12.5   De-seasonalising the actual data

One result of all these activities is that we can de-seasonalise the data. Official publications frequently publish 'seasonally adjusted' figures which have been adjusted to show the general trend more clearly by removing the seasonal effects. Such data as unemployment figures may be more meaningful if adjusted in this way to reveal the underlying trends. On the other hand, they may be given in this form to suit a particular political viewpoint.

When de-seasonalising data we alter the actual figures by removing the seasonal variation from them. This can be a little tricky because of the signs. It is easy to get confused. In Table 12.5 on page 202 the data of Table 12.1 have been de-seasonalised, and the difficulty about signs has been explained in the notes below the table. The de-seasonalised data have been given to the nearest whole number.

12.6   Other aspects of time series analysis

In this chapter so far we have been looking at the analysis of a time series from the point of view that the actual data are made up of three parts, as follows:

Actual data = underlying trend + seasonal variations + random variations (sometimes called residual variations)

We could abbreviate this to:

Actual data = T + S + R

This is often called the '*additive model*'. Many statisticians dislike the additive model because they think that it is unrealistic to add on a constant amount, or subtract a constant amount, for any particular quarter. It would be better to take the trend figure and multiply it by a constant factor (ie a constant percentage) which takes account of the seasonal influences at work in each quarter. This revised approach changes the formula given above to:

Actual data = (T × seasonal variation) + R

This is called the '*multiplicative model*'. Instead of regarding the seasonal variation as the average of the (actual minus trend) values, the multiplicative model views the seasonal variation as the average of the proportional change in the figures. The proportional change is found by taking the actual figure for any quarter and dividing it by the trend figure. (Continues on page 202.)

Table 12.4 A full-time series analysis

(i) Year	(ii) Quarter	(iii) Sales (£'000)	(iv) Centred trend	(v) Deviation from trend	(vi) Seasonal variation	(vii) Random variation
1	1	1508	—			
	2	3852	—			
	3	2875	2359.25	+515.75	+676.148	−160.398
	4	1151	2385.625	−1234.625	−1397.040	+162.415
2	1	1610	2406.875	−796.875	−931.477	+134.602
	2	3961	2429.125	+1531.875	+1652.367	−120.492
	3	2936	2458.125	+477.875	+676.148	−198.273
	4	1268	2509.125	−1241.125	−1397.040	+155.915
3	1	1725	2592.75	−867.75	−931.477	+63.727
	2	4254	2654.50	+1599.50	+1652.367	−52.867
	3	3312	2683.125	+628.875	+676.148	−47.273
	4	1386	2784.50	−1398.50	−1397.040	−1.46
4	1	1836	2973.25	−1137.25	−931.477	−205.773
	2	4954	3057.625	+1896.375	+1652.367	+244.008
	3	4122	3045.50	+1076.50	+676.148	+400.352
	4	1251	2970.5	−1719.5	−1397.040	−322.46
5	1	1874	2803.625	−929.625	−931.477	+1.852
	2	4316	2739.875	+1576.125	+1652.367	−76.242
	3	3425	—			
	4	1438				

Notes

i The seasonal variation (column (vi)) is the same in each quarter of each year. Thus in quarter 1 the seasonal variation is −931.477 in year 2, year 3, year 4 and year 5.

ii The actual deviation from trend (column (v)) is different from the corrected seasonal variation of column (vi). This shows that random variations also occurred. Being random they may be positive or negative. The reader may be confused by the signs. The detailed explanation below may help.

iii Consider the 3rd quarter of year 1. We would have expected a seasonal variation from the trend of +676.148. Actually the variation was +515.75. This was smaller than expected, so a negative random variation must have acted to drag the data down to +515.75. This negative random variation was −160.398.

iv Now consider the situation in year 4. We would again have expected, in the 3rd quarter, a deviation of +676.148. Actually the deviation was +1076.50, so it is clear that in year 4 the random variation did not reduce the seasonal variation but increased it. It was therefore a positive random variation of 400.352.

v Now consider quarter 4, year 1. We would have expected a seasonal variation of −1397.040. In fact we only had a seasonal variation of −1234.625. A random variation was at work to reduce the negative seasonal variation, so it must have been a positive random variation. The situation was different in quarter 4, year 4. Here an expected seasonal variation of −1397.040 was actually turned into a larger variation of −1719.5. It follows that a negative random variation, −322.46, operated to make the expected negative variation even bigger.

vi In each case, the statistician must ask 'How big is the random variation?' and 'What sign must it have to produce the change that the figures reveal?'.

(*Now return to page 199, at Section 12.5.*)

Thus, using the figures given earlier in Table 12.2 (see page 192), the change in sales for quarter 3, year 1 would not be the actual change shown of £515.75 ('000), but would be the proportional change, found by dividing the actual figure by the trend figure.

$$\text{Proportional change} = \frac{\text{Actual}}{\text{Trend}} = \frac{£2875}{£2359.25} = 1.2186$$

In other words, the trend figure of £2359.25 is increased by almost a quarter by the seasonal variation and, if we calculate 0.2186 of £2359.25, it does come to the actual increase of £515.75 shown in Table 12.2. (*See page 203.*)

Table 12.5 De-seasonalised data

(i)	(ii)	(iii)	(iv)	(v)
Year	Quarter	Sales (£'000)	Seasonal variation (£'000)	De-seasonalised data (£'000)
1	1	1508	− 931.477	2439
	2	3852	+ 1652.367	2200
	3	2875	+ 676.148	2199
	4	1151	− 1397.040	2548
2	1	1610	− 931.477	2541
	2	3961	+ 1652.367	2309
	3	2936	+ 676.148	2260
	4	1268	− 1397.040	2665
3	1	1725	− 931.477	2656
	2	4254	+ 1652.367	2602
	3	3312	+ 676.148	2636
	4	1386	− 1397.040	2783
4	1	1836	− 931.477	2767
	2	4954	+ 1652.367	3302
	3	4122	+ 676.148	3446
	4	1251	− 1397.040	2648
5	1	1874	− 931.477	2805
	2	4316	+ 1652.367	2664
	3	3425	+ 676.148	2749
	4	1438	− 1397.040	2835

Notes

i If the seasonal variation has a negative sign, as in quarters 1 and 4, it means that in this season actual sales are below the trend. To de-seasonalise the data we must therefore *add* the seasonal variation to the actual data. This gives us the figure that sales would have been had the adverse seasonal effect not occurred.

ii When the seasonal variation has a positive sign, as in quarters 2 and 3, it means that sales exceeded the trend in these quarters. To de-seasonalise the data we must therefore *deduct* the seasonal variation from the actual data. This gives us the figure that sales would have reached had there not been a favourable seasonal effect.

iii Remember that de-seasonalised data have been rounded. (*Now return to page 199.*)

If we therefore rework Tables 12.2 and 12.3 to find the seasonal variations, we have the following results. Some of the detail of Table 12.2 (the 4-quarterly moving average column) has been omitted here, because we only need to show the centred trend figures. The reworking has been done in Tables 12.6 and 12.7.

Table 12.6 Seasonal variation by the multiplicative method

(i)	(ii)	(iii)	(iv)	(v)
				Seasonal variation
		Sales	Centred	Actual sales (iii)
Year	Quarter	(£'000)	trend	Trend (iv)
1	1	1508		
	2	3852		
	3	2875	2359.25	1.2186
	4	1151	2385.625	0.4825
2	1	1610	2406.875	0.6689
	2	3961	2429.125	1.6306
	3	2936	2458.125	1.1944
	4	1268	2509.125	0.5054
3	1	1725	2592.75	0.6653
	2	4254	2654.50	1.6026
	3	3312	2683.125	1.2344
	4	1386	2784.50	0.4978
4	1	1836	2973.25	0.6175
	2	4954	3057.625	1.6202
	3	4122	3045.50	1.3535
	4	1251	2970.50	0.4211
5	1	1874	2803.625	0.6684
	2	4316	2739.875	1.5753
	3	3425		
	4	1438		

Table 12.7 Averaging the seasonal variation ratios

Year	Quarter 1	Quarter 2	Quarter 3	Quarter 4
1	—	—	1.2186	0.4825
2	0.6689	1.6306	1.1944	0.5054
3	0.6653	1.6026	1.2344	0.4978
4	0.6175	1.6202	1.3535	0.4211
5	0.6684	1.5753	—	—
Totals	2.6201	6.4287	5.0009	1.9068
Average (÷)	0.6550	1.6072	1.2502	0.4767

We would expect the four ratios to add up to 4, but in fact they add up to 3.9891. This means the average ratios are slightly understated, and we must increase them in the proportion 4/3.9891. Multiplying each of the four averages by this fraction we find that the four seasonal variations are:

Quarter 1	Quarter 2	Quarter 3	Quarter 4
0.6568	1.6116	1.2536	0.4780

These do sum to 4.

De-seasonalising the data with the seasonal variation ratios

If we now wish to produce a de-seasonalised series of data we divide the actual data by the ratio for the quarter concerned. For example in quarter 1 of year 1 the sales figure is £1508 ('000). The seasonal variation in ratio form is 0.6568. Therefore if we find how many times 0.6568 goes into 1508 we shall have the trend figure for that quarter. The de-seasonalised data in both Table 12.5 and in Table 12.8 below, are the revised trend figure as a result of our calculation. For quarter 1, year 1

Table 12.8 De-seasonalising data with the seasonal variation ratios

(i)	(ii)	(iii)	(iv)	(v)
				De-seasonalised
		Sales	Seasonal	data
Year	Quarter	(£'000)	variation	(£'000)
1	1	1508	0.6568	2296
	2	3852	1.6116	2390
	3	2875	1.2536	2293
	4	1151	0.4780	2408
2	1	1610	0.6568	2451
	2	3961	1.6116	2458
	3	2936	1.2536	2342
	4	1268	0.4780	2653
3	1	1725	0.6568	2626
	2	4254	1.6116	2640
	3	3312	1.2536	2642
	4	1386	0.4780	2900
4	1	1836	0.6568	2795
	2	4954	1.6116	3074
	3	4122	1.2536	3288
	4	1251	0.4780	2617
5	1	1874	0.6568	2853
	2	4316	1.6116	2678
	3	3425	1.2536	2732
	4	1438	0.4780	3008

this figure is:

$$\frac{1508}{0.6568} = £2\,296\,000$$

De-seasonalising the data in this way in Table 12.8, we can compare the results with Table 12.5 which used the additive model.

When we de-seasonalise data we would expect to get back to figures which are fairly close to the trend, but they will not necessarily be very close because the random (or residual) variations are still present. Even so there are many situations in business where it is helpful to de-seasonalise data. If a commercial traveller has landed some big orders we shall be less impressed at a time when seasonal increases are expected than at other times when they are less influential, or even adverse. Conversely, when planning future targets for sales staff (see the section on Gantt charts in Chapter 6) we shall take the seasonal variations into account when deciding what is a reasonable monthly target for each member of the sales group.

12.7 Forecasting with the trend

Suppose we now wish to forecast sales for the coming period. We have a much clearer understanding of the original erratic sales data in Table 12.1 because we now have two sets of trend figures – those found in Table 12.5 by the additive model and those found in Table 12.8 by the multiplicative model. If we want to forecast sales we can use either set of trend figures, but if we stick to the multiplicative model for the moment we can see that the trend has been a gradually rising trend, thrown into slight disarray in year 4 when there was an unusual influence at work in the 2nd quarter producing very high sales.

If we wish to forecast sales in the next year we need to look at the figures for each quarter and estimate what the trend will be. Suppose we say that the trend will move in the coming year as shown below:

Year	Quarter	Trend forecast (£'000)
6	1	2900
	2	2850
	3	2900
	4	3000

The awkward point in predicting the trend is the fall-off that occurred in year 5, from the position in year 4, when the random event that triggered off large sales distorted the picture. The figures suggested for year 6 envisage some growth on year 5. What we now have to do is to turn these trend figures into likely sales figures. We do this by taking the seasonal variation into account. This time we multiply the trend by the seasonal variation:

Year	Quarter	Trend forecast (£'000)	Seasonal variation	Quarterly figures forecast (£'000)
6	1	2900	0.6568	1905
	2	2850	1.6116	4606
	3	2900	1.2536	3635
	4	3000	0.4780	1434

Such quarterly forecast figures may make it easy to allocate sales targets to representatives, with a view to meeting the planned sales figures.

Summary

1 A time series is a set of data collected over months and years. By comparing such data we can discover economic, business and social trends.
2 The trend is the long-term pattern underlying the data. It can be isolated by a moving average, which averages out seasonal and random variations to reveal the underlying pattern.
3 The period to be averaged is usually a natural period, such as twelve monthly periods or four quarterly periods, but some data may need to be analysed over other periods.
4 Once the trend has been discovered it can be used to predict future data by extrapolation from the trend.
5 Once the trend has been found it is possible to isolate any seasonal variations. The differences between the data and the trend are found, and each quarter's data are averaged to average out any random variations. The resulting data have to be corrected so that they sum to zero.
6 Having found the seasonal variations we can now discover the random variations. These cause the data for a particular quarter to be more, or less, than the seasonal variations would lead us to expect.
7 All these data can then be used to assist management to plan for the future, and to set targets for sales representatives, production, staff, etc.

Exercises on time series analysis

1 What is a time series of data? When we analyse a time series what are we hoping to discover and what uses can we make of the resulting derived statistics?
2 *a* Explain what is meant by a moving average.
   b Using a moving average analyse the trend in the following set of data, which relates to the sales of artificial fertiliser during the first 5 years of the activities of Prolific Ltd.

c Draw a graph showing the data and the trend.

Sales ('000 tonnes)

	Quarter			
Year	1	2	3	4
1	17	37	48	29
2	23	46	84	36
3	37	64	72	52
4	39	83	93	61
5	52	94	105	63

3 *a* Explain what is meant by 'extrapolation from the trend'.
   b Use a moving average to find the trend in sales of Rainproofer out-
   door wear. The details of sales are as follows:

Sales ('000 garments)

Month	Year 1	Year 2	Year 3
January	48	60	73
February	52	64	78
March	56	67	81
April	72	83	94
May	56	67	83
June	34	42	62
July	22	31	48
August	20	28	38
September	88	96	105
October	90	88	94
November	66	69	77
December	56	60	70

Now extrapolate from your trend line to predict the sales in year 4.
What reservations have you about this figure?

4 The quarterly sales of ice cream by a retail vending cooperative are
   given below. Analyse this data to determine *a* the trend, *b* the
   seasonal variation from the trend and *c* any residual random
   variations.

Sales of ice cream (hl)

	Quarter			
Year	1	2	3	4
1	37	146	325	84
2	39	138	318	87
3	48	192	436	172
4	57	171	342	107

5   The quarterly production of garments in a garment factory is affected by both seasonal influences and random influences. The sales of personal apparel are as shown below. Year 3 was affected by a public event of international importance. You are asked to determine *a* the trend, *b* the seasonal variation from the trend and *c* the random variations.

Sales of garments ('000)

Year	Quarter			
	1	2	3	4
1	98	115	128	103
2	136	150	164	129
3	108	120	131	116
4	120	132	140	124

6   What are the constituent elements in any time series? How can they be separated from one another to discover the various influences at work? Briefly describe the various stages in a full analysis of a time series of data.

7   Analyse the trend, seasonal variations and random variations in the data below. De-seasonalise the data and give the data in its de-seasonalised form.

Sales of bulk sulphur ('000)

Year	Quarter			
	1	2	3	4
1	1160	1985	3250	1768
2	1254	2836	4860	1958
3	1865	3425	5845	2482
4	1938	3856	6216	2999
5	2856	4250	6325	3524

8   Using the multiplicative method of finding seasonal variations as a ratio of the trend, analyse the following data provided by a hotel chain with 37 hotels.
    You are asked to *a* find the trend using a moving average, *b* find the seasonal variation as a ratio of the trend, and *c* provide a de-seasonalised series of data.

Visitors ('000)

Year	Quarter			
	1	2	3	4
1	37	47	56	29
2	39	49	62	33
3	42	51	73	52
4	45	55	81	42

9 Using the multiplicative model for finding seasonal variations as a ratio of the trend, analyse the following data for housing starts in the United Kingdom.

Housing starts – all dwellings ('000)

	Quarter			
Year	1	2	3	4
1	27	54	58	28
2	33	57	62	41
3	26	62	63	27
4	28	60	60	25
5	27	67	64	28
6	31	66	63	36

You are required to produce *a* the trend, *b* the seasonal variations from the trend, in ratio style, and *c*, the actual seasonal variations from the trend.

13 Probability

13.1 The meaning of probability

It is very common to hear people discuss problems or situations in a probabilistic manner. We make statements like 'There is a good chance of it raining this afternoon'; 'Are you likely to visit our area in the near future?'; 'The horse was favourite at 5 to 1 to win'; 'The probability is that the government will get a landslide victory.'

These statements are all probabilistic in nature and are also imprecise. We do not specify the chance of it raining this afternoon because we cannot predict the probability accurately. In television weather reports a forecaster can sometimes be heard to state 'There is a 50% chance of rain in the Midlands today!' This refinement of the general probabilistic forecast is based on the knowledge of national and local weather forecasters whose professional assistance is sought to calculate the probability of it raining. The 5 to 1 odds on a horse winning is again based initially on a professional assessment of the horse's ability by the turf accountant. These odds may change as people start to bet on the horse and will alter according to the amount of money placed on the horse. Finally, the probability of the government getting a landslide victory in an election is wide open to speculation. All sorts of factors can affect election results and it is a brave political pundit who would place a figure on the probability of an election result. Nevertheless, with the aid of information in the form of opinion polls it is easier to predict election results and a probability figure may sometimes be given.

Thus making generalised probabilistic statements is easy and we all use them. However, quantifying probabilities, chance and likely outcomes is particularly difficult and such quantification requires considerable skill and statistical knowledge.

In this chapter the ideas of probability are introduced and methods of quantification described. Whilst these methods are relatively simple they can be used to great advantage in running a business and making management decisions. Very rarely is there a clear-cut case for a particular decision. Invariably the probabilities of a sequence of events have to be assessed and comparisons made of the different management options. In such situations, probability theory can be of real benefit and is often the only way of assessing the situation. *Probability may be defined as a concept which seeks to quantify the relative frequencies of occurrences of events by answering the question: if a given coincidence of circumstances takes place a large number of times, on what proportion of these occasions would a particular event occur?*

13.2   Quantifying probability

The smallest value that a probability statement can have is 0, indicating that the event is impossible, and the largest value it can have is 1 (or 100% in percentage terms), indicating that the event is certain to occur. If we wish to calculate the probability of an event A occurring all we need do is count the number of times the event occurs, a, and the total number of experiments or observations, b, and use the formula:

$$P(A) = \frac{a}{b}$$

Here P(A) is the probability of A occurring and is determined by the *relative frequency* of the event occurring. The simplest example of this method of determining probability is to toss a coin 20 times and count the number of times it falls as heads. Because the coin is balanced it is just as likely to fall 'heads' as it is to fall 'tails' and we would expect to obtain heads 10 times. The probability of getting heads is therefore:

$$P(H) = \frac{10}{20} = 0.5$$

We may get 9 or 11 heads or even 8 or 12 but if enough experiments (ie tosses of the coin) are completed we would expect the probability to be very close to 0.5.

An alternative to the relative frequency approach is the *a priori* (reasoning from cause to effect) or *classical* approach to probability. If there are a possible outcomes favourable to the occurrence of an event A, and b possible outcomes unfavourable to the event, then the probability of A occurring is:

$$P(A) = \frac{a}{a+b}$$

provided that all the possible outcomes are equally likely.

Consider drawing a king from a pack of cards. There are 4 kings in a pack and 48 other cards and hence 4 possible favourable outcomes, and 48 possible unfavourable outcomes. The probability of drawing a king is therefore:

$$P(K) = \frac{4}{4+48} = \frac{4}{52} = 0.077$$

Note that the probability of an event occurring is represented by P(E) or some other relevant letter, like P(K) for king or P(H) for heads if we are tossing a coin. The set of all possible outcomes is called the sample space. We all have a birthday and a few people even have a birthday on 29 February in a leap year. Therefore the size of 'sample space' for possible birthdays is 366. However, there are four times as many chances of being born on some other day than 29 February, so perhaps we should say the sample space has $365\frac{1}{4}$ equally likely outcomes.

The calculation for P(K) above assumes that the outcomes are equally likely and *mutually exclusive* or *disjoint*. By mutually exclusive we mean that the events cannot occur together so that the occurrence of one event automatically precludes the occurrence of another event. Consider the two possible events 'queen' and 'king' being drawn from a pack of playing cards. These two events are mutually exclusive since any given card cannot be both a queen or a king. However, if we were to say the two events were 'queen' and 'spades' that it is quite possible that a card could be drawn to satisfy both events. Such events are termed *non-exclusive* or *joint* since it is possible for them to occur together.

Another factor that affects probability calculations is whether the events are *independent* or *dependent*. Two events are said to be independent when the occurrence of one event has no effect on the probability of the other event. Thus the tossing of a coin produces independent events since obtaining heads on one occasion will have no effect on the result of the next event. However, in the case of dependent events the probability of occurrence is affected by other events. If an ace is drawn from a pack of cards, there are only three aces left in the pack and therefore the probability of drawing an ace as the next card is reduced.

13.3 Rules of addition

Rules of addition are used when we wish to determine the probability of one event or another occurring in a single observation. Symbolically we can represent the probability of event A or event B occurring by P(A or B). In the case of mutually exclusive events the probability of either A or B occurring is obtained by summing the probability of the event occurring separately:

$$P(A \text{ or } B) = P(A) + P(B)$$

For events that are not mutually exclusive, the probability of the joint occurrence of the two events is subtracted from the sum (otherwise outcomes for which A and B both occur would be counted twice):

$$P(A \text{ or } B) = P(A) + P(B) - P(A \text{ and } B)$$

This formula is called the **general rule for the addition of probabilities.**

Thus, in our playing cards example, the probability of drawing either a queen or a king from a pack of cards would be:

$$P(Q \text{ or } K) = P(Q) + P(K) = \frac{4}{52} + \frac{4}{52} = \frac{8}{52} = 0.154$$

and the probability of drawing a queen or a spade is:

$$P(Q \text{ or } S) = P(Q) + P(S) - P(Q \text{ and } S) = \frac{4}{52} + \frac{13}{52} - \frac{1}{52} = \frac{16}{52} = 0.308$$

There are 4 chances of drawing a queen and 13 chances of drawing a spade, but one of these is the queen of spades which has already been counted, so we must deduct one possibility.

It is quite useful to portray probabilities using *Venn diagrams* as shown in Fig 13.1. With a Venn diagram the total sample space is represented by a rectangle within which two shaded areas symbolise possible events. No attempt is made to give a correct size to these areas,

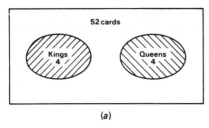 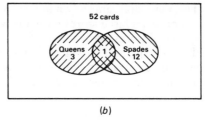

(a)   (b)

Fig 13.1 Venn diagrams for card selection

the values of which are written in. Fig 13.1*a* indicates the two mutually exclusive events and the probability of either the king or the queen being drawn from the pack of cards is equivalent to adding the values of the shaded areas. In the case of non-mutually exclusive events the total summed shaded area is reduced by the overlapping area of intersection, as indicated in Fig 13.1*b*. The chance of drawing either a queen or a spade is reduced by the fact that one of the queens is a spade.

As a more practical example consider a businessman who has to select shops or department stores for testing a new product. He may have 100 stores to choose from but would like to select 20 randomly. Of the 100 stores, 30 are large stores in high street locations and 70 are smaller stores. Ten of the high street locations are stores specialising in the type of product he is interested in selling and 15 of the smaller stores are also specialist. He would like to calculate the probability of selecting either a large or a specialist store if the selection is random.

In calculating the probability we must use the general rule of addition of probabilities: 30 stores are large and hence the probability of selecting a large store is 30/100; 25 stores are also specialist and the probability of selecting a specialist store is 25/100; however, 10 of the large stores are also specialist and therefore the probability of selecting a large and specialist store is 10/100; the probability of selecting either a large or a specialist store is therefore:

$$P(\text{L or S}) = \frac{30}{100} + \frac{25}{100} - \frac{10}{100} = \frac{45}{100} = 0.45$$

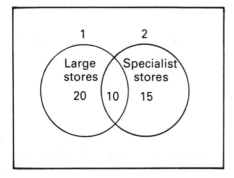

Fig 13.2 Venn diagrams for store selection

The Venn diagram shown in Fig 13.2 also illustrates this problem. Circle 1 represents large stores with a total of 30 stores and circle 2 represents specialist stores, with a total of 25. The overlapping area of 10 represents the 10 large and specialist stores. The probability of selecting either a large or a specialist store is obtained by adding up the values indicated in the Venn diagram and dividing by the total number of stores. Therefore:

$$P(L \text{ or } S) = \frac{20 + 10 + 15}{100} = \frac{45}{100} = 0.45$$

13.4 Rules of multiplication

The rules of multiplication are used to determine the probability of the joint occurrence of two events. For example, if we want to determine the probability of obtaining tails twice if a coin is tossed twice we would multiply the probabilities of obtaining tails in each toss of the coin. Thus:

$$P(\text{tails and tails}) = P(\text{tails}) \times P(\text{tails}) = \tfrac{1}{2} \times \tfrac{1}{2} = \tfrac{1}{4} = 0.25$$

The rule for two such independent events, A and B, is:

$$P(A \text{ and } B) = P(A)P(B)$$

For dependent events we have to account for the **conditional** probability of B given A, represented as $P(B|A)$. Thus the **general rule for multiplication** is:

$$P(A \text{ and } B) = P(A)P(B|A)$$

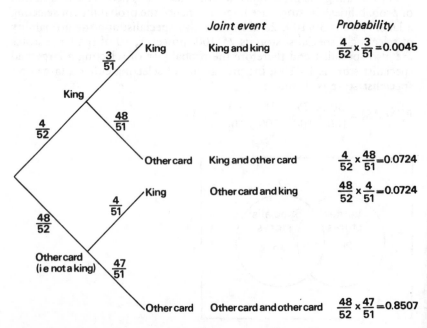

Fig 13.3 A tree diagram (selecting kings from a pack of cards)

Consider our playing cards example. Calculate the joint probability of selecting two kings from a pack of cards. The probability of drawing the first king is 4/52 since there are 4 kings in a pack of 52 cards. The probability of selecting a second king is 3/51 since there are now 3 kings left in a pack of 51 cards. The joint probability is therefore:

$$P(K_1 \text{ and } K_2) = P(K_1)P(K_2 \mid K_1)$$

$$= \frac{4}{52} \times \frac{3}{51} = 0.0045$$

Quite a useful technique in investigating probabilities is to make use of a **tree diagram** as shown in Fig 13.3 on page 214. All **possible outcomes** are evaluated using the tree diagram and the probabilities calculated. The tree diagram can be extended to evaluate as many events as required. Extend the tree diagram yourself by considering the next card to be drawn and calculate the probability of obtaining a further king.

When you do so you will find that in choosing the third card there are 8 possibilities in the full sequence. They are:

First choice	Second choice	Third choice
1 King	King	King
2 King	King	Other card
3 King	Other card	King
4 King	Other card	Other card
5 Other card	King	King
6 Other card	King	Other card
7 Other card	Other card	King
8 Other card	Other card	Other card

Working out the probability of the first of these occurring: king, king, king, we have:

$$\frac{4}{52} \times \frac{3}{51} \times \frac{2}{50} = 0.00018$$

This is about 1 chance in every 5000 that it would occur.

By contrast the probability that the last of these 8 possibilities would occur (ie other card, other card, other card) is:

$$\frac{48}{52} \times \frac{47}{51} \times \frac{46}{50} = 0.7826$$

or 78 chances in every 100.

Summary

1 Probability theory is a branch of statistics which attempts to predict the likelihood of a particular event occurring out of a large population of events.

2   The smallest value that a probability can have is 0 (the event is impossible) while the largest value is 1 (or 100%) (the event is certain to occur).
3   With mutually exclusive events (events which cannot occur together, so that the occurrence of one precludes the occurrence of any other) the formula for probability is $P(A) = a/(a+b)$. (Thus the probability of drawing a king from a pack of cards is $4/(4+48) = 4/52 = 0.077$.)
4   The addition rule of probability says that the probability that either of two mutually exclusive events will occur is the sum of the probabilities of each of them occurring. Thus the chances of drawing either a queen or a king from a pack of cards is $4/52 + 4/52 = 2/13 = 0.154$.
5   For non-mutually exclusive events the probability is the sum of their probabilities of occurring alone, less the probability of them appearing together. Thus the chances of drawing either a queen or a spade from a pack of cards are $4/52 + 13/52 - 1/52 = 16/52 = 4/13 = 0.308$.
6   Venn diagrams may be used to portray probabilities (see Figs 13.1 and 13.2 on page 213).
7   The rules of multiplication are used to determine the probability of the joint occurrence of two or more events. Thus the chance of heads when tossing a coin is $\frac{1}{2}$. The chance of the results being heads on two successive occasions is $\frac{1}{2} \times \frac{1}{2} = \frac{1}{4}$. The formula for independent events is $P(A \text{ and } B) = P(A)P(B)$. The formula for dependent events is $P(A \text{ and } B) = P(A)P(B|A)$. $P(B|A)$ means the probability of B happening given that A has already happened.
8   A tree diagram is useful for investigating probabilities (see Fig 13.3 on page 214 to refresh your memory).

Exercises on probability

1   Consider rolling a normal six-sided die. What is the probability of obtaining a 4?
2   Consider rolling the die twice. What is the probability of throwing a 4 twice?
3   If the die is thrown twice, what is the probability of throwing a 6 at least once?
4   Given a normal pack of 52 cards, what is the probability of drawing *a* a Jack (Knave), *b* a Jack or a diamond?
5   Statistical data collected from a hospital showed that 300 out of 9000 patients suffered from heart attacks during a year. Calculate the probability value for the heart attack diagnosis.
6   In the same hospital 500 patients during the year had cancer. *a* What was the probability of the cancer diagnosis? *b* What was the probability of a cancer patient having a heart attack?
7   Of 200 business students at a college, 50 are studying economics and 80 are studying accountancy. Thirty students are enrolled in both courses. What is the probability of a randomly chosen student being enrolled in either economics or accountancy or both? Draw a Venn diagram illustrating the situation.

8 The probability that a salesman will sell a vacuum cleaner is 0.2. If the probability of sales at successive houses is independent and a salesman selects 3 houses randomly, what is the probability that he will sell 3 vacuum cleaners? *b* Draw a tree diagram to represent the sales patterns and calculate the probability of the salesman making at least 1 sale.

14   Probability distributions

14.1   The nature of probability distributions

When discussing probabilities we must expect a range of results which might come out of any collection of data or experimentation with variables. The set of possible results, together with the relative frequencies with which they occur constitute a **probability distribution**. Consider, for example, the experiment discussed in Chapter 11 of tossing 10 coins to see how many times they come down heads. Remember that the result of the experiments was that the distribution of results obtained was in the form of a bell-shaped, symmetrical curve, the normal distribution curve (see Fig 11.2 on page 164).

When a collection of observed data is tabulated we can produce a list of probabilities from the data which is a probability distribution. Consider the data for the hire of video tapes by customers in a video shop, given in the first two columns of Table 14.1 on page 219. The demands shown are the midpoints of groups, ie 50 is the midpoint of a '45 and less than 55' group.

From the table there are 4 days on which 50 tapes are hired, 18 days when 60 tapes are hired and so on down to 5 days when 110 tapes are hired. The probability is calculated from the observed frequencies and presented in the third column of the table. Thus the probability of 60 tapes being hired is 0.18. The list of probabilities represents a distribution for the discrete variables.

It is often useful to summarise a probability distribution. We can do this in terms of its mean and the deviation of the data from the mean. Chapter 11 introduced the idea of the distribution of data around the mean and the concept of standard deviation. The mean tells us what is the average of the data, and the standard deviation tells us how much the data are spread out on either side of the mean. We saw in Fig 11.3 how two normal curves could have the same mean but different standard deviations, so that the shape of the normal curves differed considerably. The distribution with a large standard deviation was flatter than the one where the standard deviation was small.

Returning to the distribution of Table 14.1, how shall we describe the distribution in terms of probability? First, the mean is called the **expected value** or **expectation** of the distribution and is denoted by E(A). The expected value of a probability distribution is calculated as a weighted average according to the formula:

$$E(A) = \Sigma \ AP(A)$$

Table 14.1 Demand for hire of video tapes over 100-day period

Possible demand (A)	Number of days	Probability P(A)	Weighted values AP(A)	Squared demand, A²	Weighted square, A²P(A)
50	4	0.04	2.0	2 500	100
60	18	0.18	10.8	3 600	648
70	25	0.25	17.5	4 900	1225
80	23	0.23	18.4	6 400	1472
90	15	0.15	13.5	8 100	1215
100	10	0.10	10.0	10 000	1000
110	5	0.05	5.5	12 100	605
	100	1.00	E(A) 77.7		E(A²) 6265

Notes

i The data shows that out of 100 days there were 4 days when 50 tapes were hired, so the probability of 50 hirings is 0.04. Other probabilities are calculated similarly (column 3).

ii If we multiply the probability by the demand – which gives the AP(A) terms of column 4 – and sum the results we get the expected value or expectation of the distribution, which is the same as saying the mean of the distribution. In this case the mean E(A) is 77.7. This must be so, since any average is derived from the probability of the various numbers being averaged occurring.

iii Having found the mean we must now find how the various probabilities are distributed around the mean, in other words their standard deviation. To do this we square the demand (column 1) to give A² (column 5) and multiply by the probability to give the A²P(A) column (column 6).

iv The standard deviation is found by taking the sum of this column (E(A²)), deducting the square of the mean [E(A)]² and finding the square root of the answer. In mathematical terms:

$$\sigma(A) = \sqrt{E(A^2) - [E(A)]^2}$$

The explanation continues in the main text.

The expected value E(A) is the sum of the probabilities weighted to take account of the size of the demand at each level of probability. Thus this weighted value for the first line in the table is $50 \times 0.04 = 2.0$, and this appears as the first entry in the AP(A) column.

Thus from Table 14.1 E(A) is calculated as the summation of all the AP(A) terms, which, in the case of the video tapes, is 77.7.

The standard deviation of the distribution is denoted by the formula:

$$\sigma(A) = \sqrt{(E(A^2) - [E(A)]^2}$$

For the video data the result is:

$$\sigma(A) = \sqrt{6265 - (77.7 \times 77.7)} = \sqrt{227.71} = 15.09$$

The distribution can therefore be described as having a mean of 77.7 and a standard deviation of 15.09.

It is important to understand probability distributions since many statistical tests assume a particular distribution type. Also, if empirical data do not conform to an expected distribution we might suspect either that we have not made enough observations or that there is something peculiar or unexpected about the system we are sampling.

We must now consider some of the possible distributions. These are:

a the binomial distribution
b the normal distribution
c the Poisson distribution

14.2 Binomial distributions

A common distribution is the binomial distribution which is derived from a situation where each trial of an experiment has just two possible outcomes which may often be thought of as 'success' and 'failure'. The earlier example of tossing a coin generates a binomial distribution since we obtain either heads or tails. Each trial is independent of every other and the probability of each event does not change from trial to trial. Consider the tree diagram shown in Fig 14.1 on page 221.

Each time a coin is tossed it can only come down as a head (H) or as a tail (T). The probability of getting a head is 1/2 (or 50%) and the probability of getting a tail is the same.

Following the tree diagram, we can see that to get 3 heads, HHH, occurs only once, but to get 2 heads in a series of throws can occur in three ways, HTT, HTH and THH. Similarly, there are three ways to get 2 tails, THT, TTH and HTT.

The probability of obtaining three heads is $P(H)^3$, where $P(H)$ is the probability of throwing heads in one trial. The probability of throwing heads twice in the three trials is $3P(H)^2P(T)$, if we add up the probabilities of the three times when heads are thrown twice from the diagram. Similarly the probability of throwing heads once is $3P(H)P(T)^2$ and the probability of throwing tails three times is $P(T)^3$.

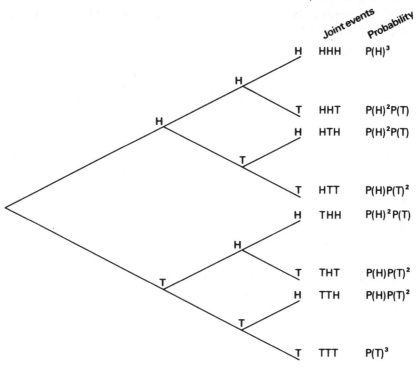

Fig 14.1 Tree diagram for tossing a coin

We may now list these probabilities as:

No of heads occurring	Probability calculation	Probability
3	$0.5 \times 0.5 \times 0.5$	0.125
2	$3 \times (0.5 \times 0.5) \times 0.5$	0.375
1	$3 \times 0.5 \times (0.5 \times 0.5)$	0.375
0	$0.5 \times 0.5 \times 0.5$	0.125
		1.000

Since the probabilities of heads and tails are both 0.5, the brackets are really unnecessary. There is in fact a pattern to these probabilities since these terms can be derived from a **binomial expansion** of $(P(H) + P(T))^3$. By a binomial expression we mean an algebraic expression containing two parts, such as $(a + b)$ or $(x + y)$, raised to a power. Thus:

$(x + y)^0 = 1$
$(x + y)^1 = x + y$
$(x + y)^2 = x^2 + 2xy + y^2$
$(x + y)^3 = x^3 + 3x^2 y + 3xy^2 + y^3$

As the power increases so the combinations of x and y, such as the $x^2 y$

and xy^2 terms, increase. Thus in the case of $(P(H) + P(T))^3$ the expanded expression is:

$$P(H)^3 + 3P(H)^2P(T) + 3P(H)P(T)^2 + P(T)^3$$

which gives the probabilities obtained using the tree diagram. The binomial expansion can, of course, be applied up to any whole positive power and a useful method of determining the binomial coefficients (the numbers 1, 3, 3 and 1 in the above example) is to use Pascal's triangle, which is written as follows:

Power								
0					1			
1				1		1		
2			1		2		1	
3		1		3		3		1
4	1		4		6		4		1
5	1		5		10		10		5		1
6	1		6		15		20		15		6		1

To obtain the next line add the overlying two numbers together and remember that each line starts and finishes with a 1. For the seventh power the figures are therefore:

1   7   21   35   35   21   7   1

The triangle shows the binomial coefficients, multiplying each factor. Thus for the power 3 the coefficients are $1, 3, 3, 1$ as before and for the sixth power the coefficients are $1, 6, 15, 20, 15, 6, 1$. If we wished to know the probability of throwing 4 heads and 2 tails in 6 trials of tossing a coin, all we need do is write the binomial expansion of $(P(H) + P(T))^6$. This is:

$$P(H)^6 + 6P(H)^5P(T) + 15P(H)^4P(T)^2$$
$$+ 20P(H)^3P(T)^3 + 15P(H)^2P(T)^4 + 6P(H)P(T)^5 + P(T)^6$$

The probability is $15P(H)^4P(T)^2$ and since we know that $P(H)$ is 0.5 and $P(T)$ is 0.5 the calculated probability is $15 \times (0.5)^4 \times (0.5)^2 = 0.234$.

When a large number of trials is envisaged it becomes awkward to use Pascal's triangle because of the large number of terms and a formula can be used to calculate the coefficients. The coefficient for x heads from n trials is:

$$\frac{n!}{x! \, (n-x)!}$$

Here ! is called the factorial and is a shorthand method of writing the product of n and all the integers down to 1. Factorial 6 is therefore $6 \times 5 \times 4 \times 3 \times 2 \times 1$ which is 720 and factorial 4 is $4 \times 3 \times 2 \times 1$ which is 24. By convention factorial 0 is 1. Thus in our heads and tails example the coefficient for 4 heads from 6 trials would be:

$$\frac{6!}{4! \, (6-4)!} = \frac{6 \times 5 \times 4 \times 3 \times 2 \times 1}{(4 \times 3 \times 2 \times 1) \times (2 \times 1)}$$

We can cancel out a lot of the common numbers leaving the coefficient as:

$$\frac{6 \times 5}{2} = \frac{30}{2} = 15$$

and this agrees with the result from our Pascal's triangle method.

We can further generalise our probability calculations by noting that the formula for calculating the probability of any combination of events is:

$$\frac{n!}{x! \, (n-x)!} \, P^x (1-P)^{n-x}$$

where n is again the number of trials, x is the number of successes and P is the probability of one event occurring. Since we are dealing with only two possible events the probability of the other event occurring is $(1-P)$.

Consider a salesman wishing to calculate the probability of making 4 sales from visiting 10 shops. From previous experience he knows the probability of each sale is 0.3. Using the binomial formula above the probability is:

$$\frac{10!}{4! \, (10-4)!} \times 0.3^4 \times 0.7^6$$

$$= \frac{10 \times 9 \times 8 \times 7 \times 6 \times 5 \times 4 \times 3 \times 2 \times 1}{4 \times 3 \times 2 \times 1 \times (6 \times 5 \times 4 \times 3 \times 2 \times 1)} \times 0.3^4 \times 0.7^6$$

$$= \frac{10 \times 9 \times 8 \times 7}{4 \times 3 \times 2 \times 1} \times 0.3^4 \times 0.7^6$$

$$= 210 \times 0.0081 \times 0.117649 = 0.20$$
(correct to two decimal places)

Thus there is a 0.2 probability of him making the number of sales he wants to, providing the shops are independent of one another.

Sometimes we wish to know the cumulative probability of x or more successes or n or fewer successes in n trials. In such a case we make use of the rule of addition and simply add the probabilities of all the possible successes. Thus with our salesman example, if we wish to know the probability of one or fewer sales we use the following expression:

$$P(A \leqslant 1) = P(A = 0) + P(A = 1)$$

$$P(A = 1) = \frac{10!}{1! \, (10-1)!} \times 0.3^1 \times 0.7^9 = 10 \times 0.3^1 \times 0.7^9$$

$$= 0.1211$$

$$P(A = 0) = \frac{10!}{0! \, (10-0)!} \times 0.3^0 \times 0.7^{10} = \frac{10!}{1 \times 10!} \, 0.3^0 \times 0.7^{10}$$

$$= 0.3^0 \times 0.7^{10} = 0.0282$$

$$\therefore \, P(A \leqslant 1) = 0.1211 + 0.0282 = 0.1493$$

Expressing this as a percentage, we could say that there is a 14.9% chance that the salesman will make no sales, or one sale.

If we wish to know the probability of nine or more sales we compute the probability as:

$$P(A \geqslant 9) = P(A = 9) + P(A = 10)$$

where

$$P(A = 9) = \frac{10!}{9! \ (10 - 9)!} \times 0.3^9 \times 0.7^1 = 10 \times 0.3^9 \times 0.7^1 = 0.000138$$

and where

$$P(A = 10) = \frac{10!}{10! \ (10 - 10)!} \times 0.3^{10} \times 0.7^0 = \frac{10!}{10! \ 0!} \times 0.3^{10} \times 0.7^0$$

$$= 0.3^{10} \times 0.7^0 = 0.0000059$$

the combined probability $P(A \geqslant 9)$ is therefore:

$$\begin{aligned} P(A \geqslant 9) &= 0.000138 + 0.0000059 \\ &= 0.0001439 \end{aligned}$$

Again, in percentage terms, this means that there is a 0.014% chance that the salesman will make a sale at all 10, or at all but one of the 10 shops he proposes to visit.

14.3   The normal distribution

The **normal probability distribution** is important since the observations from many random processes are known to follow it. In addition, normal distributions can be used to approximate to other types of distribution. This means that where a calculation on some other distribution is excessively awkward – for example, a binomial expression with a very

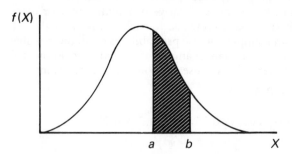

Fig 14.2 The normal probability distribution curve

Notes
  i The curve is a symmetrical bell-shaped curve.
 ii Since the normal distribution is continuous we cannot use it to calculate the probability of a discrete event occurring.
iii However, we can use it to calculate the probability of a variable lying between two numbers, or above or below a particular number.
iv The areas under the graph are *proportional to probability*, with the whole area under the graph equal to one.

large number of trials – we can use the normal distribution instead and get very close to the answer we would have produced by doing the tedious binomial calculation.

Because the normal distribution is continuous we cannot use it to calculate the probability of a discrete event occurring. We can use it, however, to calculate the probability of a variable lying between two numbers or above or below a particular number. In order to do this we make use of the **standard normal distribution** which has a mean of zero and a variance of one. A graph of such a distribution is shown in Fig 14.2 on page 224.

As explained in the notes under Fig 14.2 the areas under portions of the graph – such as the area $a - b$ in the diagram – are proportional to probability with the total area under the graph being equal to one. These areas have been tabulated, as shown in Table 14.2 on page 226. They are easy to use in probability calculations. For example, Fig 14.2 shows a normal distribution with two points a and b. Suppose we wish to determine the probability of a variable occurring between a and b. We first have to transform or scale our distribution to match the standard normal distribution. This is achieved using the formula:

$$Za = \frac{a - \mu}{\sigma}$$

where a is one point of interest (see Fig 14.2), μ is the mean of our data series and σ is the standard deviation. So Z is the symbol used to refer to the difference between a and μ in units of the standard deviation. Similarly for the point b:

$$Zb = \frac{b - \mu}{\sigma}$$

We then make use of Table 14.2, which gives the area under the standard normal curve for each point Z.

For example, suppose the values of Z_b and Z_a are obtained from the table and the area between Z_b and Z_a is calculated by subtracting the two areas. Thus if Z_b is 1.5 and Z_a is 1.0 then the area between points a and b is 0.4332 (for Z_b) minus 0.3413 (for Z_a) which is 0.0919. *The area is the probability that we are seeking.* In other words there is a probability of 0.0919 or 9.19% of the variable lying between points a and b.

As an example of how we would use probability information of this type, suppose we wish to manufacture 20 000 pairs of men's shoes for the European market. It is not proposed to make shoes of every possible size, since the numbers of men with very small feet or very large feet are not great, and are usually catered for by specialist manufacturers. We would want to know the number to manufacture in each size range. There would be little point in either making them all size 40 or making the same number in each size. Suppose we find out that the mean size for the population is 41 with a standard deviation of 2 and we assume the distribution of sizes to be normal. In order to find out how many shoes to manufacture for a shoe range from 39 to 45 we calculate the Z score for each size from 38 onwards. It is necessary to calculate the probability

Table 14.2 Probability table for the standard normal distribution
(Reproduced by courtesy of McGraw-Hill Book Company Ltd)

z	0.00	0.01	0.02	0.03	0.04	0.05	0.06	0.07	0.08	0.09
0.0	0.0000	0.0040	0.0080	0.0120	0.0160	0.0199	0.0239	0.0279	0.0319	0.0359
0.1	0.0398	0.0438	0.0478	0.0517	0.0557	0.0596	0.0636	0.0675	0.0714	0.0753
0.2	0.0793	0.0832	0.0871	0.0910	0.0948	0.0987	0.1026	0.1064	0.1103	0.1141
0.3	0.1179	0.1217	0.1255	0.1293	0.1331	0.1368	0.1406	0.1443	0.1480	0.1517
0.4	0.1554	0.1591	0.1628	0.1664	0.1700	0.1736	0.1772	0.1808	0.1844	0.1879
0.5	0.1915	0.1950	0.1985	0.2019	0.2054	0.2088	0.2123	0.2157	0.2190	0.2224
0.6	0.2257	0.2291	0.2324	0.2357	0.2389	0.2422	0.2454	0.2486	0.2513	0.2549
0.7	0.2580	0.2612	0.2642	0.2673	0.2704	0.2734	0.2764	0.2794	0.2823	0.2852
0.8	0.2881	0.2910	0.2939	0.2967	0.2995	0.3023	0.3051	0.3078	0.3106	0.3133
0.9	0.3159	0.3186	0.3212	0.3238	0.3264	0.3289	0.3315	0.3340	0.3365	0.3389
1.0	0.3413	0.3438	0.3461	0.3485	0.3508	0.3531	0.3554	0.3577	0.3599	0.3621
1.1	0.3643	0.3665	0.3686	0.3708	0.3729	0.3749	0.3770	0.3790	0.3810	0.3830
1.2	0.3849	0.3869	0.3888	0.3907	0.3925	0.3944	0.3962	0.3980	0.3997	0.4014
1.3	0.4032	0.4049	0.4066	0.4082	0.4099	0.4115	0.4131	0.4147	0.4162	0.4177
1.4	0.4192	0.4207	0.4222	0.4236	0.4251	0.4265	0.4279	0.4292	0.4308	0.4319
1.5	0.4332	0.4345	0.4357	0.4370	0.4382	0.4394	0.4406	0.4418	0.4429	0.4441
1.6	0.4452	0.4463	0.4474	0.4484	0.4495	0.4505	0.4515	0.4525	0.4535	0.4545
1.7	0.4554	0.4564	0.4573	0.4582	0.4591	0.4599	0.4608	0.4616	0.4625	0.4633
1.8	0.4641	0.4649	0.4656	0.4664	0.4671	0.4678	0.4685	0.4693	0.4699	0.4706
1.9	0.4713	0.4719	0.4726	0.4732	0.4738	0.4744	0.4750	0.4756	0.4761	0.4767
2.0	0.4772	0.4778	0.4783	0.4788	0.4793	0.4798	0.4803	0.4808	0.4812	0.4817
2.1	0.4821	0.4826	0.4830	0,4834	0.4838	0.4842	0.4846	0.4850	0.4854	0.4857
2.2	0.4861	0.4864	0.4868	0.4871	0.4875	0.4878	0.4881	0.4884	0.4887	0.4890
2.3	0.4893	0.4896	0.4898	0.4901	0.4904	0.4906	0.4909	0.4911	0.4913	0.4916
2.4	0.4918	0.4920	0.4922	0.4925	0.4927	0.4929	0.4931	0.4932	0.4934	0.4936
2.5	0.4938	0.4940	0.4941	0.4943	0.4945	0.4946	0.4948	0.4949	0.4951	0.4952
2.6	0.4953	0.4955	0.4956	0.4957	0.4959	0.4960	0.4961	0.4962	0.4963	0.4964
2.7	0.4965	0.4966	0.4967	0.4968	0.4969	0.4970	0.4971	0.4972	0.4973	0.4974
2.8	0.4974	0.4975	0.4976	0.4977	0.4977	0.4978	0.4979	0.4979	0.4980	0.4981
2.9	0.4981	0.4982	0.4983	0.4983	0.4984	0.4984	0.4985	0.4985	0.4986	0.4986
3.0	0.4987									
3.5	0.4997									
4.0	0.4999									

Notes

i The column headed Z shows the Z score – the scores achieved when our distribution is transformed into a standard normal distribution.

ii The other column headings show decimal developments of the Z score.

iii The proportion of area under a standardised normal curve is shown in the table for each Z score. The areas are only those between the mean of the distribution and the corresponding Z score. As the whole distribution has an area of 1, the table only reaches 0.5.

iv Reproduced with permission from Schaum's Outline: *Theory and Problems of Business Statistics.*

area between 38 and 39 to find the number of shoes that must be manufactured for the 38–39 size range.

For 38:

$$Z = \frac{38-41}{2} = \frac{-3}{2} = -1.5$$

For 39:

$$Z = \frac{39-41}{2} = \frac{-2}{2} = -1.0$$

For 40:

$$Z = \frac{40-41}{2} = \frac{-1}{2} = -0.5$$

and so on, giving the results in Table 14.3. From Table 14.2 the area under the standard normal distribution between 38 and the mean is 0.4332 which is found by looking up the Z score of 1.5 and the area between 39 and the mean is 0.3413. The area *between* 38 and 39 is therefore the *difference* between these two areas, ie 0.4332 – 0.3413 which is 0.0919. The other probabilities are shown in Table 14.3. They reveal that the total probabilities come to 0.9104. This is less than the total of one, because the extreme parts of the distribution represented by sizes 46 and above and 38 and below are not being manufactured, but are being left to be supplied by the specialist 'outsize' manufacturers. The number of pairs of shoes of each size to be manufactured can therefore be calculated as follows:

$$\text{Size } 39 = \frac{0.0919}{0.9104} \times 20\,000 = 2\,019 \text{ pairs}$$

The list is as shown in Table 14.3.

Thus the normal distribution is very useful for determining frequencies in the population and is widely used.

Table 14.3 Probabilities and frequency of shoe manufacture

Size range	Z score	Area (between range and mean)	Probability	Number to manufacture (out of 20 000)
38	– 1.5	0.4332		
39	– 1.0	0.3413	0.0919	2 019
40	– 0.5	0.1915	0.1498	3 291
41	0	0.0	0.1915	4 207
42	0.5	0.1915	0.1915	4 207
43	1.0	0.3413	0.1498	3 291
44	1.5	0.4332	0.0919	2 019
45	2.0	0.4772	0.0440	967
Total			0.9104	20 001

14.4 The Poisson distribution

Another type of distribution is the **Poisson distribution** which can be used to determine the probability of a designated number of successes when the events occur over a period of time or over space. This compares with the binomial distribution, where it is the number of events which is fixed. For example, if we wish to know the probability of a certain number of incoming calls into a telephone exchange in a fixed time period we would use the Poisson distribution. Such information might be required to assess the number of telephone operators needed to manage the exchange. The Poisson distribution probability for a occurrences of a desired event in a given time period is:

$$P(A = a) = e^{-\mu} \frac{\mu^a}{a!}$$

where μ is the mean number of times the event occurs in the time period and e is a constant, called the exponential number. The number e has the value 2.7183 correct to four decimal places.

Suppose that on average a telephone exchange receives 3 calls in a 2-minute period. The manager would like to know the probability of not more than 3 calls being received in a 2-minute period because he estimates the telephone exchange staff cannot cope with more than 3 calls in the 2 minutes. Thus $\mu = 3$, the mean number of calls, and the Poisson probability of a calls being received in the period is:

$$P(A = a) = e^{-3} \frac{3^a}{a!}$$

Thus:

$$P(A = 0) = \frac{e^{-3} 3^0}{0!} = \frac{e^{-3} 1}{1} = \frac{1}{e^3} = 0.0498$$

$$P(A = 1) = \frac{e^{-3} 3^1}{1!} = \frac{e^{-3} 3}{1} = \frac{3}{e^3} = 0.1494$$

$$P(A = 2) = \frac{e^{-3} 3^2}{2!} = \frac{e^{-3} 9}{2} = \frac{9}{2e^3} = 0.2240$$

$$P(A = 3) = \frac{e^{-3} 3^3}{3!} = \frac{e^{-3} 27}{6} = \frac{27}{6e^3} = 0.2240$$

Thus the probability of not more than 3 calls being received is the sum of these probabilities, which is 0.6472 or 0.65 to two decimal places. The manager would be concerned at this situation since it suggests his staff could cope for only 65% of the time. He may wish to employ a further operator or might decide that he cannot justify the extra cost and that for the remaining 35% of the time some people phoning in will get an engaged call.

14.5   Normal approximations to the binomial distribution

The mathematical application of the binomial distribution when n, the number of trials, becomes large is very involved. In such cases we can make use of the normal distribution which approximates to the binomial distribution when n is moderately large and p is not too close to 0 or 1 – a rough guide is that np and $n(1-p)$ should both be at least 5.

Consider a sample of 200 items from a production line where the probability of an item being defective is 0.15. With 200 items this would lead us to expect 30 defective items on average. We may wish to know the probability of obtaining more than 40 defective items in the sample. In order to calculate the total probability we must find the sum of the following probabilities $P(41) + P(42) + P(43) \ldots P(200)$. Each of these probabilities is determined from the expansion of $(0.85 + 0.15)^{200}$. This is a very tedious calculation.

Since $np = 30$ and $n(1-p) = 170$ are both greater than 5 we can simplify the calculation by using the normal distribution as an approximation. It can be proved that the mean, μ, of a binomial distribution is np and the standard deviation, σ, is $\sqrt{np(1-p)}$. Thus for our example $p = 0.15$, $(1-p) = 0.85$, $n = 200$ and therefore $\mu = np = 200 \times 0.15 = 30$ and $\sigma = \sqrt{np(1-p)} = \sqrt{200 \times 0.15 \times 0.85} = 5.05$ (to two decimal places).

Since the normal distribution is continuous we must apply a **continuity correction** to take account of the fact that the binomial expansion considers whole numbers of events occurring. Thus for an event of 41 in the binomial distribution the correction requires us to view 41 as a step in the normal curve for 40.5–41.5. We must determine the area under the normal curve between 40.5 and 41.5 to give us the 41 area. To calculate the probability of *more* than 40 defective items we require the total probability (ie the area under the normal curve) for all items greater than 40.5. We can use our Z score approach described previously to calculate this area, ie:

$$Z = \frac{x - \mu}{\sigma} = \frac{40.5 - 30}{5.05} = 2.079 = 2.08 \text{ (to two decimal places)}$$

The area under the curve for all items to 40.5 has a Z score of 2.08. From the table of areas under the normal curve (Table 14.2) this area between the mean and 40.5 is found to be 0.4812. The area beyond 40.5 is $0.5 - 0.4812$ which is 0.0188. The probability that more than 40 items will be defective is therefore 0.0188, or 1.88%.

14.6   Normal approximation to the Poisson distribution

The normal distribution approximates to the Poisson distribution when μ becomes large (say μ greater than 20) in the function:

$$P(A = a) = \frac{e^{-\mu}\mu^{a}}{a!}$$

As in the case of the binomial distribution the mathematical determination of Poisson distributions for μ greater than 5 becomes tedious. The mean of the Poisson distribution is always μ and the standard deviation can be proved to be $\sqrt{\mu}$.

Suppose we wish to know the probability of more than 30 people (ie 31, 32, etc) entering a shop in an hour given that the average was 25 people. Once again we must apply the continuity correction, and work from 30.5. Using the normal approximation and the continuity correction the Z score is calculated as:

$$Z = \frac{x - \mu}{\sigma} = \frac{30.5 - 25}{\sqrt{25}} = \frac{5.5}{5} = 1.1$$

The normal distribution probability table (Table 14.2) with a Z score of 1.1 gives the area between the mean and 30.5 as 0.3643. The area beyond is therefore $0.5 - 0.3643$ which is 0.1357. In other words the probability of more than 30 people entering the shop is 0.1357, or 13.57%.

Summary

1 A probability distribution is a set of possible results arising from the observation of, or experimenting with, variables, together with the relative frequencies with which they occur.

2 The mean of the distribution is called the expected value, or expectation of the distribution. Its formula is $E(A) = \Sigma\ AP(A)$. The standard deviation of the distribution is $\sigma(A) = \sqrt{E(A)^2 - [E(A)]^2}$.

3 The three possible distributions are the binomial distribution, the normal distribution and the Poisson distribution.

4 A binomial distribution is an expansion of a binomial expression (one containing two parts only) raised to a power. The coefficients of a binomial expansion may be found using the method of Pascal's triangle.

5 Where a large number of trials is envisaged Pascal's triangle becomes awkward and we find the coefficients by the formula $n!/[x!\ (n - x)!]$.

6 The normal probability distribution is one assumed by many random processes. The areas under the curve of such a distribution are proportional to probability. This fact is used to prepare a table of Z scores, the term Z meaning the difference between any point a on the horizontal scale and the mean, measured in standard deviations.

7 The Poisson distribution can be used to determine the probability of a designated number of successes occurring in a given time period. The formula is $P(A = a) = e^{-\mu}\mu^a/a!$, where μ is the mean number of times the event occurs in the time period and e is a constant, 2.7183.

8 Both the binomial and the Poisson distributions can be approximated by the normal distribution in certain circumstances.

Exercises on probability distribution

1 Explain what is meant by a probability distribution.
2 Calculate the number of screws that need to be manufactured for lengths 2, 3, 4, 5, 6, 7, 8 and 9 cm given that the mean length is 5 cm and the standard deviation is 1.2. Assume that the distribution is normal and that a maximum of 3 000 screws can be manufactured. Plot the distribution of screws as a histogram.
3 Calculate the probability of the following results from an experiment in which a coin is tossed 6 times, assuming that the probability of obtaining a head or a tail is 0.5:
   a 1 head and 5 tails
   b 3 heads and 3 tails
   c 4 heads and 2 tails
   d 0 heads and 6 tails
4 For the above example calculate the probabilities to three decimal places of all combinations of heads and tails and check that they sum to one.
5 Repeat Exercises 3 and 4 assuming the coin is weighted so that the probability of obtaining heads is 0.6 and the probability of obtaining tails is 0.4. What can you say about the probabilities?
6 A car salesman has a probability of 0.05 of selling a car. Calculate the probability of him exactly meeting his quota of 5 cars per month if on average 200 people make inquiries about cars per month. Suppose the quota had been specified as greater than 2 cars per month – calculate the probability of him satisfying this quota. Calculate the probability if the quota is changed to at least 5 cars per month.
7 Suppose a large van hire firm hires on average 35 vans per week. Calculate the probability that fewer than 30 vans will be required each week. Also calculate the probability that greater than 45 vans per week will be required.

15   Quality control

15.1   The nature of quality control

There is no such thing as 'quality' *per se*. Quality is always judged from
the subjective viewpoint of the customer or the producer. It is a waste
of time making an item better than it needs to be, and the quality controller aims for a quality that *a* satisfies the customer, and *b* is as cheap
as possible. A third requirement may be to meet any delivery deadline.
A quality-control procedure has to be tailor-made for the product and for
the contract being undertaken. It may be appropriate in some situations
to devise a statistical approach to ensure the quality of the items being
produced, but in other circumstances a more practical approach may be
best. It is said that Josiah Wedgwood, the founder of the pottery firm,
did all his quality control at the close of work each day with a hammer.
Anything he didn't like was hit with the hammer and put in the dustbin.
His method was a special case of attribute acceptance (see Section 15.4
below).

The essential elements of quality control are:

a Decide the quality required by the customer. This may require careful
consideration of the customer's specification or, if the customer leaves
it to the manufacturer, the engineer or other specialist must set
the specification in house, to meet the customer's needs in terms of
function, appearance, expected lifetime, final finish, etc.
b Cost the item to discover the likely price, and set up a system for
checking variances (ie difference between expected and actual costs
discovered) as the work proceeds.
c Evaluate the likely performance of machines, operators, etc to ensure
that the item can be made, and that price and delivery dates can be
achieved.
d Plan the manufacture: the materials required, the machines required
and their availability, the labour situation and the skills needed and
the inspection processes (at all stages). (For example, we need to
inspect material as it is delivered; the setting-up of machines as they
start to be used; the components as they are produced; and any final
assembly activities.)
e As quality-control data are collected, use them to feed back information and advice to areas needing help. We may need to shut out
suppliers of poor quality goods; to train up staff who produce failed
items, etc.

In any manufacturing process there will be a certain degree of variability in the goods manufactured. We all know of the possibility of buying a car that has more faults than we would expect. Variations in machine performance can cause such variability in the final product, and so can poor workmanship or the use of faulty parts.

A manager of a factory will want to know when the firm's products are unsatisfactory, and will seek to control their quality. We may express the quality in a variety of ways. It might be the length of a nail or screw, the thickness of a sheet of glass or the colour of a piece of pottery. We may decide that the final product is unsuitable if any of these matters fail to meet specifications, or if any other sort of malformation or damage is suffered.

In order to manage the manufacturing process successfully it is necessary to detect adverse trends in the quality of the goods so that any significant deviation from standards can be corrected. For example, a machine producing nails may drift so that the length increases slowly. If this is not detected the machine will continue to produce long nails with a resultant increase in material required. Moreover, it may be impossible to sell the nails. Whilst it would be impractical to measure every nail it is possible to sample the nails and measure the mean length of the sample. This mean length can be compared with the expected or desired mean length and if the difference is statistically significant then management action is required to restore the machine to its correct setting. The main features of the quality-control scheme are therefore the sampling of the product and the identification of a change in a quality-control variable. If the product is classified just as 'good' or 'bad' then this attribute is used so that the proportion of defective items is compared with the expected proportion of defective items.

15.2 Control charts

Control charts are used to compare the sample means with the overall process mean, as shown in Fig 15.1.

The mean of the control variable is plotted on the chart. In the case we are considering, if each sample consists of 5 nails the mean we want to plot on the chart is the average length of the 5 nails selected at random. The control chart features the intended length of the nails as a continuous central line. Also shown on the chart are two warning lines and two action lines. These are specified to be at the 95 and 99% confidence bounds, respectively. In the case of the 95% confidence bounds we would expect the sample mean to stay within these bounds for 95% of the time (ie 5 in 100 sample means might lie beyond the warning line). In the case of the 99% bounds the mean should stay within the lines for 99% of the time (ie 1 in 100 samples might lie beyond the action line). If the mean moves outside the 95% line then we would suspect something is wrong with our process. If it moves outside the 99% line something is almost certain to be wrong and we should check our process machinery immediately.

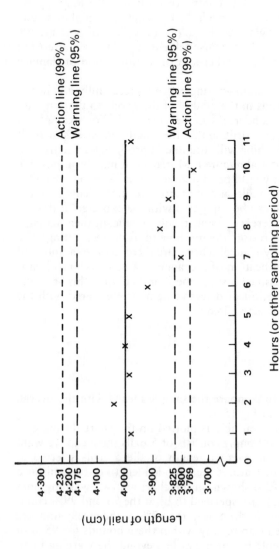

Fig 15.1 A quality-control chart

Notes

i The overall process mean (the specification length of a nail) is marked on the chart as a horizontal line. This is the standard against which our quality is to be judged – in this case it is the standard length of a nail.

ii The two sets of confidence bounds are calculated as shown later in this chapter.

iii At regular intervals, perhaps hourly or daily, we would sample the output – for example, take 5 nails from the bin into which new nails are falling. We would measure these and find the mean length. This mean is plotted on the chart and should lie within the two 95% warning lines. If the mean length is outside the warning lines it may mean that it is one of the 5 out of 100 samples that will fail. We would heed the warning and try another sample – if this was outside the warning line too we would suspect that something is wrong with the process. *iv* If the means of samples get outside the 99% line something is clearly wrong and we must take action to check the process and improve the

15.3 Confidence bounds

The key to a quality-control system is calculating the position of the confidence bounds relative to the expected mean of the quality-control variable. A distribution of product quality will exist around a mean level since we know that because of machine tolerance levels there will inevitably be some variations in product quality.

Confidence bounds are easily calculated if information on the mean and the standard deviation of the distribution is known. In our example on the machine for producing nails, the manufacturer may know that the mean length of the nails is 4 cm and the standard deviation is 0.2 cm. If we assume that the distribution is normal, from Table 14.2 (page 226) we find that for 95% of the area under the curve to be enclosed the number of standard deviations from the mean is 1.96. At the 99% level the number of standard deviations from the mean is 2.58. The confidence limits may be expressed as:

$$\text{Confidence bound} = \bar{x} \pm \frac{Z\sigma}{\sqrt{n}}$$

where $\bar{x}$ is the mean, Z is the number of standard deviations from the mean, n is the number of samples taken and σ is the standard deviation. Thus at the 95% level for a 4-cm nail the confidence limits for a sample of 5 nails are:

$$4 \pm \frac{1.96 \times 0.2}{\sqrt{5}} = 4.175 \text{ and } 3.825$$

For the 99% level the confidence levels are:

$$4 \pm \frac{2.58 \times 0.2}{\sqrt{5}} = 4.231 \text{ and } 3.769$$

These levels are marked as the warning and action lines on the control chart (as in Fig 15.1).

A further safeguard which is sometimes marked on the chart is to enter the **range** of each sample – preferably in a different colour. This means the lengths of the longest and shortest nails in a sample would be recorded if they came outside the action-line measurements. This is because the mean length might conceivably be within the limits and yet every nail be longer or shorter than the permissible limits. While such erratic behaviour on the part of any machine would be a cause for serious concern, and the much more likely event is that all the nails would be shorter or all longer than required, the cautious quality-control engineer might ask for this extra record to be kept.

The great merit of this type of quality-control system is that it can be kept by relatively unskilled staff once the specifications for each sample test have been laid down (perhaps on a standard record sheet which is available in pad form).

15.4 Attribute acceptance sampling

If the quality-control variable cannot be measured and the product is either good or bad then attribute-acceptance sampling can be used to maintain quality control. In attribute sampling the proportion, p, of products that are defective is specified and a control chart drawn as before. In acceptance sampling a certain proportion, say p, of defective items is accepted as tolerable. Samples of size n are taken periodically from the output of the process, and action is taken to correct machine performance if too many items in the sample are defective. The maximum acceptable number of defective items in the sample (the **acceptance number**) is calculated using the binomial distribution.

If the sample size is large enough ($np \geqslant 5$), the normal approximation to the binomial may be used. In this case the largest acceptable proportion of defective items is:

$p + 1.64\sqrt{p(1 - p)/n}$ at 95% significance level

$p + 2.33\sqrt{p(1 - p)/n}$ at 99% significance level

Note that because we are only interested in deviations above the proportion, p (rather than in deviations in either direction from a mean level, as in the previous sections), we use the one-sided confidence limits 1.64 and 2.33 for the standard normal distribution rather than the more familiar two-sided limits ± 1.96 and ± 2.58.

The lower limits need not be drawn in the control chart since a lower proportion of defective items implies better-than-expected quality. Thus for a 5% proportion of defective items $p = 0.05$ and, assuming a sample of 20 items, the 95 and 99% confidence limits are, respectively:

$$\text{Acceptance no.} = 0.05 + 1.64\sqrt{\frac{0.05 \times 0.95}{20}} = 0.13 \text{ or } 13\%$$

$$\text{Acceptance no.} = 0.05 + 2.33\sqrt{\frac{0.05 \times 0.95}{20}} = 0.164 \text{ or } 16.4\%$$

Thus if the proportion of defective items moves from 5% (or 1 in 20 samples) to above 13% (or about 3 in 20 samples) action is required to correct the machine or production line performance.

The limits may explained as an increase in the acceptable level of defective items in a sample which cannot be explained by the normal expectations of a random sample at the 95 or 99% level of probability and must therefore be due to some defect in production procedures. The formulae given above are similar to those for confidence limits, but in this case the standard deviation σ is approximated by $\sqrt{p(1 - p)}$ which is derived using the normal approximation to a binomial distribution (see Chapter 14).

15.5 Pareto curve analysis

A Pareto curve is a curve which brings out the influences of various factors on any given situation. It draws its name from an Italian economist who used it to study the distribution of wealth in Italy, but it has wide application in other fields, including quality control. Suppose we have a product which has to be fully inspected before final acceptance as meeting the quality standards we have laid down. Some units will pass first time, having been correctly manufactured. Others will be rejected for all sorts of reasons and have to be diverted into a rectification work-shop where faults can be corrected, or arrangements can be made with the department at fault for their return and eventual rejoining of the 'test' line. Suppose there are 20 different reasons for failure. It would be very surprising if the faults occurred exactly the same number of times. In 100 rejections, it would be very unlikely that each of the 20 faults occurred 5 times. The much greater probability is that some faults occurred more frequently, and other faults were pretty rare – perhaps only a single example occurring of some of them. Effective quality control would therefore take account of the frequency of particular faults and give priority to sorting out the most frequently-occurring problems.

Analysis of the reaction rates can be made in many ways, but if we take the *numbers* of units which are defective for various reasons, from our analysis of the reports coming through from the inspection department, we might have figures as follows, in the order of frequency (ie most frequent defect given first).

Fault no	Defect	Frequency	% defective	Cumulative % defective
1	Component X	86	25	25
2	Final painting	74	21	46
3	Electrical fault	62	18	64
4	Bad assembly	49	14	78
5	Component Y	33	10	88
6	Lighting fault	22	6	94
7	Brake failure	13	4	98
8	Component Z	4	1	99
9	Door fault	2	1	100
10	Window fault	1	0	100
		346	100	

Figure 15.2 shows a curve drawn to illustrate these data in a manage-ment report, although for practical purposes the data themselves (once we have analysed our reports to see what they say) are enough to get work put in hand to eliminate the fault. In Fig 15.2 the cumulative per-centage of faults has been plotted against the (equally spaced) fault number on the horizontal axis, plotting having been made against the midpoint of the space allotted to each fault. As a matter of interest, the 45° line drawn in shows the shape the curve would be if all 10 faults had occurred with equal frequency – ie 10% of the total frequencies arising from each fault.

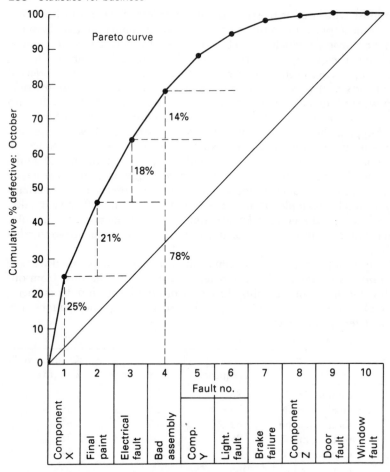

Fig 15.2 Illustrating fault frequencies with a Pareto curve

Notes
i The vertical axis shows the cumulative % of defective items.
ii The horizontal axis shows the faults found, equally spaced.
iii Plotting of the cumulative % against the midpoints of the space allocated to each fault gives a curve which rises steeply at first (because the faults are arranged in decreasing order, with the most frequent fault in first place).
iv The curve flattens out at the end as less and less frequent occurrences mean that the increase each time is smaller.
v We can see that 78% of the trouble is caused by only 4 of the faults.

Although in this case we have used the numbers of faults as our guide in plotting the Pareto curve, we could have used others, for example:

a We could have used the value (in money terms) lost by the fault. For example, suppose the window fault, no 10, which in numerical terms did not amount to even 1%, in cost terms came to a very large amount. Plotting the graph on the basis of the value lost would make no 10 more influential – a greater percentage of the total cost.

b We could have plotted part numbers rejected.

c We could have plotted 'operator responsible' and thus pinpoint where retraining was required.

d We could plot the inspector who found the fault. This would discover inspectors who show excessive zeal, or have a grudge against a particular operator or department. (Bias can creep into our statistics at any level.)

Summary

1 All manufacturing processes are subject to variations caused by machine wear, quality variations in raw materials, human error, etc. To supervise quality it is necessary to implement sampling procedures known as quality controls.

2 In quality control we sample the product, find the mean error (the mean variation from standard) and see if this error comes within the permitted margin of error. If a product is simply classified as 'good' or 'bad' we use the method of attribute sampling. This compares the number of defective items with the expected proportion of defective items.

3 A quality-control chart shows the standard expected as the overall process mean, with the 95 and 99% confidence bounds on either side of it. If a sample is taken and the mean measurement comes within these confidence bounds we have no need to adjust the production system. If samples come outside the confidence bounds the system needs adjusting.

4 The formula for calculating confidence bounds is: confidence bound $= \bar{x} \pm Z\sigma/\sqrt{n}$, where $\bar{x}$ is the standard laid down for an average product, Z is the number of standard deviations from the mean for the confidence level required (1.96 or 2.58), σ is the standard deviation and n is the number of samples taken.

5 With attribute sampling the product is assessed by a skilled craftsman for its various attributes – shape, colour, glaze, etc, in pottery, for example – and is judged either good or bad. A proportion of defective items is agreed, and if this is exceeded the process is investigated for possible malfunctions or other defects. The formula is $p + Z\sqrt{p(1-p)/n}$, where p is the permitted proportion of defective items, Z is the number of standard deviations (using 1.64 for the 95% confidence limit and 2.33 for the 99% limit, since we are dealing with a one-sided limit) and n is the number of samples taken.

6 Pareto curve analysis is a procedure which shows what faults in a product are most frequent and therefore the most urgent if customer dissatisfaction is to be reduced.

Exercises on quality control

1 Draw a control chart for the manufacture of small batteries given that the mean life of a battery is 9 hours and the standard deviation is 1

hour. Assume that the distribution is normal and that a sample of 10 batteries can be tested each day.

2 For the same sample as Exercise 1 redraw the control chart assuming the number of samples is increased to 20 batteries per day. Explain why the confidence limits should be different.

3 A television manufacturer wishes to ensure that the proportion of defective sets leaving his factory is less than 1%. Design a quality-control scheme which will enable him to do this.

4 A machine fills bags of coffee so that the net weight of coffee in each bag is 0.5 kg with a standard deviation of 0.04 kg. The machine can be adjusted and a sample of 12 bags has a mean weight of 0.55 kg. Test the hypothesis that the machine needs adjusting.

5 A final inspection department at a fork-lift truck factory produces inspection data which shows that the following faults occurred in the 100 trucks produced on 7 May 19—:

Fault	Number
Fuel tanks	5
Engines	13
Assembly	17
Final painting	23
Fork alignment	1
Tyres	3
Seats	4
Steering	19
Brakes	8
Pedals	3
	96

Draw a Pareto curve to illustrate the data by frequency of defect.

16 Correlation and regression

16.1 The association of two variables

In business it is often necessary to analyse data to determine a relationship between two variables. The two variables may be linked in some manner so that a knowledge of one can be used to infer or predict the other. Such a prediction can then be used to aid a management decision. For example, a business proposing to undertake a further advertising campaign would want to examine past advertising costs and sales figures to determine whether a further increase in advertising costs could be justified by the potential increase in sales. Similarly, a farmer would not want to increase applications of expensive fertiliser unless an increased crop yield could be anticipated. In both these cases an analysis of past data will reveal the association between the variables which may be used to predict the effects of increased advertising or increased fertiliser application. There is said to be a **causal relationship** between the variables (increased advertising causes increased sales and increased fertiliser causes increased crop yield). The sales and crop yield are called **dependent variables** and the advertising costs and fertiliser costs are termed **independent variables**.

The extent to which one variable is dependent on another is often measured using **correlation analysis**. Whilst we might expect advertising revenue and sales to be **positively correlated** we would be surprised to see any correlation between variables such as the sales of paint brushes and chairs, unless people stand on new chairs to paint their houses, which is rather unlikely. It is possible, however, to come across **spurious correlations** and an example of this is the relationship between interest rates and house prices. When interest rates are falling people can afford larger mortgages and house prices tend to rise. A *negative correlation* is obtained between interest rates and house prices. If this correlation applied for all time then when interest rates rise we would expect house prices to fall. However, this does not happen because people are more reluctant to move and cannot afford the higher mortgage rates with the result that prices stagnate or rise more slowly, rather than fall. Thus the correlation is spurious when applied over the longer time scale. Quite often business decisions are made on the basis of spurious correlations, with disastrous results for the company involved. It is important, therefore, to understand correlation analysis and to be able to use it effectively as an aid to business management.

16.2 Scatter diagrams

The simplest method of investigating the relationship between two variables is to plot a scatter diagram. Consider the transport and delivery data shown in Table 16.1. The scatter diagram is obtained by plotting the delivery time against the distance travelled as shown in Fig 16.1.

We can see a variety of scatter diagrams in Fig 16.2. Sometimes the points tend to cluster about a straight line as indicated in Fig 16.2(a) and (b). In the first diagram the variables may be said to have a *strong positive linear correlation* since y is increasing with increasing x. In the second diagram, y is decreasing with increasing x and the relationship has a *strong negative linear correlation*. In Fig 16.2(c) there is no obvious relationship and *zero-correlation* is assumed. However, in Fig 16.2(d)

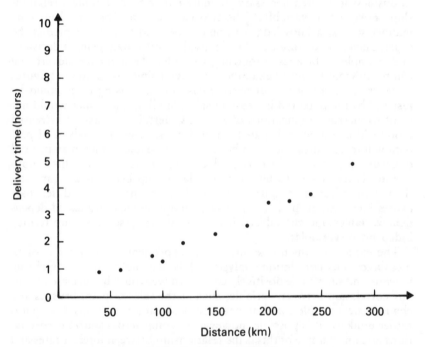

Fig 16.1 Scatter diagram of delivery time against distance

Notes
  i In general, the vertical axis is used for the dependent variable and the horizontal axis for the independent variable.
  ii In this case the time varies according to the distance the delivery vehicle has to travel. This means that time is the dependent variable and distance is the independent variable plotted on the horizontal axis.
  iii A scatter of points is obtained by plotting the delivery time values against the corresponding distances and making a series of dots on the graph. The pattern of these points often indicates immediately whether the two variables are associated in any way and whether the relationship is *linear* or not. The relationship is linear if the points tend to cluster about a straight line.
  iv In this figure they do appear to lie fairly close to a straight line.

Table 16.1 Transportation distance and time in transit

Journey number	Distance (kilometres)	Time taken (hours)
1	40	0.9
2	200	3.5
3	90	1.5
4	180	2.6
5	280	4.9
6	60	1.0
7	120	2.0
8	240	3.8
9	150	2.3
10	220	3.5
11	100	1.3

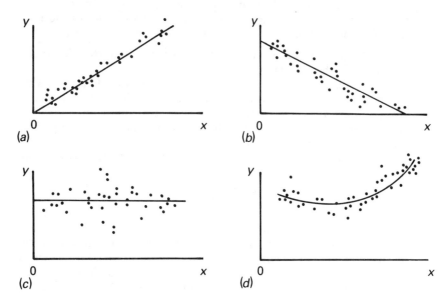

Fig 16.2 Generalised scatter diagrams

there does seem to be a relationship since a curved line can be drawn through the points. In this case a *non-linear* or *curvilinear* relationship exists between the variables. In this chapter we are concerned with linear relationships between two variables.

Bivariate distributions

The scatter diagrams we have drawn are the graphs of bivariate distributions, that is they are graphs of the way in which one variable changes relative to another variable. From our knowledge of the situation where the data were collected we may be able to say with reasonable certainty which is the independent variable and which is the dependent variable (for example, it is usually advertising that causes changes in sales, rather than vice versa). We can usually assume that one variable is a function of the other and our analysis will seek to discover the exact relationship between them – the degree of association between the variables. Having found some measure of this relationship we should be able to predict how to expand our business activity most effectively, and how to avoid adverse developments.

16.3 Lines of best fit

If there is a linear relationship between two variables it is often useful to determine a **line of best fit** or **regression line** through the data. (The word 'regression' is something of a misnomer – for historical reasons it has come to be used in statistics to describe a line which indicates the general path of change of data which are interrelated.) The drawing of 'lines of best fit' is not easy, and involves some use of mathematics if accurate regression lines are to be produced. There are three methods:

a *Inspection*. We just look at the pattern of dots and draw in a line that seems to fit the pattern.
b *The arithmetic means method*. This uses groups of data to find the arithmetic mean of parts of the scatter, and finds the line of best fit by joining up these partial means. Since the minimum number of means required to draw a straight line is three points it is sometimes called the **three-point method**.
c *The method of least squares*. This is a more mathematical method.

a Lines of best fit by inspection

The aim is to draw in an average line, equidistant from the scatter of points. This means we shall try to leave an equal amount of distance from the points to the regression line on either side. This may not mean that an equal number of points is on either side of the line, for one which was 2 cm above the line might 'balance' two below the line each 1 cm from it. A good way to try to find such a line is to hold a piece of cotton taut between thumb and forefinger of each hand and line it up to equalise the scatter on either side of the line. This has the advantage over a ruler that you can see the scatter on both sides of the line. When you have found the line of best fit draw it in with a ruler. One helpful point here is that the line of best fit, being an 'average' line, will always pass through the means of the two sets of data. Thus in the transportation data in Table 16.1 the mean distance is 153 km and the mean delivery time is 2.5 hours. If we plot this mean on the graph, as in Fig 16.3 we have a starting point for observing our stretched piece of cotton. The piece of cotton must be stretched so as to pass over this mean point, and pivot round it to find the line of best fit. (In Fig 16.3 some other means are also plotted. Ignore these for the present.) The result is a pretty good judgement of the line of best fit.

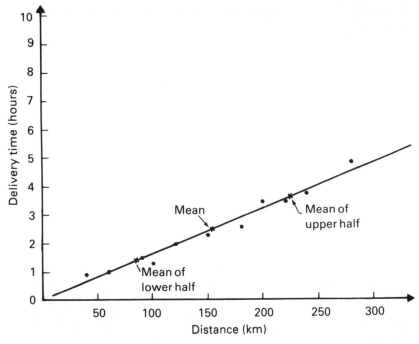

Fig 16.3 Scatter diagram showing the line of best fit, drawn in by inspection, or by the 'arithmetic means' method

b The arithmetic means method

In this method we take the arithmetic means of all the data as explained in *a* above and plot this point as an additional scatter point on the diagram. It is best to plot it in a distinctive way (in Fig 16.3 a tiny cross has been used). We now need at least two more arithmetic means from part of the data but we could put the whole set of data into a frequency distribution of, say five, groups, and plot the means of each group of data. In Fig 16.3 we have used only two groups. To find these groups we rearrange the table of data in order of the distance travelled, as shown in Table 16.2 on page 246. We divide this rearranged table into two sections, as shown, ignoring the central pair of figures if there is one, as in this case. We now work out the means for each group and plot them on the scatter diagram as additional crosses. For the transport data Group 1 has means of 82 km and 1.34 hours for distance and time respectively, and Group 2 has means of 224 km and 3.66 hours respectively. These locations are marked on the scatter diagram shown in Fig 16.3.

If the number of pairs of data is even, a straight line – the regression line – can be drawn through all three crosses. If the number of pairs is odd, as in our case, the line is drawn through the middle cross and approximately through the other crosses. We shall then find that some of the scatter points lie on one side of the line of best fit, and the rest on the other side. The data show a strong positive linear correlation – the

Table 16.2 Transportation distance and time in transit in order of increasing distance

Group	Distance (km)	Time taken (hours)
1	40	0.9
	60	1.0
	90	1.5
	100	1.3
	120	2.0
	150	2.3
2	180	2.6
	200	3.5
	220	3.5
	240	3.8
	280	4.9

scatter points are all close to the line of best fit and there is a relationship between distance and time taken. We must then decide from our knowledge of the problem whether the relationship is **causal**.

Thus the arithmetic means can be used to evaluate the line of best fit. It is, however, a fairly crude method and not as accurate as the method of least squares.

c The least squares method of regression analysis

The least squares method utilises the fact that the equation of a straight line is always of the form:

$y = a + bx$

where y and x are our dependent and independent variables as before, and a and b are constants. Such a relationship may be described as the regression of y upon x. Figure 7.7 (see page 100) shows that the constant a is equal to the **intercept on the y axis** and the constant b is determined as the **slope** or **gradient** of the line. By slope or gradient we mean the increase in y for every unit of x. In Fig 7.7 y increases by one-half of a unit (ie 0.5) for every single unit of x.

The least squares method provides the equation of the straight line that is the best fit to the points in a scatter diagram. In trying to find the best fit to the data we note that the points are scattered on either side of any line we care to draw. The best line will be the one which minimises the deviations of the scattered points from the line. As some of them are above the line, and have positive values, while others are below the line, and have negative values, it is necessary to square the deviations to eliminate the minus signs. The deviations are measured as vertical distances. Some typical points are shown in Fig 16.4.

To fix the regression line we need to know two things:

a the intercept on the y axis (ie, a in the formula $y = a + bx$)
b the slope of the line (ie, b in the formula $y = a + bx$)

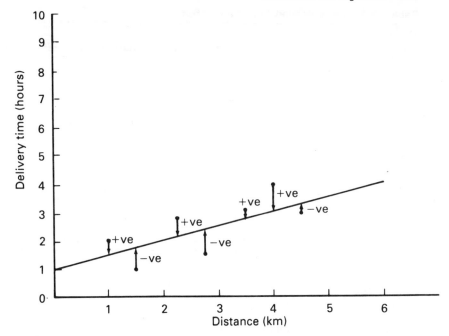

Fig 16.4 Deviations (measured as vertical distances) of scattered points from the regression line

These can be found using the following two formulae:

$$a = \bar{y} - b\bar{x}$$

where a is the intercept on the y axis, $\bar{y}$ and $\bar{x}$ are the arithmetic means of the data series and b is the slope of the line.

$$b = \frac{n \, \Sigma \, xy - \Sigma \, x \, \Sigma \, y}{n \, \Sigma \, x^2 - (\Sigma \, x)^2}$$

where b is the slope of the line, n is the number of data pairs and Σ is the symbol for a summation.

These formulae have been derived using mathematical analysis which is beyond the scope of this book. However, the formulae are relatively easy to use. Since the first of these equations has b in it, we must solve the second one first. To do this we draw up Table 16.3, as shown, using the transportation data of Table 16.2 on page 246.

Substituting these figures in our formulae above:

$$b = \frac{(11 \times 5168) - (1680 \times 27.3)}{(11 \times 317\ 000) - (1680)^2}$$

$$= \frac{56\ 848 - 45\ 864}{3\ 487\ 000 - 2\ 822\ 400}$$

Table 16.3   Table derived from Table 16.2

Distance x (km)	Time y (hours)	xy (distance × time)	x^2 (distance squared)
40	0.9	36	1 600
60	1.0	60	3 600
90	1.5	135	8 100
100	1.3	130	10 000
120	2.0	240	14 400
150	2.3	345	22 500
180	2.6	468	32 400
200	3.5	700	40 000
220	3.5	770	48 400
240	3.8	912	57 600
280	4.9	1372	78 400
$\Sigma\, x = 1680$	$\Sigma\, y = 27.3$	$\Sigma\, xy = 5168$	$\Sigma\, x^2 = 317\,000$

$$= \frac{10\,984}{664\,600}$$

$$= 0.0165 \text{ (to three significant figures)}$$

(*Note*: When calculating regression equations it is important to use at least three significant figures. Otherwise errors are introduced which can multiply up to produce an inaccurate equation.)

Now that we have found b we can find a:

$$a = \bar{y} - b\bar{x}$$

Since the arithmetic means are as follows:

$$\bar{y} = \Sigma\, y \div 11 = 27.3 \div 11 = 2.48$$
$$\bar{x} = 1680 \div 11 = 152.7$$
$$\therefore\ a = \bar{y} - b\bar{x}$$
$$= 2.48 - (0.0165 \times 152.7)$$
$$= 2.48 - 2.52$$
$$= -0.04$$

We can now draw the line of best fit on the scatter diagram, for we know that the intercept on the y axis is -0.04 (in other words the intercept is just below the zero point on the y axis) and the slope of the line is governed by b (y changes 0.0165 of a unit for every unit x changes).

In order to draw the regression line on the scatter diagram all we need do is plot some values for x and y, obtained from the regression equation, on the scatter diagram and draw the line as in the previous arithmetic means example. This has been done on Fig 16.5. The values of y when x was 0, 100, 200 and 300 were calculated as shown in Table 16.4 on page 249. As can be seen in Fig 16.5 the regression line thus plotted does indeed seem to be a very good fit to the scattered points.

Regression analysis is frequently used to forecast results by extending the regression equation outside the range of values which served as the

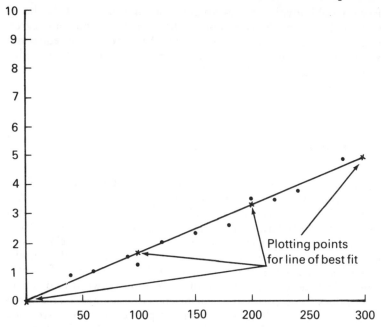

Fig 16.5 The regression line plotted from the least squares method

Table 16.4   Values of y for given values of x

	x			
	0	100	200	300
bx (ie $0.0165x$)	0	1.65	3.3	4.95
a	-0.04	-0.04	-0.04	-0.04
$y = a + bx$	-0.04	1.61	3.26	4.91

basis for calculating the a and b parameters. This can lead to errors. For example, consider our transport data. We are quite safe to interpolate (read off values from the regression line within the limits of the evidence we have at present) since the evidence seems to suggest that nothing else will affect delivery times seriously except the distance travelled. Thus we could read off the likely delivery time for a journey of 175 km as 2.86 hours, approximately. By actual calculation it is:

$$y = a + bx$$
$$= -0.04 + (0.0165 \times 175)$$
$$= -0.04 + 2.8875$$
$$= 2.8475$$
$$= 2.85 \text{ hours}$$

However, suppose we wish to determine the delivery time for a distance of 1000 km, the calculation moves outside the limits of the present data. The **extrapolated** delivery time is 16.46 hours. It is highly likely that such a journey would involve an overnight rest en route, and 12 hours should be added to the delivery time to allow for this. Thus our regression equation produces an incorrect result. When regression equations are extrapolated outside the range of the original data, reliable predictions cannot be guaranteed, and they should always be used with caution.

16.4   The coefficient of correlation

If there is a linear correlation between two sets of data it will be either **direct** or **inverse**. Alternative names are *positive correlation* and *negative correlation*. If the observed values increase together or decline together there is a positive correlation. If one increases as the other decreases there is a negative (or inverse) correlation. It is convenient if the relationship can be described in mathematical terms, and the term used is the **correlation coefficient**. A coefficient is a number. The correlation coefficient is a number which tells us the degree of correlation between two sets of observed values. The correlation coefficient is designated r and varies from -1 to $+1$, through zero. If there is a perfect positive correlation between the two sets of data $r = +1$. If there is no correlation between the sets of data $r = 0$, while if there is perfect negative correlation, with one set of data decreasing exactly in step as the other increases, the correlation coefficient $r = -1$.

The correlation coefficient (its full name is the **Pearson's product moment correlation coefficient**) enables us to quantify the correlation between two sets of variables. In Section 16.2 we discussed the correlation in a scatter diagram in qualitative terms (strong positive correlation, weak negative correlation, etc). When quantified we can test the statistical significance of the relationship between two variables. The formula for the correlation coefficient is:

$$r = \frac{[\Sigma\,(x - \bar{x})(y - \bar{y})/n]}{[\sqrt{\Sigma\,(x - \bar{x})^2/n}]\,[\sqrt{\Sigma\,(y - \bar{y})^2/n}]}$$

where $\bar{x}$ and $\bar{y}$ are the arithmetic means of the two variables, n is the number of pairs of data and Σ is a symbol meaning 'the sum of'.

The formula may be written in words as:

$$r = \frac{\text{covariance of } x \text{ and } y}{\text{standard deviation of } x \times \text{standard deviation of } y}$$

This is explained later. The formula can be simplified mathematically but at this stage we will make use of a tabular presentation to simplify the calculations. The formula looks complicated, but the solution is quite straightforward if you construct a table of products as given in Table 16.5 on page 251. Once again the transportation data given in Table 16.1 have been used to illustrate the calculations.

Table 16.5   Table of products, etc.

(i) Distance, x (km)	(ii) Time, y (hours)	(iii) $x - \bar{x}$, where $\bar{x} = 152.7$	(iv) $y - \bar{y}$, where $\bar{y} = 2.48$	(v) $(x - \bar{x})^2$	(vi) $(y - \bar{y})^2$	(vii) $(x - \bar{x})(y - \bar{y})$
40	0.9	−112.7	−1.58	12 701.29	2.4964	178.066
60	1.0	−92.7	−1.48	8 593.29	2.1904	137.196
90	1.5	−62.7	−0.98	3 931.29	0.9604	61.446
100	1.3	−52.7	−1.18	2 777.29	1.3924	62.186
120	2.0	−32.7	−0.48	1 069.29	0.2304	15.696
150	2.3	−2.7	−0.18	7.29	0.0324	0.486
180	2.6	+27.3	+0.12	745.29	0.0144	3.276
200	3.5	+47.3	+1.02	2 237.29	1.0404	48.246
220	3.5	+67.3	+1.02	4 529.29	1.0404	68.646
240	3.8	+87.3	+1.32	7 621.29	1.7424	115.236
280	4.9	+127.3	+2.42	16 205.29	5.8564	308.066
$\Sigma x = 1680$	$\Sigma y = 27.3$	0	0	60 418.19	16.9964	998.546

Notes
Columns (iii) and (iv) must sum to zero – although the tiny errors do not sum exactly.

Substituting into the formula from Table 16.5, we have:

$$r = \frac{[\Sigma \ (x-\bar{x})(y-\bar{y})/n]}{[\sqrt{\Sigma \ (x-\bar{x})^2/n}] \ [\sqrt{\Sigma \ (y-\bar{y})^2/n}]}$$

$$= \frac{[998.546/11]}{[\sqrt{60 \ 418.19/11}] \ [\sqrt{16.9964/11}]}$$

$$= \frac{90.777}{\sqrt{5 \ 492.56} \times \sqrt{1.5451}}$$

$$= \frac{90.777}{74.1118 \times 1.243}$$

$$= \frac{90.777}{92.121}$$

$$= \underline{0.985}$$

We can see that there is almost perfect positive correlation between the two sets of data. Perfect correlation would be when $r = +1$, but here it is $+0.985$ which is very close to perfect correlation.

Note: To return to the written form of the formula:

$$r = \frac{\text{covariance of } x \text{ and } y}{\text{standard deviation of } x \times \text{standard deviation of } y}$$

The covariance is the average of the products of the deviations of each pair of data from their respective means. The deviations from the mean in columns (iii) and (iv) are multiplied together (column (vii)), added up and the total is divided by the number of pairs. This is the upper part of the formula:

$$\frac{\Sigma \ (x-\bar{x})(y-\bar{y})}{n}$$

What this means for the value of r is as follows. If the values of x and y show some correlation − in other words if x is large when y is large and their deviations from the mean keep in step − r is going to be positive and also large, because the sum of the products of the deviations will be large. By contrast, if there is negative correlation − in other words as x gets larger y gets smaller − then r is going to be negative, but it will still be large because the products will have the same sign and the sum of the products will be large but negative. But if there is no correlation, and positive or negative deviations of x coincide indiscriminately with positive or negative deviations of y, the products will have different signs and the sum of the products will be small, and consequently r will be small. That is why a small r indicates absence of correlation.

However, this value of r (which is dependent on the degree to which deviations of x and y move in sympathy) is not yet a mere coefficient − a mathematical number − because it is still expressed in the terms of the original data (in the case used, in kilometres and hours). r will be affected both by the units used − for example, if metres had been used instead of kilometres – and also by the number of pairs of data. We therefore have to eliminate both these elements in the calculation for r. We remove the influence of the number of pairs of data by dividing by n – to give us an average covariance for just one pair of data. This is why the covariance formula is $\Sigma\,(x - \bar{x})(y - \bar{y})/n$. We remove the influence of the absolute size of the units used by dividing by the standard deviations of both the variables. These standard deviations are themselves affected by the absolute size of the units used, and when we divide the covariance (which is affected by the same problem) by the two standard deviations the units cancel out and leave us with an r which is in numerical form only, and not affected by the units used in the original data.

Obviously this is not an easy formula to remember for examination purposes, and it *must* be learned by heart – but remembering it is easy if the purpose of the various bits is remembered. It is sometimes written:

$$r = \frac{\Sigma\,(x - \bar{x})(y - \bar{y})}{n\sigma x\sigma y}$$

but this is only a shorthand version of the full formula:

$$r = \frac{[\Sigma\,(x - \bar{x})(y - \bar{y})/n]}{[\sqrt{\Sigma\,(x - \bar{x})^2/n}]\,[\sqrt{\Sigma\,(y - \bar{y})^2/n}]}$$

It is hoped that the explanation provided above will help students remember each part, the purposes of which may be summarised as follows:

$(x - \bar{x})(y - \bar{y})$ multiplies the deviations from their means of each pair of data, to reveal *i* the sign of the covariance and *ii* the size of the covariance

$\sqrt{\Sigma\,(x - \bar{x})^2/n}$ (over n) finds the average of this covariance per pair of data / eliminates the influence of the size of the absolute units used for x upon the size of r

$\sqrt{\Sigma\,(y - \bar{y})^2/n}$ eliminates the influence of the size of the absolute units used for y upon the size of r.

All this leaves r as a coefficient only – a number between -1 and $+1$ indicating the degree of correlation between the data.

Note: The formula for correlation coefficients can be rearranged into several forms; these may be given in books of statistical formulae. One such form is:

$$r = \frac{n\,\Sigma\,xy - \Sigma\,x\,\Sigma\,y}{[\sqrt{n\,\Sigma\,x^2 - (\Sigma\,x)^2}]\,[\sqrt{n\,\Sigma\,y^2 - (\Sigma\,y)^2}]}$$

This formula requires fewer computational steps and is useful when dealing with large numbers of data pairs.

To illustrate its use, consider the figures given in Table 16.6 on page 254.

You are asked to establish whether there is any association between capital available and housing starts commenced in the year. The scatter graph which illustrates the data graphically is shown in Fig 16.6. There would appear to be some correlation but it is not markedly close.

Table 16.6 Housing starts by Construction (Camside) PLC

Year	Capital available to Construction (Camside) PLC (£m)	No of housing starts
1	5	68
2	8	72
3	14	54
4	25	285
5	36	460
6	38	325
7	42	360
8	60	238

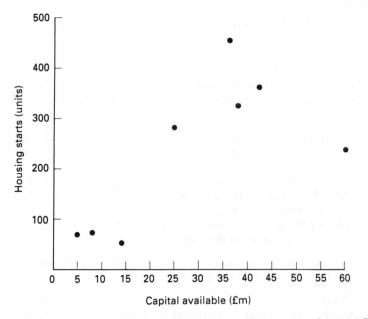

Fig 16.6 Scatter diagram for housing starts by Construction (Camside) PLC

If we calculate a coefficient of correlation using the formula given above we may get a more objectives assessment of the association. The figures for the calculation are found in Table 16.7.

Substituting into the formula, we have:

$$r = \frac{n \Sigma xy - \Sigma x \Sigma y}{[\sqrt{n \Sigma x^2 - (\Sigma x)^2}] [\sqrt{n \Sigma y^2 - (\Sigma y)^2}]}$$

$$= \frac{(8 \times 67\ 107) - (228 \times 1862)}{[\sqrt{(8 \times 9014) - (228)^2}] [\sqrt{(8 \times 597\ 418) - (1862)^2}]}$$

Table 16.7 Calculations

Capital available x (£m)	No of housing starts y	xy	x^2	y^2
5	68	340	24	4 624
8	72	576	64	5 184
14	54	756	196	2 916
25	285	7 125	625	81 225
36	460	16 560	1296	211 600
38	325	12 350	1444	105 625
42	360	15 120	1764	129 600
60	238	14 280	3600	56 644
$\Sigma x = 228$	$\Sigma y = 1862$	$\Sigma xy = 67\,107$	$\Sigma x^2 = 9014$	$\Sigma y^2 = 597\,418$

$$= \frac{536\,856 - 424\,536}{[\sqrt{(72\,112 - 51\,984)}]\,[\sqrt{(4\,779\,344 - 3\,467\,044)}]}$$

$$= \frac{112\,320}{[\sqrt{20\,128}]\,[\sqrt{1\,312\,300}]}$$

$$= \frac{112\,320}{141.8731828 \times 1145.556633}$$

$$= \frac{112\,320}{162\,523.7656}$$

$$= \underline{0.69} \text{ (correct to two decimal places)}$$

16.5 Interpretation of correlation coefficients

It has already been said that a coefficient close to $+1$ or -1 indicates a significant correlation between the sets of data, while if r is close to 0 there is little correlation between the data. It is important to remember when interpreting correlation coefficients that a significant correlation does not necessarily indicate causation. It may simply indicate a common linkage to other events. For example, sales value, wages, prices and many other sets of data are greatly influenced by inflation, and a relationship between data might appear to indicate causation, but in fact both may have been influenced by the general trend of inflation in the economy concerned. Also, a high degree of correlation is not necessarily indicative of a *significant* correlation. This is because the number of data pairs affects the correlation coefficient. It is easier for the 11 points of our transportation data to lie close to a straight line than 60 points. We would expect the correlation coefficient to fall as more points are included. The key issue is whether the correlation coefficient is significantly different from zero. If it is not then the two variables cannot be said to be related in a linear sense and it would be very misleading to use the *insignificant* correlation to aid a management decision. The methods of significance testing are relatively simple and are discussed in the next chapter. One helpful indication is as follows.

The coefficient of determination

The square of the value of r is called the **coefficient of determination** and is generally expressed as a percentage. It can be regarded as the percentage of change in y resulting from the change in x. In the first example given above $r^2 = 0.985^2 = 0.97$ or 97%. In other words, 97% of the change in y (time taken) can be explained by the change in x (distance) in the transportation data used. This is called the explained variance; the other 3% is unexplained, and may be due to a variety of factors.

In the second example about Construction (Camside) PLC the correlation coefficient = 0.69. The coefficient of determination

$$= (0.69)^2$$

$$\underline{= 0.47 \text{ or } 47\%}$$

So only 47% of the increase in housing starts is due to the greater availability of capital, and 53% is due to other reasons (it might be a bulge in the birth rate 20 years before, or immigration into the area, or any of a dozen other reasons.

Finally, note that the correlation coefficient is only a number, to show whether or not correlation exists. It tells us nothing about the nature of the correlation – it is for the business person to interpret the relationship and use it to influence his/her activities and results.

Whatever linear correlation coefficient may be obtained it is possible that a more significant non-linear or curvilinear relationship exists. It is often possible to transform the data in some manner (eg by taking logarithms, etc) so that the relationship between the transformed variables is linear. However, this is outside the scope of the present volume.

16.6 Rank correlation

An alternative approach to the Pearson product moment correlation coefficient discussed previously is to investigate the ranking of data and to determine the **Spearman rank correlation coefficient**. There are many situations where numerical values are not available, but data have been assembled in a *relative* order, the best being in the first rank, the second best next, and so on – like the starting grid for a Grand Prix motor race. This approach may be used to compare the performance of potential recruits to a company, or existing staff of the company, by the personnel officer. Suppose a company advertises for staff and requires some objective tests for comparing interviewees. It may set two types of test, an aptitude test and a training course. It may be impractical to give an overall mark for these tests and the trainees are ranked in order of merit. However, the personnel manager will want to investigate whether there is any correlation between the performance in the two tests. In order to do this the Spearman rank correlation coefficient (R) is calculated from the following formula:

$$R = 1 - \frac{6 \, \Sigma \, d^2}{n(n^2 - 1)}$$

where d is the difference in ranking between the two sets of observations and n is the number of data pairs. Note that this Spearman rank correlation has been designated with a capital R to distinguish it from the Pearson product moment correlation coefficient, designated r.

Consider the data in Table 16.8.
Substituting into the formula gives:

$$R = 1 - \frac{6 \times 22}{8(8^2 - 1)}$$

$$= 1 - \frac{132}{8 \times 63}$$

$$= 1 - \frac{132}{504}$$

$$= 1 - 0.26$$

$$= 0.74 \text{ (correct to two decimal places)}$$

As in the case of the Pearson correlation coefficient, R can vary between $+1$ and -1. In this particular case R is 0.74 which suggests a positive correlation between the two tests but not a particularly strong correlation.

Rank correlation techniques can also be applied to data sets such as our earlier example of transportation distance and delivery time data. Table 16.9 shows the data displayed in terms of ranking.

Table 16.8 Ranking from aptitude and training tests

Interviewee	Aptitude test ranking	Training course ranking	Difference in ranking, d	d^2
F Smith	4	3	1	1
G Williams	1	1	0	0
P Jones	8	6	2	4
P Brown	5	7	−2	4
J Blythe	2	4	−2	4
F Black	7	5	2	4
S Prune	3	2	1	1
K Tatler	6	8	−2	4
Total				22

Table 16.9 Ranking of transportation data

Distance, x (km)	Time, x (hours)	Ranking of x	Ranking of y	Difference in ranking, d	d²
40	0.9	1	1	0	0
60	1.0	2	2	0	0
90	1.5	3	4	− 1	1
100	1.3	4	3	+ 1	1
120	2.0	5	5	0	0
150	2.3	6	6	0	0
180	2.6	7	7	0	0
200	3.5	8	8.5	− 0.5	0.25
220	3.5	9	8.5	+ 0.5	0.25
240	3.8	10	10	0	0
280	4.9	11	11	0	0
Total					2.5

Substituting into the formula:

$$R = 1 - \frac{6 \; \Sigma \; d^2}{n(n^2 - 1)}$$

$$= 1 - \frac{6 \times 2.5}{11(11^2 - 1)}$$

$$= 1 - \frac{15}{11(120)}$$

$$= 1 - \frac{15}{1320}$$

$$= 1 - 0.011$$

$$= 0.99 \text{ (correct to two decimal places)}$$

This value is slightly higher than the Pearson correlation coefficient calculated previously. In general, the ranking correlation coefficient gives an approximate value of the correlation only but since it is easier to calculate for small data sets it can be used to provide a rapid assessment of a data set. The formula for R should be used with care when there are tied ranks (ie when two or more observations have the same value and hence the same rank). In such a situation give each tied rank the arithmetic mean of the ranks they occupy.

Summary

1   Correlation and regression are techniques for investigating the association between two variables.
2   The first stage of investigating two data series is to plot a scatter diagram; from an inspection of this it should be possible to detect whether the points lie on a straight line and the relationship is linear or whether a non-linear or curvilinear relationship exists.

3 If the relationship is clearly non-linear, a transformation of the data is required to obtain a linear relationship.

4 If the relationship appears linear the line of best fit or regression line can be determined. A rough idea of the regression line can be determined by inspection – using the stretched cotton thread technique. More accurate lines can be drawn using the arithmetic means method or the least squares method.

5 The regression equation can be determined and used to predict the dependent variable, but remember that extrapolation to values outside the range of the data series can produce unreliable predictions.

6 To evaluate the statistical significance of the relationship between the two variables we can calculate a correlation coefficient (r) which expresses the relationship as a number between $+1$ and -1. A value of r close to $+1$ implies a strong positive correlation; a value close to -1 implies a strong negative correlation but a value for r close to zero implies absence of correlation between the variables.

7 The formula for Pearson's correlation coefficient is:

$$r = \frac{[\Sigma \ (x - \bar{x})(y - \bar{y})/n)}{[\sqrt{\Sigma \ (x - \bar{x})^2/n}] \ [\sqrt{\Sigma \ (y - \bar{y})^2/n}]}$$

8 The coefficient of determination is calculated as the square of r and describes the percentage of explained variance to total variance.

9 Another method for determining correlation is to use the ranking of data grouped together in order of merit. Thus results in two examinations could be tested for correlation. The formula for Spearman's rank correlation coefficient is:

$$R = 1 - \frac{6 \ \Sigma \ d^2}{n(n^2 - 1)}$$

Exercises on correlation and regression

1 What is a scatter diagram? Make use of scatter diagrams to distinguish variables which display *a* perfect positive correlation, *b* weak negative correlation and *c* zero correlation.

2 The number of houses on which building commenced in England and Wales ('000) were as follows:

Year	Local government	Private
1	40	64
2	43	62
3	48	45
4	55	42
5	77	37
6	100	31
7	104	30
8	108	29
9	110	28
10	112	27

  a Draw a scatter diagram to represent this data.
  b Draw a regression line for the data by inspection.
  c Comment on this regression line.

3 The statistics shown below relate to a group of school leavers who
  left school in the year 19—. The first line shows the number of cer-
  tificates gained in examinations before leaving school. The second
  shows the salary earned 5 years later.

  a Draw a scatter diagram to represent this data.
  b Draw a regression line for the data by inspection.
  c Comment on this regression line.

	School leaver							
	A	B	C	D	E	F	G	H
Certificates	5	8	15	26	7	8	14	10
Salary (£)	7600	9000	13 200	17 200	8400	9200	14 400	13 600

4 The following data relate to the years of experience in the fashion
  trade of a group of fashion designers in the age range 20–30 years:

	Designer								
	Z	Y	X	W	V	U	T	S	R
Years of experience	2	3	8	13	14	12	8	6	7
Salary (£'000)	12	10	16	30	30	24	22	24	30

  a Draw a scatter diagram of these variables.
  b Using the least squares method draw a line of best fit.
  c Comment on this line of best fit.

5 The following data relate to the licences issued for colour and
  monochrome television licences in the 8 years shown:

	Year							
Licences issued (millions)	1	2	3	4	5	6	7	8
Monochrome	14.1	12.3	10.6	9.4	8.4	7.4	6.5	5.4
Colour	2.8	5.0	6.8	8.3	9.6	10.7	11.9	12.8

  a Draw a scatter diagram of these variables.
  b Using the least squares method draw a line of best fit.
  c Comment on this line of best fit.

6 Using the data of Exercise 2 above calculate the product moment
  correlation coefficient. Comment upon your result.

7 The figures below show the average weekly turnover (£ sterling) and average weekly profit (£ sterling) achieved by eight retail shops in a certain town:

	Shop							
	1	2	3	4	5	6	7	8
Average profit	45	60	85	90	240	125	70	40
Average turnover	250	210	476	432	1400	800	350	240

a Draw a scatter diagram to represent this data.
b Calculate the product moment correlation coefficient.
c Comment on your results.

8 Salesmen were asked to report the entertainment expenses incurred with various customers, and these were compared with the value of the orders gained. The results were as follows:

Customer	Value of orders gained (£'000)	Entertainment expenses (£)
A	5.0	85
B	—	56
C	7.5	180
D	3.0	24
E	0.2	154
F	1.5	36
G	2.5	42
H	—	85
J	4.0	—
K	16.8	260

Calculate the product moment coefficient of correlation between value of orders and entertainment expenses and comment on the results.

9 The following official statistics show two indexes each based on a base year 4 years earlier. The figures given are monthly figures for the year 19—.

Index of industrial production	Index of average earnings
102	154
104	156
106	166
108	164
108	169
109	176
109	181
109	186
107	189
106	191
106	200
104	208

Calculate the correlation coefficient and comment briefly on the results.

10 Monthly incomes and expenditures on fuel and light for 12 single-parent families are given as follows:

	Family											
	1	2	3	4	5	6	7	8	9	10	11	12
Income (£)	162	145	230	156	192	140	185	165	154	120	180	148
Fuel, etc (£)	29	24	42	27	34	20	28	30	21	22	32	25

Calculate the coefficient of correlation of these data and comment on the result.

11 a What are the problems of using regression lines for forecasting purposes?

b The figures for the Index of Retail Prices for the year 19— are given as follows (January 1974 = 100):

Jan.	Feb.	Mar.	Apr.	May	June
245.3	248.8	252.2	260.8	263.2	265.7
July	Aug.	Sept.	Oct.	Nov.	Dec.
267.9	268.5	270.2	271.9	274.1	275.6

Find the equation of the regression line of the Index of Retail Prices on time.

c Forecast the Index of Retail Prices for January in the year ahead.

12 a What are the chief differences between the product moment correlation coefficient and the rank correlation coefficient for two characteristics measured on a number of individuals?

b Calculate a rank correlation coefficient between home-produced steel used domestically and imported steel in the years shown below. Comment on your result.

Year	Home-produced consumption	Consumption of imported steels
1	16.8	3.4
2	16.4	3.8
3	15.7	4.3
4	15.2	3.6
5	15.3	4.8
6	14.4	5.8
7	14.1	4.1
8	12.8	6.2

17 **Sampling and significance testing**

17.1 Estimating the mean of a population

In previous chapters the notion of sampling a population has been introduced. Quite often we cannot afford the time or cost to measure the statistics of an entire population and we can make use of sampling techniques to provide estimates of the statistics of interest.

If we decide to collect data about a sample, the question then arises 'How representative of the whole population is the sample data we have collected?' In order to be sure that our **sample statistics** are representative of the **population statistics** we need to know the errors associated with the sample statistics; as a measure of these errors the **confidence limits** are frequently calculated. This term, confidence limits, may be understood as follows:

a We have taken a sample of the whole population in order to make statements about the population.

b If the sample is representative of the whole population the statements we make will be valid.

c The difficulty is that any one sample may be unrepresentative and we can never be sure that the sample we have taken is representative.

d What we can do is lay down confidence limits which say that provided the population mean lies between these limits, our sample is representative of the population in so far as 95% (or 99%) of all possible samples would look something like ours.

The mean, $\bar{x}$, of a sample is an estimate of the true population mean, which is called μ. Clearly, if we take a number of sample sets from a population there will be a distribution of values of $\bar{x}$ (sample means), as shown in Fig 17.1. The 95% confidence limits are located at the points $\bar{x}_a$ and $\bar{x}_b$ in Fig 17.1 such that the shaded area under the normal curve is 95% of the total area. Since the given areas in the Z score table (Table 14.2 on page 226) relate to the area under the curve *from the mean* we have to look up the area 0.95/2 or 0.475. From Table 14.2 the Z value corresponding to $\bar{x}_b$, the upper 95% limit, is 1.96 and by symmetry the Z value corresponding to $\bar{x}_a$ is -1.96.

It is convenient at this point to discuss the distribution illustrated in Fig 17.1. The distribution arises because each particular sample inevitably displays a **random sampling error**. This does not mean any mistake has been made, simply that chance variations cause the sample mean to be different from the population mean. The standard deviation of the distribution of the sample means is known as the **standard error of the**

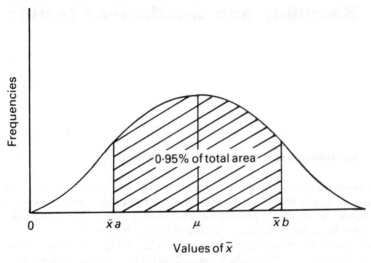

Fig 17.1 The distribution of sample means $\bar{x}$

mean. The use of the term 'standard error' denotes that we are considering a sample distribution, not a sample, or the whole population. This may be calculated by the formula:

$$\sigma_{\bar{x}} = \frac{\sigma}{\sqrt{n}}$$

where $\sigma_{\bar{x}}$ is the standard error of the sample distribution, σ is the standard deviation of the population and n is the size of the sample. The larger the sample the smaller the standard error and the closer we are to the population mean.

There are several theoretical results associated with this distribution. First, the mean of the distribution of sample means is the same as the population mean, μ. Second, as explained above, the standard deviation of the sample means, $\sigma_{\bar{x}}$, is equal to the standard deviation of the population, divided by the square root of the sample size.

Third, as the sample size, n, increases the distribution approaches the normal distribution and for n greater than 30 it can usually be assumed to be normal. When the normal approximation to the distribution of the sample mean is valid, we can use the Z score approach of Chapter 14 to obtain confidence limits for the sample mean. Since $\bar{x}$ has mean μ and standard deviation $\sigma_{\bar{x}} = \sigma/\sqrt{n}$, its Z score is:

$$Z = \frac{\bar{x} - \mu}{\sigma/\sqrt{n}}$$

From Chapter 14 we know that the symmetric 95% confidence limits for the Z score are -1.96 and $+1.96$. Thus the 95% confidence limits for $\bar{x}$ are $\bar{x}_a$ and $\bar{x}_b$, where:

$$\frac{\bar{x}_a - \mu}{\sigma/\sqrt{n}} = -1.96$$

$$\therefore \bar{x}_a - \mu = -1.96\sigma/\sqrt{n}$$
$$\therefore \bar{x}_a = \mu - 1.96\sigma/\sqrt{n}$$

and similarly:

$$\bar{x}_b = \mu + 1.96\sigma/\sqrt{n}$$

Confidence limits are often misunderstood. It is important to recognise that we are *not* saying that there is a 95% probability that the population mean lies between the limits $\bar{x}_a$ and $\bar{x}_b$: the population mean is a single number, it does not have a probability distribution, and either it lies between the confidence limits or it does not – there is no middle ground. What *is* true is that if the population mean lies outside the 95% confidence limits, then we have observed an event – namely, that the difference between $\bar{x}$ and μ exceeds $1.96\sigma/\sqrt{n}$ – whose probability is less than 5%. Thus, having observed the sample mean $\bar{x}$ and calculated the confidence limits $\bar{x}_a$ and $\bar{x}_b$, we can say 'either μ lies between $\bar{x}_a$ and $\bar{x}_b$, or a very unlikely event has occurred'. It is in this sense that we can have confidence that μ (the true population mean) lies between $\bar{x}_a$ and $\bar{x}_b$.

Thus the quantities $-1.96\sigma/\sqrt{n}$ and $+1.96\sigma/\sqrt{n}$ represent the confidence limits for μ and can be evaluated given n and the population standard deviation σ.

Suppose we attempt to find the cost of rented accommodation in Newtown (which has 2000 rented houses) by taking a random sample of 50 houses. The result is that we find the mean rent is £40 per week and the sample has a standard deviation of £6.40. This is the usual way to present the results of any sample survey, to show the mean and the standard deviation of the sample.

How confident can we be that these sample results are representative of the rents of houses in Newtown generally? The confidence limits for μ are:

$$-1.96\,\frac{\sigma}{\sqrt{n}} \qquad \text{and} \qquad +1.96\,\frac{\sigma}{\sqrt{n}}$$

We could therefore work out these limits if we knew the value of σ, which is the standard deviation of the population. Unfortunately we do not know this, and could only find it out by doing a complete census of rents. However, we *can* use the standard deviation of our sample, S, to approximate (get reasonably close to) the standard deviation of the population. It can be shown mathematically that for large samples $(n \geqslant 30)$ the standard deviation of the sample approaches very closely the standard deviation of the population. Using £6.40 as the standard deviation our results above become:

$$\frac{-1.96 \times £6.40}{\sqrt{50}} \qquad \text{and} \qquad \frac{+1.96 \times £6.40}{\sqrt{50}}$$

$$= \frac{-£12.544}{7.071} \qquad \text{and} \qquad \frac{+£12.544}{7.071}$$

$$= -£1.774 \qquad \text{and} \qquad +£1.774$$
$$= -£1.77 \qquad \text{and} \qquad +£1.77$$

We can therefore state that the mean rent payable for rented property in Newtown lies within £1.77 either side of our figure of £40, found by the sample investigation we carried out, with a 95% degree of confidence in this estimate.

17.2 Estimating the proportion of a population

Determining the confidence limits for a proportion of the population is similar in principle to the method described above for estimating the mean. A proportion of the population is used in business a great deal in market research, where we might investigate the proportions of populations displaying a particular characteristic. Thus if 77% of housewives prefer a particular brand of baked beans according to our sample of 200 families, what are the confidence limits for this proportion?

Provided np and $n(1-p)$ are both greater than 5 we may use $\sqrt{p(1-p)/n}$ as the standard deviation of the sample distribution of the proportions. In this case 200×0.77 (np) and 200×0.23 $(n(1-p))$ are both over 5. Therefore the standard deviation of the sample is:

$$\sqrt{\frac{p(1-p)}{n}} = \sqrt{\frac{0.77(0.23)}{200}} = 0.0297$$

The 95% confidence limits for the proportion are therefore:

$$0.77 \pm 1.96(0.0297) = 0.77 \pm 0.0582$$
$$= 0.8282 \text{ or } 0.7118$$

Therefore we can state with 95% confidence that between 71.18 and 82.82% of housewives prefer that particular brand of baked beans.

17.3 Estimating the difference between two means

Suppose we have taken two samples from different populations (for example, from the products of two manufacturers). Our samples have different means and different standard errors. We may wish to know the confidence limits for the difference between the means from the two populations. Consider samples from two manufacturers each of 100 batteries which we have been testing for longevity. The data are as follows:

Sample 1   mean 25 hours, standard deviation 5 hours
Sample 2   mean 22 hours, standard deviation 3 hours

Is there any difference between these two means, really? Obviously there is a difference of 3 hours between these samples, but is this difference significant or is it just a matter of chance? The significance of results is dealt with later in this chapter – here we are simply trying to establish confidence limits for the difference between the two means. Could they really be so close to one another that they could have been drawn from the same general population (batteries of a particular specification) and there is no real difference between the products from the two manufacturers?

In order to find the confidence limits for the difference between the two means we need to consider the distribution of the differences between the means. If the means of the two sample sets are $\bar{x}_1$ and $\bar{x}_2$ and the standard deviations of the populations are σ_1 and σ_2 then the 95% confidence interval is $(\bar{x}_1 - \bar{x}_2) \pm 1.96\sqrt{\sigma_1^2/n_1 + \sigma_2^2/n_2}$. Here $\sqrt{\sigma_1^2/n_1 + \sigma_2^2/n_2}$ is an estimate of the standard deviation of the difference between the population means $\mu_1 - \mu_2$, assuming that the standard deviations are unequal. The limits $\bar{x}_1 - \bar{x}_2 \pm 1.96\sqrt{\sigma_1^2/n_1 + \sigma_2^2/n_2}$ are valid in the following cases:

a both samples come from normal distributions with known standard deviations (not necessarily equal)
b both samples are large ($n_1\, n_2 \geqslant 30$) but not necessarily normal and both sample standard deviations are known
c in addition, the above limits are valid if both samples are large (not necessarily normal) and the standard deviations σ_1, σ_2 are not known, provided that the sample standard deviations s_1 and s_2 are used instead of σ_1 and σ_2

If either sample is small and both samples can be assumed to be approximately normal we can use confidence limits based on the t distribution, discussed in Sections 17.6 and 17.7 on pages 269 to 273. Confidence limits cannot be established for other non-normal small samples.

Our example fits the circumstances of (c) above. As before, we may not know the standard deviations of populations 1 and 2 but, if n is large and we know the standard deviations of our samples s_1 and s_2, we can use these instead of σ_1 and σ_2.

The 95% confidence limits for the difference between the means are:

$$(\bar{x}_1 - \bar{x}_2) \pm 1.96\sqrt{\frac{s_1^2}{n_1} + \frac{s_2^2}{n_2}} = 3 \pm 1.96\sqrt{\frac{5^2}{100} + \frac{3^2}{100}}$$

$$= 3 \pm 1.143$$

Thus the 95% confidence levels for the difference between the means are 4.14 and 1.86 correct to two decimal places. Since the lower limit does not encompass zero we can say that the difference between the means is significant at the 95 per cent level. This is further considered on pages 269–270.

17.4 Selecting the size of the sample

From the preceding analysis it is clear that confidence limits change as the sample size, n, changes. Thus we can design our sampling programme to match some desired confidence limit. For example in the case of the population of rents in Newtown we might wish to ensure that our estimate of the mean is very accurate. In such a case we might specify that 95% confidence limits are to be at $\pm £1.00$. The confidence limits would be:

$$\frac{1.96 \times £6.40}{\sqrt{n}} = £1.00$$

Rearranging this to find n we have:

$$n = \left(\frac{1.96 \times £6.40}{£1.00}\right)^2$$

$$= \left(\frac{1.96 \times 6.4}{1}\right)^2$$

$$= 157.35$$

To meet our accuracy requirements the sample size would have to be at least 157.35 – say a round figure of 160 houses investigated out of the total of 2000 rented properties in Newtown.

17.5 Hypothesis testing

We often need to ask questions like 'Are house rents in Newtown more than £45 per week on average?' or 'Do X's batteries last longer than Y's?' Questions like these can be expressed in statistical terms, and the procedure for answering them is known as **hypothesis testing**.

The first requirement of hypothesis testing is the **null hypothesis**. This is the statement which we want to test, usually formulated as a restriction on the parameters of a probability distribution. The **parameters** are the quantities which characterise a distribution: mean, standard deviation, population correlation coefficient, etc. Examples of null hypotheses would be 'the population mean of house rents in Newtown is £45' or 'the mean lifetimes of X's batteries and Y's batteries are equal'.

In hypothesis testing the **level of significance** is the statistical standard specified for rejection of the null hypothesis. This is usually specified in terms of the 5% significance level, such that the null hypothesis would be rejected only if the sample result was sufficiently far from the hypothesised result for there to be a 5% probability only of it occurring if the null hypothesis were true. The 5% level is normally chosen. However, it is also common to see the 1% significance level applied.

We are therefore going to answer the question posed about batteries in Section 17.3, 'Is it reasonable to assume that these two samples were drawn from the same population?', by discovering whether the difference between the two means, 3 hours, is significant or not. To do this we calculate the standard error of difference between the two means, using the formula:

$$\sqrt{\frac{\sigma_1^2}{n_1} + \frac{\sigma_2^2}{n_2}} = \sqrt{\frac{5^2}{100} + \frac{3^2}{100}}$$

$$= 0.58$$

Using our knowledge of the sampling distribution we know that the chance of a difference between sample means being greater than 1.96 times the standard error is only 5%, while the chance of it being more than 2.58 times the standard error is only 1%. Therefore at the 95% level we can expect the difference between the means to be

$$1.96 \times 0.58 \text{ hours} = 1.14 \text{ hours}$$

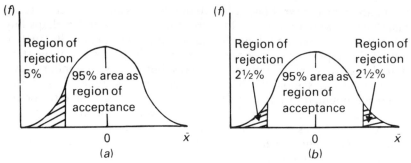

Fig 17.2 Regions of rejection in *(a)* a one-tailed test and *(b)* a two-tailed test

At the 99% level we can expect the difference between the two means to be:

2.58×0.58 hours $= 1.50$ hours

As our samples give a difference of 3 hours there is some statistical significance in the difference between the samples and the batteries in the first sample really do have a longer life than those in the second sample.

Hypothesis tests depend upon **critical values** for the test statistic. Critical values mark the boundary between acceptance and rejection of the null hypothesis. They may be the values at either end of a distribution in **two-tailed tests**, or a single value in the case of **single-tailed tests**. An example of the two-tailed test is testing whether the expected population mean is significantly different from the observed mean of the population. The mean could be on the high side or the low side, hence the need for a two-tailed test. If the hypothesis is that the mean is less than an expected value then the single-tailed test would be used. Figure 17.2(a) and (b) shows regions of rejection for one- and two-tailed tests.

Errors in hypothesis testing

There are two types of errors in hypothesis testing.

Type 1 errors are errors in which we reject a null hypothesis when it is, in fact, true. Because our sample is chosen randomly from the population there is a chance that we will mistakenly reject a null hypothesis. The maximum probability of committing such an error is called a **significance level**, mentioned previously.

Type II errors are committed when we accept a null hypothesis when it is in fact false. The analysis of Type II errors requires advanced statistics and is outside the scope of this book.

17.6 The Student *t*-test

When testing a hypothesis we often consider data from a small sample of a larger population. For example, if we wished to check that a certain manufacturer's car tyres lasted for 30 000 km as claimed in advertising material, we would not buy 1000 tyres to test. We would perhaps buy 20, test them to see how long they lasted and then statistically analyse our small sample. In this case we do not know the true value of the standard deviation, σ, of the full batch of tyres, but we have a standard deviation, s, of our sample batch of tyres. For small samples (ie $n < 30$), where the population standard deviation, σ, is not known and the population is assumed to be normally distributed, we use the Student t-test to test our hypothesis. In our example we would use it to test that the tyre sample mean, $\bar{x}$, is not significantly different from the manufacturer's value of μ.

The Student t-test is so called because W S Gosset, who developed the test, wrote under the pen name 'Student'. Instead of working with the normal variate Z score:

$$Z = \frac{\bar{x} - \mu}{\sigma/\sqrt{n}}$$

the test uses the variate t:

$$t = \frac{\bar{x} - \mu}{s/\sqrt{n}}$$

What the t-test does is compensate for the small size of the samples we have been using by changing the shape of the distribution to take account of the fact that small samples contain less information and therefore display a greater variation in results.

Note that the sample standard deviation (s) replaces the standard deviation of the population mean and that t is determined from Table 17.1 on page 271. The t distribution is different from the normal distribution because of the low sample numbers, but becomes more and more like the normal distribution as n increases.

Suppose that in our tyre example the 20 tyres gave a sample mean life $\bar{x}$ of 29 000 km with a standard deviation of 4 000 km, then:

$$t = \frac{29\ 000 - 30\ 000}{4000/\sqrt{20}} = \frac{-1000}{4000/\sqrt{20}}$$

$$= -1.118$$

We now have to determine the value of t for a given significance level. Table 17.1 gives a table of t values for different significance levels with 0.1 representing a 10% probability, 0.05 representing 5% probability and 0.01 representing 1% probability; df in the table represents the number of **degrees of freedom**, normally defined as $n - 1$ for tests involving a single mean.

A brief explanation of the degrees of freedom may help. Suppose we have found the mean of 4 numbers to be 16. In finding what these numbers are, we have $4 - 1$ degrees of freedom because fixing the mean has robbed us of one degree of freedom. We could say 'Let us call 3 of these numbers 9, 15 and 27'. Then the fourth number is 13 because the total must be 64 (4×16). We cannot choose any 4 numbers we like, because if we do the mean will not be 16. If we had 20 items in our

Table 17.1 t-distribution areas

df	0.10	0.05	0.025	0.01	0.005
1	3.078	6.314	12.706	31.821	63.657
2	1.886	2.920	4.303	6.965	9.925
3	1.638	2.353	3.182	4.541	5.841
4	1.533	2.132	2.776	3.747	4.604
5	1.476	2.015	2.571	3.365	4.032
6	1.440	1.943	2.447	3.143	3.707
7	1.415	1.895	2.365	2.998	3.499
8	1.397	1.860	2.306	2.896	3.355
9	1.383	1.833	2.262	2.821	3.250
10	1.372	1.812	2.228	2.764	3.169
11	1.363	1.796	2.201	2.718	3.106
12	1.356	1.782	2.179	2.681	3.055
13	1.350	1.771	2.160	2.650	3.012
14	1.345	1.761	2.145	2.624	2.977
15	1.341	1.753	2.131	2.602	2.947
16	1.337	1.746	2.120	2.583	2.921
17	1.333	1.740	2.110	2.567	2.898
18	1.330	1.734	2.101	2.552	2.878
19	1.328	1.729	2.093	2.539	2.861
20	1.325	1.725	2.086	2.528	2.845
21	1.323	1.721	2.080	2.518	2.831
22	1.321	1.717	2.074	2.508	2.819
23	1.319	1.714	2.069	2.500	2.807
24	1.318	1.711	2.064	2.492	2.797
25	1.316	1.708	2.060	2.485	2.787
26	1.315	1.706	2.056	2.479	2.779
27	1.314	1.703	2.052	2.473	2.771
28	1.313	1.701	2.048	2.467	2.763
29	1.311	1.699	2.045	2.462	2.756
30	1.310	1.697	2.042	2.457	2.750
40	1.303	1.684	2.021	2.423	2.704
60	1.296	1.671	2.000	2.390	2.660
120	1.289	1.658	1.980	2.358	2.617
∞	1.282	1.645	1.960	2.326	2.576

Note
Table 17.1 is taken from Table III of Fisher & Yates, *Statistical Tables for Biological, Agricultural and Medical Research*, published by Longman Group UK Ltd, 6th edition (previously published by Oliver & Boyd Ltd, Edinburgh) and by permission of the authors and publishers.

sample and the mean was 36, we could choose 19 numbers (provided that they did not exceed 20×36) but the last number is decided for us by the mean. If we have two statistics involved, say the mean and the standard deviation, we have $20 - 2$ degrees of freedom. Thus in our example, we have $20 - 1$ or 19 degrees of freedom. The number of degrees of freedom depends upon the number of items (n) in our data. This number must be reduced by the number of statistics being used — for example, if we are using the mean we have 1 less degree of freedom. In the case of the difference between 2 means we have 2 less degrees of freedom.

The hypothesis to determine whether the sample mean is significantly different from the manufacturer's figure is written as follows:

The null hypothesis, H_0:   the mean life of the tyres is 30 000 km or
$\mu = 30\ 000$ km

Against this null hypothesis we also set up an alternative hypothesis:

The alternative hypothesis, H_1:   the mean life of the tyres is less than the claimed 30 000 km or
$\mu < 30\ 000$ km

The alternative hypothesis will be accepted only if the null hypothesis is rejected by the test.

We are dealing with a single-tailed problem since we want to test that the mean is not less than 30 000 km. We therefore require to know the value of t such that an area of 0.05 lies beyond t in the lower tail, for a 5% significance level with 19 degrees of freedom. From Table 17.1 the corresponding value of t is 1.729 and the decision criterion becomes:

If $t > -1.729$, do not reject H_0
If $t < -1.729$, reject H_0

The test statistic t was calculated previously as $t = -1.118$ and since this value is greater than -1.729 (ie less negative than -1.729) we cannot reject H_0. There is insufficient evidence to suggest that the mean life of the tyres is significantly less than 30 000 km. It is worth considering why this should be the case. The sample standard deviation is, in fact, quite large, suggesting a wide variety of distances before the tyres wear out. If the standard deviation had been 2000 instead of 4000 this would have produced a test t statistic of -2.236 and this value would have been less than the 5% level of -1.729. In such a case the null hypothesis is not accepted at the 5% significance level and we would be justified in doubting the manufacturer's tyre figures. Of course, if the number of samples had been greater than 30 we would use the Z score to test the manufacturer's tyre statistics. For example, suppose the sample had been 50 tyres instead of 20 tyres.

The score is:

$$Z = \frac{29\ 000 - 30\ 000}{4000/\sqrt{50}} = -1.768$$

The Z score corresponding to the 5% rejection level is -1.96. Since -1.768 is greater than -1.96 the null hypothesis cannot be rejected.

As another example of using the t statistic, consider the coefficient determined for the transportation data in Chapter 16 (see p. 252). The correlation coefficient was 0.985 based on 11 observations. We want to determine whether this correlation coefficient is significantly different from zero. The null hypothesis is that the correlation coefficient is not significantly different from zero. In this case the t statistic is calculated as:

$$t = \frac{r\sqrt{n-2}}{\sqrt{1-r^2}}$$

where r is the correlation coefficient and n is the number of samples. Using this formula gives:

$$t = \frac{0.985\sqrt{9}}{\sqrt{1-0.985^2}}$$

$$= \frac{0.985 \times 3}{0.1725}$$

$$= 17.13$$

Since we are dealing with two sets of data, x and y in the correlation analysis, we have $n-2$ or 9 degrees of freedom. In this case we also have to consider a two-tailed test since our null hypothesis is:

H_0: $r = 0$

with the alternative hypothesis:

H_1: $r \neq 0$

ie r can be either greater than or less than 0. Thus at the 0.05 significance level, 0.025 of the distribution area can be at either tail of the distribution. The t value from Table 17.1 is therefore determined for $t = 0.025$ and df $= 9$ and gives t as ± 2.262. Since the test t statistic of 17.13 is larger than 2.262 the null hypothesis is rejected and we conclude that there is a significant relationship between the two variables.

17.7 Applying the *t*-test to estimating population statistics

In earlier sections of this chapter methods of estimating population statistics were given. The Z score approach was used to provide information on the area under the normal distribution. However, in many applications we are dealing with small samples of a population. Provided that the population has a normal probability distribution, we can take the t statistics used in the previous section and apply them to the problem of determining confidence limits for the mean. Thus in establishing confidence limits for the population mean, for example, we would use the value of t obtained using Table 17.1. Assuming $n-1$ degrees of freedom the confidence limits can be found from:

$$\bar{x} \pm t \frac{s}{\sqrt{n}}$$

where s is the sample standard deviation.

Consider the example about tyres on page 270. The mean life of 20 tyres was 29 000 km and the standard deviation was 4000 km. We can calculate the 95% confidence limits for the true mean of the population, but we have to use the t statistic because the sample size is less than 30. The number of degrees of freedom is $20 - 1 = 19$. We need to know the t statistic at the 0.025 level since we are dealing with a 2-tail problem (confidence limits either side of the mean). From Table 17.1 it is determined as 2.093 and the confidence limits are:

$$\bar{x} \pm t \frac{s}{\sqrt{n}} = 29\,000 \pm 2.093 \times \frac{4000}{\sqrt{20}}$$

$$= 29\,000 \pm 2.093 \times \frac{4\,000}{4.472}$$

$$= 29\,000 \pm 1872$$

$$= 30\,872 \text{ km and } 27\,128 \text{ km}$$

Thus there is a 95% probability that the true mean life of our population of tyres lies between 30 872 km and 27 128 km.

In the case of the difference between two means the confidence limits are calculated as:

$$(\bar{x}_1 - \bar{x}_2) \pm t \sqrt{\frac{s_1^2}{n_1} + \frac{s_2^2}{n_2}}$$

where t has $n_1 + n_2 - 2$ degrees of freedom.

Consider a random sample of 8 light bulbs with a mean life of 4600 hours and a standard deviation of 250 hours. For another brand of bulb a random sample of 10 bulbs has a mean of 4000 hours and a standard deviation of 200 hours. The 95% confidence limit for estimating the differences between the mean operating lives is:

$$(\bar{x}_1 - \bar{x}_2) \pm t \sqrt{\frac{s_1^2}{n_1} + \frac{s_2^2}{n_2}}$$

The number of degrees of freedom is $8 + 10 - 2 = 16$ and the corresponding t at the 95% confidence interval is 2.12. The confidence interval is therefore:

$$(4600 - 4000) \pm 2.12 \sqrt{\frac{250^2}{8} + \frac{200^2}{10}} = 600 \pm 2.12 \sqrt{7812 + 4000}$$

$$= 600 \pm 230 = 830 \text{ to } 370$$

In other words, with a 95% degree of confidence, we can say that the first brand has a longer life (between 370 and 830 hours longer) than the second brand.

17.8 The χ^2 (chi-squared) test

The χ^2 test is used to compare observed and expected frequencies. It is particularly useful if we wish to hypothesise that a data series has a

normal or any other distribution. We can apply the test and determine
to a chosen significance level whether the observed data conform to the
expected distribution.

The symbol χ (pronounced kigh) is determined using the formula:

$$\chi^2 = \sum \frac{(F_o - F_e)^2}{F_e}$$

where F_o is the observed frequency, F_e the expected frequency and Σ is
the summation of all the terms.

Consider the frequency of shoes manufactured in the example used
previously (see page 225). The expected frequency which follows a
normal distribution can be compared with the actual observed demand,
as shown in Table 17.2. Note that as the number of shoes manufactured
(see column (iii)) was in some cases less than the demand we could not
actually sell all that were demanded. In other cases we could. The
heading 'observed demand' could therefore read 'observed sales' in some
cases, but for sizes 39 and 41 the observed sales would be only the
number of expected sales – we would have been out of stock for the
other customers. χ^2 is calculated as:

$$\chi^2 = \frac{18^2}{2019} + \frac{(-40)^2}{3291} + \frac{44^2}{4207} + \frac{(-40)^2}{4207} + \frac{(-51)^2}{3291} + \frac{(-40)^2}{2019} + \frac{(-44)^2}{967}$$

$$= 0.160 + 0.486 + 0.460 + 0.380 + 0.790 = 0.792 + 2.002$$

$$= 5.070$$

In order to test whether the observed sales follow the normal distribution
we must compare the χ^2 value with the test statistic obtained from
Table 17.3. The degrees of freedom, df, in goodness of fit tests is one less
than the number of categories. In this case we have 7 categories – the 7
sizes of shoes. Also 1 degree of freedom is subtracted for each parameter

Table 17.2 Expected and observed demand for shoes

(i)	(ii)	(iii)	(iv)	(v)
Size	Probability	Expected sales, F_e	Observed demand, F_o	$F_o - F_e$
39	0.0919	2019	2037	18
40	0.1498	3291	3251	– 40
41	0.1915	4207	4251	44
42	0.1915	4207	4167	– 40
43	0.1498	3291	3240	– 51
44	0.0919	2019	1979	– 40
45	0.0440	967	923	– 44

Notes
i The figures in column (v) represent the extent to which demand exceeded or fell
short of supply.
ii Size 39 shoes were demanded by 2037 customers but we had only manufactured
2019 so that 18 customers could not be supplied.
iii Size 40 shoes were supplied to 3251 customers but 40 pairs of these shoes were
eventually unsold because demand was less than the supply.

Table 17.3 The χ^2 distribution

df	$\chi^2_{0.05}$	$\chi^2_{0.025}$	$\chi^2_{0.01}$	$\chi^2_{0.005}$	df
1	3.841	5.024	6.635	7.879	1
2	5.991	7.378	9.210	10.597	2
3	7.815	9.348	11.345	12.838	3
4	9.488	11.143	13.277	14.860	4
5	11.070	12.832	15.086	16.750	5
6	12.592	14.449	16.812	18.548	6
7	14.067	16.013	18.475	20.278	7
8	15.507	17.535	20.090	21.955	8
9	16.919	19.023	21.666	23.589	9
10	18.307	20.483	23.209	25.188	10
11	19.675	21.920	24.725	26.757	11
12	21.026	23.337	26.217	28.300	12
13	22.362	24.736	27.688	29.819	13
14	23.685	26.119	29.141	31.319	14
15	24.996	27.488	30.578	32.801	15
16	26.296	28.845	32.000	34.267	16
17	27.587	30.191	33.409	35.718	17
18	28.869	31.526	34.805	37.156	18
19	30.144	32.852	36.191	38.582	19
20	31.410	34.170	37.566	39.997	20
21	32.671	35.479	38.932	41.401	21
22	33.924	36.781	40.289	42.796	22
23	35.172	38.076	41.638	44.181	23
24	36.415	39.364	42.980	45.558	24
25	37.652	40.646	44.314	46.928	25
26	38.885	41.923	45.642	48.290	26
27	40.113	43.194	46.963	49.645	27
28	41.337	44.461	48.278	50.993	28
29	42.557	45.722	49.588	52.336	29
30	43.773	46.979	50.892	53.672	30

such as the mean or standard deviation used to calculate the expected frequencies. In our case the mean and standard deviation are used to calculate the expected sales and therefore the degrees of freedom are $7-1-2=4$. From Table 17.3, assuming a 0.05 significance level, the χ^2 test value is 9.49. Since our calculated χ^2 is 5.070 and less than the test value of 9.49, the null hypothesis is accepted and the observed frequencies follow a normal distribution.

Note that the χ^2 test is not accurate if the numbers of observed frequencies are very small. If a particular sample of data – say an investigation of the ages of motorcycle accident victims in Newtown in a given day – has only very small frequencies in each age range (less than 5) the χ^2 test will not accurately determine the nature of the distribution.

The χ^2 test can be used to test binomial or Poisson distributions. Provided the probability, p, in the binomial distribution is known the number of degrees of freedom is $n - 1$. If p is not known and has to be estimated (using $\bar{x} = np$) from the observed set of frequencies then there are $n - 2$ degrees of freedom. For the Poisson distribution to be evaluated we need to know the mean of the observed data, the Poisson parameter. If the mean is estimated from the observed frequencies there are $n - 2$ degrees of freedom.

Summary

1 Significance testing is a statistical standard used to test hypotheses. We formulate a null hypothesis such as 'A's batteries have the same length of life as B's batteries.' The significance level for the rejection of this hypothesis is usually stated at the 5% or 1% level. If a sample test gives a result which is beyond the significance level, so that it would only have a 5% or 1% chance of occurring if the null hypothesis was true, we conclude that the null hypothesis is not true, and A's batteries have a different length of life from B's batteries.

2 The mean of a sample is called $\bar{x}$, and the mean of the population is called μ. Any difference between $\bar{x}$ and μ is referred to as a sampling error. The word 'error' here does not mean 'mistake', but only a result differing from the population mean as a result of chance.

3 A large number of samples taken from the same population would have means distributed around the population mean μ. The standard deviation of such a sampling distribution is found by the formula $\sigma_{\bar{x}} = \sigma / \sqrt{n}$, where σ is the standard deviation of the whole population and n is the sample size. The larger the sample the closer the sample mean gets to the population mean.

4 The Z score approach is used to find the confidence limits associated with such a distribution (see Chapter 14 for the Z score approach). The 95% confidence limits are $-1.96\sigma / \sqrt{n}$ and $+1.96\sigma / \sqrt{n}$.

5 When estimating the proportion of a population (for example, the proportion of defective items in quality-control work), the formula is $\sigma = \sqrt{p(1 - p)/n}$, provided that np and $n(1 - p)$ are both greater than 5.

6 When comparing sets of data – for example, sample results investigating the products of two manufacturers – we need to check the difference between the two means. Here $1.96\sqrt{\sigma_1^2/n_1 + \sigma_2^2/n_2}$ is an estimate of the difference between the population means μ_1 and μ_2. Provided that both samples are large, in circumstances where the standard deviations of the populations are not known, the standard deviations of the samples can be used to calculate the possible differences between the means. If our data is within the limits found by the formula $\bar{x}_1 - \bar{x}_2 \pm 1.96\sqrt{s_1^2/n_1 + s_2^2/n_2}$ we can say that there is no significant difference between the two sets of results at the 95% confidence level.

7 It is possible to use the formula for confidence limits to decide what size of sample we need to give us a given degree of accuracy.

$\pm 1.96\sigma/\sqrt{n}$ gives us the 95% confidence limits. If we know the confidence limits we want we can find what sample size n is needed to give these limits. The formula simply has to be rearranged.

8 The Student t-test is used when the sample used is small and normally distributed, and consequently (when $n < 30$) we cannot rely on the sample distribution being close to the population distribution. Instead of the Z test we use a t-test whose formula is:

$$t = \frac{\bar{x} - \mu}{s/\sqrt{n}}$$

9 The χ^2 test is used to compare observed with expected frequencies. It is therefore useful in deciding whether an observed distribution is a normal (or any other) distribution. The formula is $\chi^2 = \Sigma(F_o - F_e)^2/F_e$, where F_o is the observed frequency and F_e is the expected frequency.

Exercises on sampling and significance testing

1 Calculate the 95 and 99% confidence limits for the mean height of the male population having a standard deviation of 15 cm. Assume a sample of 50 males gave a mean height of 170 cm.

2 Calculate the 95 and 99% confidence limits in Exercise 1 for a sample of only 15, a mean of 170 cm and a sample standard distribution of 10 cm. You may assume that the sample is normally distributed.

3 Pottery fired in a kiln is found to have 6% of defective items from a sample of 200. Calculate the 99% confidence limits for the proportion.

4 Sheets of glass manufactured by a continuous process are found to have 5% of sheets defective from a sample of 100 sheets. Calculate the confidence limits for the proportion at the 95% level.

5 Design a sampling programme to check that the mean weight of a bag of sugar is 1 kg $\pm$ 0.1 kg given that the population standard deviation is 0.23.

6 A manufacturer of car batteries claims that the mean life of a battery is 7 years. From a sample of 40 batteries the mean is found to be 6.2 years with a standard deviation of 0.5 years. Test whether the manufacturer's figures are significantly different from the sample.

7 Test the manufacturer's figures in Exercise 6 assuming that only 15 samples had been taken but the same mean and standard deviations were obtained. You may assume that the distribution is normal.

8 In a regression analysis between the yield of a crop of sweet corn and solar radiation levels a correlation coefficient of 0.67 was obtained from a sample of 10 field experiments. Test whether this correlation coefficient is significantly different at the 95% and 99% levels.

9 Four coins are tossed 240 times and the following results were obtained and compared with the theoretical frequencies from a binomial distribution.

No heads	Observed frequency	Expected frequency
0	10	15
1	68	60
2	83	90
3	57	60
4	22	15

Is there any evidence at the 5% level that the coins are biased?

10 Calculate whether there is a significant difference at the 5% level between two sets of samples of 40 tyres given that the mean life of the tyres is 25 000 km and 27 000 km respectively and the standard deviations are 4000 km and 2500 km respectively.

18 Computer-based statistical packages

18.1 Computers and statistics

The essential feature of any statistical work is that it is an attempt to bring order out of a chaotic collection of raw data. This may have been collected by questionnaires, or by interview procedures, or by observation (as with road traffic censuses). Today a lot of measurements are made by telemetry, for example the sensing of information such as temperatures, pressures, acidity, oxygen content and similar data through a variety of technical instruments. In seeking to bring order out of a mass of raw data, we have created numerous ways of classifying data, averaging it, finding the distribution of the data around the average, etc. All these activities are pretty routine, fairly laborious, time consuming and in many ways tedious. They lend themselves easily to computerisation, because it is possible to write fairly simple, logical programs which can perform these basic tasks.

With the rapid development of fast microcomputers, there has been a corresponding development and application of computer-based statistical packages. These can perform all the basic tasks and types of analysis required for business purposes, and often include many more sophisticated techniques. For example, the packages described in this chapter can do all the routine activities such as tabulation and the presentation of data in pictorial or graphical form. They can find percentages, averages, standard deviations and other statistics dealt with in the later chapters of this book, and can analyse variances, time series data, samples, probabilities, etc. Before considering these packages it is first necessary to set the scene.

18.2 Statistical packages in business life

This book is only an introductory statistical textbook, and its purpose is to take students through the rather lengthy business of collecting, analysing and presenting data. It is hoped that with these skills, in a real-life situation, management procedures can be implemented to promote the efficient use of resources and improve productivity, marketing, profitability, etc. An industrial or commercial enterprise will obviously choose a statistical package which is appropriate to its field of activity and, once this is installed, will build up files of real-life data on production, sales, quality and quantity of inputs and outputs, upon which the computer packages will be able to operate. The socially-orientated office, such as a hospital, medical practice, social security department, environmental control office, etc, will similarly build up masses of data which will be regularly revised and updated and can form the basis for the various statistical analyses which the package is being asked to perform.

The selection of a package appropriate to a particular industry, institute or department is a matter for senior staff in the organisation and the young statistician taking employment in the organisation will need to get to know the package thoroughly and find out what it can do and which aspects are of the greatest interest to their particular organisation. Of course it would be possible to develop dedicated software unique to an organisation, performing precisely those activities of use to its management, but the costs involved are usually much greater than those incurred when purchasing a tried and tested 'off-the-shelf' package already developed in the field concerned, or a related field.

Unfortunately, in the education and training field the time available for study of this aspect of a statistics course is fairly limited, and the volume of data which can be made available as a source for the package to operate upon is not as extensive as in real life. It is, of course, helpful if the package chosen has a reasonable data disk containing a variety of files for student use giving examples of the different types of data that can be processed. At this point we will consider one particular package and see what it can do. The package chosen is STATGRAPHICS, an American package which combines an easy-to-instal, easy-to-learn and easy-to-use, menu-driven interface with analytical capabilities that are as extensive as most businesses require (there are over 250 statistical procedures available).

18.3 The STATGRAPHICS package

Computer packages may be in two modes: an automated processing mode for running routine analyses on a regular basis; and an interactive mode where the user can react to the intermediate results produced and can issue commands to the computer to change the assumptions on which the analysis is based, re-run the results and see the effects. STATGRAPHICS makes both modes available, but for the inexperienced user the system is particularly easy to use, since it is menu-driven. This means that the various programs which the software offers are listed on a screen display like the items on a menu at a restaurant. The menu items are called 'options'. The user selects the option that is required from the menu. This will probably call up a further sub-menu showing a number of programs available under that main menu heading and, when one of these is selected by the user, the computer will proceed to make the required service available in a user-friendly way. This means that it will keep the user informed what is happening – for example it might say 'Loading the Quality Control program' or 'Updating the Biological Water Quality file. Please wait'. Figure 18.1 shows the STATGRAPHICS Main Menu.

The selection of a main menu option produces a sub-menu display showing the various programs available under that main menu option.

```
┌─────────────────────────────────────────────────────────────┐
│              ┌──────────────────────────────────────┐        │
│              │ STATGRAPHICS Statistical Graphics System│      │
│              └──────────────────────────────────────┘        │
│                                                               │
│ DATA MANAGEMENT AND SYSTEM UTILITIES    TIME SERIES PROCEDURES│
│   A. Data Management                      L. Forecasting      │
│   B. System Environment                   M. Quality Control  │
│   C. Report Writer and Graphics Replay    N. Smoothing        │
│   D. Graphics Attributes                  O. Time Series Analysis│
│                                                               │
│ PLOTTING AND DESCRIPTIVE STATISTICS     ADVANCED PROCEDURES   │
│   E. Plotting Functions                   P. Categorical Data Analysis│
│   F. Descriptive Methods                  Q. Multivariate Methods│
│   G. Estimation and Testing               R. Nonparametric Methods│
│   H. Distribution Functions               S. Sampling        │
│   I. Exploratory Data Analysis            T. Experimental Design│
│                                                               │
│ ANOVA AND REGRESSION ANALYSIS           MATHEMATICAL AND USER PROCEDURES│
│   J. Analysis of Variance                 U. Mathematical Functions│
│   K. Regression Analysis                  V. Supplementary Operations│
└─────────────────────────────────────────────────────────────┘
```

Fig 18.1 The STATGRAPHICS main menu

Notes

  i At the moment in Fig. 18.1 the first option, Data Management, is highlighted.

 ii By pressing the 'cursor down' key the highlighting would move down to highlight other options – for example, pressing the key four times would move the highlight to 'Plotting Functions'.

iii By moving the cursor one step to the right from 'Plotting Functions' we could arrive at 'Categorical Data Analysis'.

iv When you have arrived at the option you require, press 'Enter' and the computer will start to display that option, usually by showing a sub-menu of the various options available on that part of the main menu.

For example, the 'Data Management' option has a sub-menu which reads:

1 Display data directory
2 File operations
3 Import data files
4 Export data files

The first of these options enables you to see what data have been made available to the computer by examining a screen display which lists the data available. It may be that you intend to create a new file of data on a subject not previously handled, in which case you will need to give it a name and add it to the directory once the data has been put in.

If you move to 'File Operations', a display such as that shown in Fig 18.2 appears. The panel highlighted, file name, invites you to key in the name of the file on which you wish to carry out some operation. The display also shows the various operations that can be carried out, each of which requires a separate program. Thus the computer when instructed to copy a file will require a different program of instructions from the 'update' program, or the 'create' program.

At the end of any particular activity it is possible to return to the sub-menu, or to the main menu and to end the STATGRAPHICS session.

```
                          File Operations

STATGRAPHICS file name:

Operations:  A. Copy        D. Erase       G. Recode      J. Update
             B. Create      E. Join        H. Rename
             C. Edit        F. Print       I. Split

Desired operation:

                        Files on Data Drive

ANOVA.ASF     CARDATA.ASF   IRONORE.ASF  LOGLIN.ASF   MVDATA.ASF    NONLIN.ASF
QCDATA.ASF    RANDOM.ASF    STATGHLP.ASF STATR1.ASF   STATF1.ASF
```

Fig 18.2 File Operations panel

Notes

i At present the screen display in Fig 18.2 highlights the 'file name' area and the 'desired operation' area.

ii By pressing a single coded key, a list of available file names appears, to remind the user which files have already been created. You can call up such a file by typing in the file name and it will then become possible for that file to be copied, updated, renamed, etc.

iii If it is desired to create a new file, a new file name is typed in and the operation 'create' is requested.

The graphics available on STATGRAPHICS

STATGRAPHICS provides all the statistical analyses required, with over 250 different procedures. Some idea of the economy of presentation is given in Fig 18.3, but note that the following main summaries of data can be calculated from any file of data available:

a mean *b* median *c* mode *d* geometric mean *e* variance
f standard deviation *g* standard error *h* minimum *i* maximum
j range *k* lower quartile *l* upper quartile *m* interquartile range

Variable:	ibm	bubbly	ggb
Sample size	120	84	168
Average	513.792	4.6838	93.9783
Standard deviation	40.988	2.58586	7.52514
Range	151	12.343	37.838

Fig 18.3 Summary statistics on request

Notes

i The request has been for the arithmetic mean (called 'the average' in STATGRAPHICS), the standard deviation and the range of three sets of data (in this case provided by the Sample Data Sets supplied (for example ggb is some data about traffic flows over the Golden Gate Bridge).

ii The data required are produced almost instantaneously and are listed as shown.

iii The statistics may be 'saved' in a file for future use or displayed in one of the graphic displays listed in Table 18.1.

n skewness   *o* standard skewness   *p* kurtosis   *q* standard kurtosis
r coefficient of variation   *s* sum.

The user selects those statistics which are of interest and the screen will display the results almost instantaneously for the data under investigation.

Figure 18.3 shows the sort of presentation that results from a typical request.

The reader will be familiar with most of the graphical presentations referred to in Table 18.1, but Fig 18.4 illustrates a 3-dimensional

Table 18.1   Types of graphics available

Procedure	Number of variables	Data type*	Description
X-Y line and scatterplots	2	C/N	Produces lineplots, scatterplots, or connected scatterplots. Options include log scaling on one or both axes, etc.
Multiple X-Y plots	2 or more	C/N	Produces lineplots, scatterplots, or connected scatterplots with one variable on the X-axis. Plots can use log scaling on one or both axes, and additional Y-axis variables can be plotted on either the left or right axis
X-Y-Z line and scatterplots	3	C/N	Like X-Y line and scatterplots procedure, except that it produces plots using three variables. Reference lines may be included to connect each point to a selected plane
Multiple X-Y-Z plots	3 or more	C/N	Plots three-dimensional lineplots, scatterplots, or connected scatterplots for three or more variables. Plots can use log scaling on one or more axes, and additional Z-axis variables can be plotted on either the left or right axis
Bar charts	1 or 2	C/N	Plots a bar chart for numeric or character data
Pie charts	1	C/N	Displays percentage breakdowns for numeric or character data
Component line charts	1 or more	N	Displays one or more time series variables in a line chart

* Character or Numeric

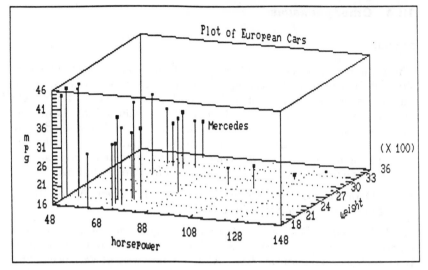

Fig 18.4 An X-Y-Z plot of three aspects of European cars

presentation which has not been shown in the earlier chapters of this book.

Where a computer has sound capability, STATGRAPHICS provides audio cues – using three tones – bell, chirp and blah. The bell indicates that STATGRAPHICS has completed the required operation and is waiting for your next piece of input. The chirp means that you pressed a key which was not defined for use at this point. It invites you to try again. The blah indicates that you made an incorrect entry. It invites you to check your entry and try again.

Visual clues are provided at many stages in the various programs, using the bottom three lines on the screen. They give instructions and information.

STATGRAPHICS is made available by STSC Inc, 2115 East Jefferson Street, Rockville, Maryland, 20852, USA. You can contact them direct on 0101-301-984-5123. For your nearest local dealer call 0101-301-984-5412 if you are outside the USA (Telex 898085 STSC Rove or Telefax 0101-301-984-5094).

The latest version of STATGRAPHICS is Version 5. Other versions are still available. System requirements: Version 5 runs on IBM PC, XT, AT, PS/2, or compatible microcomputers with a graphics adapter and compatible monochrome or colour monitor. One floppy-disk drive, a hard disk, 640K RAM memory, and DOS 2.0 or later are required. An Intelmath co-processor is recommended, but not required. For network support, DOS 3.1 or later is required. Version 5 can also use both EMS and XMS memory; an 80286 or 80386 computer it required. For XMS memory, an XMS driver and at least 64K of extended memory are required. New STATGRAPHICS packages are being produced, eg STATGRAPHICS Plus for 386/486 computers.

18.4 Other packages

Minitab

This is an interactive command-driven package produced by the University of Pennsylvania and covering such topics as descriptive data analysis, time series analysis, regression analysis, and significance tests. It is widely used in academic institutions and commercial organisations. However, since such packages are updated from time to time and commands may be changed, there is little point in describing the package in detail – the student who has access to a Minitab package will use the appropriate reference manual. Some of the features of Minitab are as follows:

Data: Data are stored in columns designated C1, C2, etc, up to C1000. This gives a very large worksheet indeed.

Analysis of data: Data are analysed by typing in the appropriate command – for example to read, edit, print, plot or carry out various analyses such as regression analysis, ANOVA (analysis of variances), etc. There are over 100 main commands and many sub-commands. For example, in editing data you can command the computer to insert, delete, copy, stack, code, sort, etc. The MINITAB Handbook by Ryan *et al* (2nd Edition 1989 published by Wadsworth) gives fuller explanations than are provided in the package manual.

Microstats

Microstats is a software package produced in 1991 which manipulates columns of numerical data. It assumes the user has the data available as a worksheet from which it is desired to derive a full range of statistics. The typing in of a command will lead to a comparison of that command with an internal directory of over 100 commands and the activation of the appropriate sub-routine.

For example, the command DESCRIBE will provide all the descriptive statistics of any one column, including the minimum; the maximum; the sum of the data; the sum of the squares of the data; the mean, median and mode (if any); the standard deviation; the coefficient of skewness; the lower and upper quartiles; and the 10th and 90th percentiles.

Microstats is available from Chapman & Hall, the publishers of *Quantitative Methods for Business Decisions* by Curwin and Slater, and is included when this text is purchased. Their telephone number is 071-865 0066. Their address is 2–6 Boundary Road, London SE1 8HN.

SPSS

SPSS stands for 'statistical package for the social sciences'. It is a widely-used package which offers the user all the routine number-crunching statistics used in social and environmental surveys.

Also available are publications accompanying software, including the book *Statistics* and its accompanying IBM-compatible disk, by Owen and Jones, published by Pitman Publishing.

18.5 Approach to employment as a statistician

When people move from being students of statistics to being statisticians they frequently find considerable difficulty in knowing what part they can play in the organisation to which they have been appointed. The computerisation of statistics has made the problem worse because of the computer's ability to perform lengthy and difficult calculations in a few seconds. This means that the answers to many problems can be provided so quickly, and with so little effort on the part of the statistician, that the untrained observer might be led into thinking that there is little point in having a statistician at all.

On the contrary, the removal of drudgery in the manipulation of data leaves the statistician free to give more attention to the problems that come up for consideration. The stages in any statistical investigation can be listed as follows:

a Whatever the proposed investigation is about, the problem should be formulated in statistical terms. What is it that you are trying to find out and why? It is necessary to interrogate the proposer fully, to find out what he/she hopes to discover from the investigation? Has the proposer just thought up the problem to give the Statistical Department something to do? There should be some worthwhile benefit accruing from the result of the investigation. For example, it may be a saving in costs, or a reduction in customer dissatisfaction, or a use for an otherwise waste product, or a reduction in labour turnover, or an extension of an existing market. How should we tackle the problem in order to form conclusions which will enable the adoption of policies to achieve the desired objectives?

b If there is likely to be literature available about the type of investigation proposed, you should search the literature and read anything you can that is relevant. If in-house data is available, you should turn it up and assess its usefulness.

c Consider what data needs to be collected and the best method of doing this – for example, a survey questionnaire. If possible, a pilot survey should be carried out, and the results reviewed to discover any errors – for example, ambiguous questions producing wrong results, or bias revealed by the answers. Questionnaires and interviewer's schedules of questions may need to be revised.

d When the main enquiry starts, the raw data should be scrutinised. This process is sometimes called an IDA (initial data analysis). The result may be a sense of satisfaction in that the data appear to be genuine, without too many misunderstandings, incorrect answers, etc. On the other hand, an uneasy feeling about the quality of the data becoming available may lead to a more cautious report when the results are being summarised for the client's or organisation's benefit.

e The level of analysis should be appropriate to the enquiry and the sophistication of the client for whom results are intended. The guiding light here is the original objective of the enquiry – you have to find from the data (if this is possible) the answer to the original problem. Do the results support and confirm the original hypothesis, or do they deny its validity? If they are inconclusive, it will be necessary to rebut possible criticisms of the conduct of the enquiry.

f The report must present the original problem, the data collected, and the conclusions to be drawn, in a clear and convincing manner, using such methods of presentation as are appropriate. If a computerised package has been used, the results should be presented fully to lighten and clarify the report. Ideally the report should end with a number of clear recommendations which go to the root of the problem. It is no good carrying out a long investigation if, in the end, you leave the client (whether an external client or one within your own organisation) to draw his/her own conclusions. You should say quite clearly what the data tells you and what, in your opinion, would be a correct course to follow. Even if the conclusion is that nothing should be done, you should say so quite clearly.

Summary

1 Many statistical activities involve the calculation of averages, distributions of data, etc, which are relatively routine activities. They lend themselves easily to computerisation because it is possible to write logical programs which will enable the raw data to be processed.
2 It is possible to develop dedicated software which will meet the needs of any particular organisation. However, this is expensive, and it is much cheaper to purchase packages of programs which have already been tried and tested and can provide the vast majority of the summaries and presentations which most organisations need.
3 Some packages are provided for educational purposes with a limited number of data files which may be used by students. In the real world more comprehensive packages are needed, with plenty of room for storing data as it accumulates from year to year, and enquiry to enquiry.
4 Some of the best packages for statistical purposes are STATGRAPHICS, Minitab, SPSS and Microstats.
5 When tackling problems in the real business world, the essential elements of any investigation are:

a to state the problem in statistical terms;
b to decide what data will be required and the best method of collection;
c to test out material at an early stage to discover in-built errors or ambiguities;
d to conduct an initial data analysis to eliminate 'joke' replies, etc;
e to analyse the data at an appropriate level of sophistication;
f to report clearly, and make firm recommendations (even if the recommendation is to do nothing).

Exercises using a computer package

Whichever package is available to you it should be possible to do nearly all the exercises in this book using the package and, of course, very much more quickly than with manual calculations. You are, therefore, recommended to go through the book, taking one or two exercises from each section and working them out on the computer. This will give you real familiarity with the computer package, calling for reference to the manual when problems arise.

The full benefits of computerisation accrue, of course, at higher levels than are dealt with in this introductory text, but a sound appreciation of the more routine activities makes success at these higher levels possible as your studies progress.

Appendix **Assignments in statistics**

Introduction

Many statistics courses today involve assignments or projects which relate statistical studies to the real world, requiring the student to apply his/her knowledge in a practical way. While these assignments can never be as realistic as a statistical exercise within a firm or government department, grappling with business or social problems, they can teach the student much about the difficulties of collecting, collating and analysing data. You will be expected to design questionnaires, conduct inquiries, collect and analyse data and present it lucidly.

One of the problems with such projects or assignments is the enormous amount of time they take. With many other calls upon your time for other subjects it may be impossible to complete an assignment and you may have to be content with only a part of the work being in a finished form. For this reason the activities in some of the assignments below have been separated off into elements, *a*, *b*, *c*, etc. The completion of each of these elements may be considered as a worthwhile and grade-earning activity, so that the completion of the whole activity might be spread over several months, with other activities interspersed.

The suggestions made may be inappropriate for the country or region in which you are studying. They may be adapted and changed to suit local conditions. Although it is often suggested that students should approach firms for help in projects, it must be remembered that even the most cooperative management may find it quite impossible to meet the needs of all those who write in. It is therefore suggested that such approaches should be left to university-level students, and lower-level students should avoid this type of approach unless the school or college has a particularly close link with a local firm or institution.

Assignment 1   A group assignment about rush-hour traffic

Which is the most commonly used method of personal transport in your own country? Which are the busiest times of the day? Prepare a traffic census form for your own area (see Fig 1.1 on page 6) but referring only to personal transport, not business transport. Produce sufficient copies to monitor every half-hour period of the day and arrange a rota to cover the census at a particular point on a main road, with separate recorders for each side of the road. Produce a report on *i* the popularity of each particular type of personal transport and *ii* the pattern of traffic flow throughout the day. Stages in this assignment are as follows:

a Preparation of the traffic census form.
b Selection of an appropriate census point in your area. Bear in mind the safety of those conducting the census in selecting your census point.
c Testing the form out on a single half-hour period to discover any weaknesses in its design – you may have left out a particular type of transport, or have left insufficient room to record the numbers of vehicles involved.
d Drawing up a rota of recorders to give a complete coverage from dawn to dusk.
e The actual taking of the census and addition of the data recorded in each box.
f Collation of the data to find the total usage of each type of transport.
g Collation of the data to reveal the hours-by-movement of traffic and consequently the rush-hour periods.
h Production of a report on the two features you have been studying.

Assignment 2 The prices of secondhand cars

Use a local or evening paper in which secondhand vehicles are frequently advertised. From a single issue or, if this gives less than 100 cars, from several issues, record the prices of secondhand cars by age, ie 1 year old, 2 years old, 3 years old, etc, up to 5 years old, with a final class of 'over 5 years old'. Calculate the average price of cars for each year. Ignore the make of car for this investigation. Is there any correlation between age and price? Present your data in a suitable form.

Assignment 3 Graph ready-reckoners

A fashion house sells garments wholesale. The minimum order is 100 garments, rising in groups of 50 to 1000 garments. When orders are greater than 1000 garments a special price is quoted. Orders at this price are only taken in groups of 500, above the 1000 base limit. It is very rare for any wholesaler to order more than 10 000 of any stock item. You are asked to draw two straight-line ready-reckoner graphs (see Section 7.4 on page 98) as follows:

a one to show the cost to the retailer of blouses wholesaling at £6 per unit for all order sizes (in groups of 50) up to 1000 items
b the other to show the cost to the retailer of the same garments at the special price of £4.50 for all order sizes (in groups of 500) up to 10 000 items

From your graphs read off the total to be charged to:

i a department store ordering 850 blouses
ii a multiple shop chain ordering 6500 blouses

Assignment 4 Earnings of employees in inflationary times

A group of employees in your factory complain that their wages have not kept up with inflation. As evidence they quote what their gross wages used to be in 1978 (£4035 per annum). Obtain a copy of the Retail Price Index (RPI) (you will find this in the library in the current copy of the *Monthly Digest of Statistics*, or in a reference book such as Croner's *Reference Book for Employers*). Calculate what their wages should now be – using the most recent monthly figure available to you at the time you are doing the assignment. Write a short report about this explaining how you calculated the figure.

Assignment 5 The price of houses

Using any edition of a local paper which features property sales, draw up a list of asking prices according to the number of bedrooms available. Use six categories, 1, 2, 3, 4, 5 and 'more than 5' bedrooms and record the asking prices in each category. Calculate the mean price for each group. Write a short report on the price of houses in the region, giving the range of prices in each category, and using an appropriate diagram to illustrate the mean prices you have discovered.

Assignment 6 Fuel availability

Using the published statistics of your own country discover the quantity of fuel available to your nation from home production in the four quarters of the last year. If these are not yet available use the figures for the last available year. Present the figures in the form of a four-quarterly component bar chart, each bar showing separately the figures for coal, petroleum, natural gas, electricity, etc. Make it clear what units are being used.

Assignment 7 The term of trade

Obtain a copy of the *Monthly Digest of Statistics* and look at the data on 'visible trade on a balance of payments basis'. You will find a column headed 'terms of trade'. It is an index number and hovers around 100.

If the price of a country's exports are low but the things it has to buy (its imports) are highly priced, the terms of trade are said to be unfavourable to the country. If its export prices are high but its imports are cheap the terms of trade are favourable, and the country will be prosperous.

To find the terms of trade we calculate as follows:

$$\text{Terms of trade index} = \frac{\text{export unit value index number}}{\text{import unit value index number}} \times 100$$

Thus if the export unit value index number is 120 (exports are earning good prices compared with former years) and the import unit value is 98 (imports are costing slightly less than in former years), the terms of trade index is:

$$\frac{120}{98} \times 100 = 122.4$$

These terms are very favourable to the exporting country.

Using the figures given below calculate the terms of trade for each year shown:

Year	Export index	Import index	Terms of trade
5	121.6	119.1	
6	124.7	117.5	
7	129.8	113.2	
8	111.6	118.9	
9	108.4	121.7	
10	103.2	123.6	

Assignment 8   A sales report

As sales manager of your company you have to present an analysis of sales to the directors at the next board meeting. You have to investigate and describe the changing pattern of sales and suggest areas where additional advertising is required to boost sales. The basic data available to you are as follows:

Year	Product 1 Quantity (units)	Price per unit (£)	Product 2 Quantity (units)	Price per unit (£)	Product 3 Quantity (units)	Price per unit (£)
1	2100	12	3000	5	6000	9
2	2500	15	3100	7	5300	12
3	2800	20	3500	9	4500	18
4	2700	24	3900	14	5100	21
5	2600	29	4500	18	4200	26
6	2650	32	6000	22	3700	33

Profits are as follows:

product 1: $12\frac{1}{2}$% of selling price
product 2: 30% of selling price
product 3: 18% of selling price

Analyse these data to show total sales by volume and value for each product and overall. What is the general trend for the individual products and overall? Prepare a written report containing your recommendations and prepare a set of overhead projector transparencies which would be useful in making your presentation to management. Bear in mind the profitability of each product when making your recommendations. The three products are not interrelated in any way.

Assignment 9   Report to the employees

It is now a statutory requirement of companies to report to the employees on the general conduct of the company. This is usually done by showing the profitability of the company, and how that profit was shared among the various claimants on the company. The chief claimants are the employees (who draw their wages and salaries), the government (which takes its share as taxation), the shareholders (who take their share as dividends) and the debenture-holders (who take their share as interest on the loans made). In addition to this it is usual to retain some profits for developing the business for the future.

The data for your firm are as follows:

Profit calculation	£m
a Sales	1140
b Materials and other costs (except wages and salaries)	480
c Excise duty paid on product (beer)	375
d Profits made (including wages and salaries)	?

(The profit is the difference between the sales value and the cost of these goods, including duty.)

Allocation of profits	%
Wages and salaries	67.2
Taxation	13.8
Dividends	5.9
Retentions	?
	100.0

Prepare a written report, and overhead projector transparencies to illustrate the situation for the enlightenment of the employees. In your report deal with the suggestion from trade union representatives that the work force is entitled to a 10% increase in pay.

Assignment 10   Sales of accountancy books

a The firm you work for produces accounts books used in preparing the financial accounts of a business. Financial accounts are usually prepared on one of three bases: a a calendar-year basis, b a tax-year basis, which means traders need a new book on 1 April, and c an anniversary basis (a new book will be needed on the anniversary of the day the business originally started). The figures shown below for sales for the last 8 years are believed by the sales manager to reflect these seasonal variations. He complains that he cannot discern from them what is the true demand for the book over the years. You are asked to:

   i explain to him the types of variation to be found in a time series of data such as this one
   ii analyse the data to display the true trend in sales over the 8-year period
   iii to estimate the sales for year 9 and year 10, showing the likely quarterly figures for each year

b A proposal is being mooted to make all firms follow a tax-year basis for presenting their financial accounts. What would be the implications of this for your firm? What problems would it present for the production and marketing of your account books?

Sales of account books ('000)

Year	Quarter 1	2	3	4
1	50	35	15	35
2	57	40	16	41
3	62	43	29	43
4	67	40	27	46
5	68	42	28	52
6	72	44	29	52
7	74	46	29	55
8	75	48	30	58

Assignment 11 Heavy metal content in river water

Imagine you have been appointed as the environmental officer of a mining company wishing to obtain planning permission for an extension of the mining operation. Consider the water quantity data shown below for the river into which your company discharges waste. The data show heavy metal concentrations at different sites along the river. Investigate the association between different pairs of these variables, which have been measured from 20 km above the present discharge site (-20 km) to 11 km downstream of the present discharge site. For each scatter diagram you do calculate regression lines and correlation coefficients. Select the most suitable site for discharge of further waste water, and prepare a report describing the data and justifying your case. At present water is extracted for use by a local town at a point 9 miles downstream from the present discharge. The mining company is prepared to finance the construction of a pipeline from a new extraction point to link up with the existing pipeline. Where would you recommend this new extraction point should be sited?

Water quality data

Sampling site	Distance from mine outlet (km)	Concentrations of metals (mg/l)			
		Lead	Nickel	Manganese	Iron
1	− 20	0.012	0.001	0.02	0.05
2	− 14	0.009	0.005	0.03	0.08
3	− 5	0.30	0.003	0.01	0.04
4	0	0.04	0.05	0.05	0.45
5	1	0.006	0.16	0.045	0.40
6	3	0.013	0.1	0.05	0.50
7	5	0.017	0.15	0.085	0.80
8	8	0.014	0.06	0.21	0.75
9	11	0.012	0.05	0.29	1.20

Note: You may take it that none of the existing levels of heavy metal pollution approaches danger level, but the ecological aim is to keep the pollution level as low as possible, particularly at any point where water is being abstracted for public water supply purposes.

Assignment 12   The price of cars in different localities

Obtain a copy of your local newspaper and also a copy of a newspaper from a town some distance away and preferably a different type of area, eg industrial, rural or residential. From both papers take out the advertisements for cars and draw up a table of car prices for all the 2-year-old and 5-year-old cars. Calculate the mean price of each group in the two areas. What conclusions can you draw about the mean price of the cars from the two towns? Test whether the prices are significantly different at the 95% confidence level.

Answers

Chapter 1 (page 9)

No numerical answers required

Chapter 2 (page 21)

No numerical answers required. In question 5 silos 2 and 4 are giving problems

Chapter 3 (page 40)

No numerical answers required

Chapter 4 (page 57)

Simple tabulation and rounding (page 52)
1 2245.5 kg; £3368.25   2 monthly totals 119 364 m; 61 290 m, grand total 180 654 m   3 22 694 (000)   4 $5000 m; percentages 7.9%, 14.8%, 7.7%, 11.4%, 25.0%, 33.1%   5 a 163 003 thousand tonnes, b 5400 thousand tonnes, c 168 403 thousand tonnes (*Note*: % is 5.60%)   6 a 374 918 serious crimes, b 0.03% were murders, 17.10%, were burglaries)   7 Total enrolments 2581, of which general education 728, business studies 885, science and engineering 445, tourism and catering 523
Arrays and frequency distributions (page 57)
1 Range 5 minutes – 5042 hours   2 no numerical answer required   3 groups contain 5, 17, 7, 7, 4, 2, 2, 2 and 4 respectively   4 groups contain 3, 6, 3, 6, 7, 4, 3, 7 and 1 items respectively   5 a groups contain 25, 7, 5, 6, 3 and 4 items respectively

Chapter 5 (page 67)

(*Note*: those using calculators may find that some of the answers given differ to a small extent from the more accurate answers given by their calculations.)

1 *a* ±3754.25, *b* ±2.6%   2 *a* +275 000 tonnes, *b* +0.19%   3 *a* −197, *b* −0.09%   4 *a* Canada 7.5%, *b* Australia 19.5%, *c* relative error ±4.1% of 7.5% = ±0.3% (ie answer is 7.5% ± 0.3%). In Australia's case it is 1.8% of 19.5% = 0.35% (ie answer is 19.5% ± 0.35%)   5 *a* A = £538, B = £683, C = £1026, Group = £782, *b i* ± £1500, *ii* ±15, *iii* ±£7   6 *a* 35 250 ± 55, *b* 21 300 ± 100, *c* 20 245 ± 52.5   7 *a* 12 500 000 ± 377 500, *b* 1 920 000 ± 225 000, *c* 450 000 ± 15 375   8 *a* 128.3 (max error +26.67), *b* 7.7 (max error +0.91)

Chapter 6 (pages 72, 79, 84, 88)

No numerical answers required

Chapter 7

Simple graphs (page 95)
No numerical answers required
Graphs (page 105)
1 and 2 no numerical answers required   3 *a* break-even point is at an output of 4300 units approximately. (We cannot given an absolutely accurate answer with graphs. Answers within 25 units may be considered correct), *b* If the selling price fell to £8 per unit the output of 10 000 units would cease to be profitable   4 Break-even point is at 2000 units, when the receipts of 2000 × £20 = £40 000 exactly cover the fixed costs of £20 000 and the variable costs of £20 000 (2000 × £10)   5 and 6 no numerical answers required

Chapter 8

Simple indexes (page 109)
1 100.0, 105.3, 113.2, 126.3, 150.0, 171.1, 215.8, 234.2, 250.0, 269.7   2 95.7, 100.0, 203.4, 211.1, 238.2   3 100.0, 98.5, 116.7, 118.9, 119.7, 128.8, 116.7   4 100.0, 101.6, 102.4, 108.1   5 50.0, 54.0, 62.0, 100.0, 106.0, 108.8, 111.2, 119.2, 122.0, 124.8
Aggregate price indexes (page 115)
1 318.3   2 274.7   3 *b i* 206.6, *ii* 206.9   4 *i* 114.3, *ii* 117.1   5 *b* Laspeyres 172.5, Paasche 158.4   6 yr 1 = 100, yr 2 = 106.5, yr 3 = 112.8
Chain-based index numbers (page 120)
1 *a* 100, 102.9, 108.8, 114.7, 116.5, *b* 100, 102.9, 105.7, 105.4, 101.5   2 *a* 100, 109.4, 115.6, 125.0, 131.2, *b* 100, 109.4, 105.7, 108.1, 105.0   3 100, 128.8, 121.2   4 100, 109.7, 116.5
Index numbers (page 131)
1 *a* no numerical answer required, *b i* 202.2, *ii* 202.9   2, 3 and 4 no numerical answers required   5 *a* 110.2, *b* 132.5   6 *b i* 120.7   7 *i* 134.0, *ii* 126.0, *iii* 129.1   8 129.0

Chapter 9 (page 140)

No numerical answers required

Chapter 10

The arithmetic mean (page 146)
1 24.25 years   2 15 348 therms   3 £6.23   4 9.458 cm   5 48 116   6
28 724   7 £30 400   8 £205   9 *a* males 19.37 years, females 19.58
years, *b* add the two means and divide by 2 since the numbers of males
and females are the same   10 *a* 973 hours, *b* the assumptions were that
the first and last groups were twice as large as the other groups, and that
the frequencies within a group were equally spread throughout the group
The geometric mean (page 149)
1 *a* 45.5, *b* 359.1, *c* 81.4, *d* 51.3, *e* 307.3
The median (page 153)
1 3   2 2   3 51.4   4 £329.62   5 *a* £19 325, *b* 48 650   6 £1444   7 *a*
85.2 kg, *b* 75.8 kg, *c* 98.5 kg, *d* 68.6 kg (*Note*: These answers are
approximate since we are interpolating from a graph. The reader should
hope for a result within 0.2 of these results)   8 *a* 8500, *b* 11 875, *c* 6250
(again, these are approximate results and an answer within £50 is acceptable)   9 *c* median time 50 secs, upper quartile time 62.5 secs, lower
quartile time 44.8 secs (again, these are only approximate as we are
reading off a graph)   10 *c* median time 72.8 secs, lower quartile time
63.8 secs, upper quartile time 79.7 secs (again, these are only approximate as we are reading off a graph)
The mode (page 159)
1 A = 4, B = 1, C = 1 and 2, D = 3 and 4   2 2 bedrooms   3 *a* size 8, *b*
sizes 4 and 5   4 £8855 (but this is an approximate answer and readers
with a result within £25 may consider they have the correct answer)   5
532 units (but again, this is an approximate answer)

Chapter 11

The range and quartile deviation (page 171)
1 no numerical answer required   2 average = 37 garments, range = 87
(5–92)   3 *a* total outputs: $x = 867$ units, $y = 684$ units, *b* range: $x = 98$
(0–98), $y = 21$ (25–46)   4 *a* range = £29 (£3–32), *b* median = £15,
lower quartile = £10, upper quartile = £19, *c* quartial deviation = £4.5   5 median price = 180 pence, quartile deviation = 15
pence   6 median turnover = £217 000, quartile deviation = £97 300,
range = £425 000 (£475 000 – £50 000)   7 median = 114 secs, quartile
deviation = 45 secs (This last answer being taken from a graph is not
accurate – answers close to the answer given may be considered correct)
Mean deviation and standard deviation (page 181)
1 *b i* 32.83 years, *ii* 8 years   2 *a* 74.2 kg, *b* 10.6 kg   3 *a* mean order
value = £2600, mean deviation = £973, *b* £2900   4 *b i* £8053, *ii* £4826
5 *a* mean = £237.50 rateable value, SD = £133   6 mean lifetime = 802.5

hours, SD = 314 hrs **7** mean weight = 71.9 kg, SD = 7.59 kg **8** no numerical answer required **9** CV = 10.6%
Skewness (page 186)
1 and **2** no numerical answers required **3** coefficient of skewness = 0.6 ie data is positively skewed to the extent of 60% of a standard deviation **4** *a* £1728.75, *b* £450.68, *c* £1750, *d* − 14.1% of SD

Chapter 12 (page 206)

1 no numerical answer required **2** *b* final trend figure 78.25 ('000 tonnes) **3** *b* in year 4 the trend line indicates monthly averages rising from 79 000 garments in January to about 87 000 in December **4** *b* seasonal variations (hl) qtr 1 − 125.177, qtr 2 − 7.844, qtr 3 + 190.114, qtr 4 − 57.094; *c* random variations (hl) range from + 32.761 in year 3 qtr 3 to − 18.739 in year 2 qtr 3 **5** *b* seasonal variations ('000 garments) qtr 1 − 7.416, qtr 2 + 3.875, qtr 3 + 15.0833, qtr 4 − 11.5416 **6** no numerical answer required **7** seasonal variations ('000) qtr 1 − 1327.016, qtr 2 + 135.516, qtr 3 + 2028.141, qtr 4 − 836.641; random variations range from − 831 (year 1 qtr 3) to + 434 (year 1 qtr 4); de-seasonalised data start at 1222 (year 1 qtr 3) and rise to 4188 (year 4 qtr 3) **8** *a* Centred trend runs from 42.5 to 57.0 (£'000), *b* corrected seasonal variations = 0.856, 1.0196, 1.345 and 0.7793 respectively, *c* de-seasonalised data = 43.2, 46.1, 41.6, 37.2; 45.6, 48.1, 46.1, 42.3; 49.1, 50.0, 54.3, 66.7; 52.6, 53.9, 60.2, 53.9 **9** *a* Trend figures = 40.0, 38.625, 39.5, 41.625, 44.875, 47.125, 47.875, 46.25, 44.75, 44.75, 44.125, 43.50, 43.125, 43.875, 45.25, 46.125, 47.00, 47.375, 47.125, *b* seasonal variations = qtr 1 0.5515, qtr 2 1.3813, qtr 3 1.3964, qtr 4 0.6708, *c* actual variations = − 12.1, + 20.6, + 23, − 9.2, − 5.8, + 21.7, + 24.6, − 13.5, − 11.7, + 23.6, + 24.9, − 8.9, − 12.6, + 22.9, + 23.8, − 8.2, − 12.1, + 25.5, + 25.4, − 9.2, − 13.9, + 25.2, + 25.0, − 11.9

Chapter 13 (page 216)

1 probability = ⅙ **2** probability = ¹⁄₃₆ **3** probability = ⅓ **4** *a* 0.077, *b* 0.308 **5** 0.033 **6** *a* 0.0556, *b* 0.00185 **7** 0.5 **8** *a* 0.008, *b* 0.488

Chapter 14 (page 231)

1 no numerical answer required **2** numbers required 15 × 2 cm, 124 × 3 cm, 467 × 4 cm, 890 × 5 cm, 890 × 6 cm, 467 × 7 cm, 124 × 8 cm, 15 × 9 cm **3** *a* 0.09375, *b* 0.3125, *c* 0.2344, *d* 0.0156 **4** probabilities are: 0.016, 0.094, 0.234, 0.312, 0.234, 0.094 and 0.016. They do sum to 1 **5** repeat of question 3 *a* 0.0368, *b* 0.2765, *c* 0.3110, *d* 0.0041; repeat of question 4: the probabilities are 0.0041, 0.0369, 0.1382, 0.2765, 0.3110, 0.1866, 0.0467. They do sum to 1. There is an obvious bias to heads, with the peak probability at 4 heads

2 tails (as distinct from 3 heads and 3 tails with an unbiased coin)   6 *a* probability is 0.03587, *b* probability is 0.9925, *c* probability is 0.9279   7 *a* probability is 0.1762, *b* probability is 0.0384

Chapter 15 (page 239)

1 limits are 95% level: 9.620 and 8.380 hours, 99% level: 9.816 and 8.184 hours   2 limits are 95% level: 9.438 and 8.562 hours, 99% level: 9.557 and 8.423 hours. The limits are narrower when the sample is larger because the chances of a sample mean being outside the limits are reduced as the sample is increased in size   3 the confidence limit at the 95% level sampling 30 sets per day is 0.046. At the 99% level it is 0.057. This works out at 1.38 sets per sample and 1.74 sets per sample respectively. Therefore the quality-control system should use a sample of 30 sets per day, and if 2 or more than 2 are defective the system should be investigated   4 the hypothesis that the machine needs adjusting is proved at the 99% confidence level   5 no numerical answer is required

Chapter 16 (page 259)

1 no numerical answer required   2 *c* the regression line slopes downwards to the right indicating a negative correlation. It appears to be quite strong, but the numbers of observations is not great   3 *c* the regression line shows a fairly strong positive correlation between examination qualifications and salary earned   4 *c* the line of best fit shows a fairly close positive correlation between experience and salary earned, but other factors clearly have a considerable impact in particular cases   5 *c* the line of best fit shows a very close negative correlation   6 $r = -0.921$. This confirms the view given in the answer to question 2 above. The correlation coefficient is high, but too much reliance cannot be placed on it because it just fails the test for significance, since the number of observations is small   7 *a* the scatter diagram seems to indicate a strong positive correlation, *b* $r = 0.988$, *c* the result confirms the impression gathered from the scatter diagram that there is a strong correlation between turnover and profit. This is in accordance with accounting experience – each time we turn over a volume of stock we make a profit on it   8 $r = 0.875$ *Comments*: there seems to be some correlation between entertainment and orders placed, but it is not very close and entertainment does not automatically ensure an order   9 $r = 0.1118$. This reveals there is hardly any correlation at all between the data. Average earnings are not significantly affected by changes in industrial production   10 $r = 0.919$. The correlation is close. Expenditure on fuel tends to be small when income is low, and to rise when more income is available   11 *b* regression equation is $y = 246.32 + 2.67x$ – January is equivalent to month 13. Therefore $y = 281.04$ 12 *b* rank correlation $R = -0.67$. Some negative correlation exists, but it is not close

Chapter 17 (page 278)

1 confidence limits 95%: 174.16 cm and 165.84 cm, 99%: 175.47 cm and 165.53 cm   2 confidence limits 95%: 175.54 cm and 164.46 cm, 99%: 177.68 cm and 162.31 cm   3 confidence limits 99%: 0.103 and 0.017 (ie at 10.3% and 1.7% of defective items)   4 confidence limits 95%: 0.0927 and 0.0073 (ie at 9.27% and 0.73% of defective items)   5 sample size is 20 bags assuming a 95% confidence level. This should be sufficient to check the weight of the bags is within the required limit at the 95% confidence level   6 the manufacturer's mean is significantly higher than the sample at a 95% confidence level   7 again, the manufacturer's mean is significantly higher than the sample at the 95% confidence level   8 at the 95% confidence level the correlation coefficient is significantly different from zero; at the 99% confidence level it is not   9 there is no evidence that the coins are biased

Index